GALILEO GALILEI:
A biography and inquiry
into his philosophy of science

Ludovico Geymonat

GALILEO GALILEI:
A biography and inquiry
into his philosophy of science

Foreword by Professor Giorgio de Santillana

**Text translated from the Italian
with additional notes and
appendix by Stillman Drake**

McGraw-Hill Book Company
New York   Toronto   London

FOREWORD
by Giorgio de Santillana

I am glad to present to the American public an Italian philosopher of science already well known in his own country. Professor Ludovico Geymonat has shown himself the worthy heir of a distinguished tradition, marked in the early years of his century by the names of Peano and Enriques. He had the good fortune of being Peano's pupil in 1932, taking the last academic course of the great logician, and soon afterward he came to know Federigo Enriques, by then in his sixties. He had already begun his scientific career as Instructor in Calculus at the University of Turin when the early whirlwinds of the coming world crisis forced him to follow unexpected paths. In 1934, all academic personnel in Italy were required to give their oath of allegiance to fascism. Being young and decisive, Dr. Geymonat did what very few other people had the courage to do: he refused the oath, broke his academic career, and became a roving scholar. His interests, which had early centered on Comte, led him to Vienna, where the famous *Wiener Schule* of scientific philosophy was becoming a cynosure; he came to know Schlick, Waismann, Karl Menger, and other members of that famous circle. He can be said to have brought to Italy the earliest interest in logical positivism. Working as a free-lance author, he wrote on various aspects of positivism, translated Frege and Russell.

When war swept over Italy, Professor Geymonat's personal position had been taken far in advance. He belonged from the first to the militant antifascist underground and commanded formations of partisan guerrillas in the *maquis* during the critical years 1943–45. With the advent of peace, he was reintegrated into the university career, but his new interests led him to occupy the chair of the Philosophy of Science at Pavia, and then, since 1957, in Milan. He is now a leading authority on the philosophy of science, a subject which is enjoying new favor as his country opens up to the contemporary concern with science, after having remained for decades under the spell of idealistic philosophies. But Professor Geymonat, in his turn, has responded to Italian traditions and has not remained anchored to the formal schemes of logical positivism. His increasing interest in the history of science as an essential component of philosophy is evidenced in the present book on Galileo, which came out in 1957, and in his splendid critical edition of Galileo's *Two New Sciences*, which he prepared with Professor Carugo in 1958. His recent *History of Mathematics* shows him to be the rightful successor in the enterprise that Federigo Enriques started fifty years ago.

The present work is a masterful example of the author's new approach. Far from being a mere biography, the biographical material is only used as a frame in which the real content is spun out; the book might be called "The making of the mind of the first physicist." That first physicist drew his inspiration from all parts of the culture of his time in order to work out a new science beyond its ken; thus in his progress he leaned on disparate and sometimes contradictory elements. He knew where he was going but he often lacked the terms. He was far from being the empiricist that unhistorical minds among scientists have so often believed him to be. He was a rationalist of a new kind, who had to establish a new link between fact and reason. His complexities and occasional ambiguities have given rise to divergent philosophical commentaries because he will fit no one philosophy. Professor Geymonat has had to dissociate himself from the idealistic interpretations of Koyré and Cassirer while recognizing much in their work that is well founded: his main point is that Galileo, while flirting with Platonism and yielding to it occasionally, retained a conception of mathematics which was logical and instrumental. On the other hand Galileo vigorously fought the Aristotelians, yet there is more of the Aristotelian in him than the superficial student suspects. He needed a metaphysics even more than he needed a method, yet his invincibly positive mind forever clipped its wings. All along, down to the very end, he was struggling to establish the meaning of that utterly new thing in history, scientific fact. It turned out to be remote from direct ex-

perience, the despair of the philosopher, yet strong and unam-
biguous enough to support the true rationalist faith. Professor
Geymonat has succeeded admirably, and in a pleasingly astringent
manner, in showing how Galileo's main political strategy, or what
we might call his problem of the public relations of science, was
his main preoccupation for twenty years, and how that political
strategy meshed with his theoretical concern, leading him to clarify his own thought and to set up the modern scientific language.
This is where humanism and science actually meet in history.

Battles, as a weary staff officer once said, are something that
usually happens at the junction of two maps; it is Professor Geymonat's merit as a historian of ideas that he elucidates the confused superposition of intellectual maps which made Galileo's
struggle heroic and creative.

Mr. Stillman Drake, who undertook the work of translation,
need not be introduced to our public; he is well known as the
most outstanding American expert on Galileo. His translations
have done much to make Galileo's works available to his country-
men. As a professional historian of science who is also a philosopher, he was in the best position to complement the work of
Professor Geyomat, who is a philosopher but only incidentally a
historian. The historical notes he has brought to the text bring the
reliability of the historical account up to the level of the philosophical critique. And, finally, may I say it was from his suggestion that the joint appendix to this book evolved.

For there is one point, crucial to the whole story, on which it
will be noticed that Professor Geymonat has carefully refrained
from commenting himself: the regularity of the trial before the
Inquisition. Professor Geymonat reports objectively on my findings as stated in *The Crime of Galileo,* but does not draw any conclusions of his own. I think I can appreciate his reasons for not
pressing the issue. It is not quite germane to his main subject,
which is scientific philosophy. Moreover, as a member by birth
of the small and respected Protestant minority of Italy (he comes
of old Waldensian stock), he felt that he had better forbear from
taking sides in what might be construed by some as a religious
polemic. Church authorities are still acutely sensitive on the sub-

ject. Still, Mr. Drake and I felt that the non-Italian reader is entitled to some clarification on the issue. We have therefore included, with the author's permission, a friendly debate between us (which will be found in the appendix) concerning the unsolved problems of the trial. The authorities stand under accusation on the part of the historian; their silence on the subject has been conspicuous since the time of Wohlwill. Mr. Drake has made himself counsel for the defence, and I have been left to play the prosecutor. That the trial was a miscarriage of justice is, I dare say, established beyond doubt; but we may still argue whether at the root there was error, misunderstanding, or overt falsification, and that is where Mr. Drake suggests an interesting conciliatory solution. First, however, I commend to the reader Professor Geymonat's penetrating study of a great and singular man.

GIORGIO DE SANTILLANA
September 20, 1963

Contents

Translator's Preface

The present translation embodies some alterations of the original text in order to adapt it to the English reader for whom it is intended. These alterations have been approved by the author.

On certain matters which are still debated among Galilean scholars, particularly those on which Professor Geymonat has preferred to reserve judgment, the translator has taken the liberty of adding comments of his own. All notes, or parts of notes, for which responsibility rests solely with the translator are enclosed in square brackets and identified by the symbol—*Tr.*

Quotations from works of Galileo are identified by references to the National Edition edited by Antonio Favaro, as in the original printing of this book. For the convenience of the English reader, references to existing English translations are also supplied. Following are the abbreviations used for this purpose, together with the full English titles of the respective books, and the original titles and dates of the works therein translated.

Motion and Mechanics:
Galileo Galilei On Motion and On Mechanics (Madison, 1960)
   De Motu (*ca.* 1590), tr. I. E. Drabkin
   Le Meccaniche (*ca.*, 1600), tr. S. Drake

Discoveries:
Discoveries and Opinions of Galileo (N.Y., 1957)
   Sidereus Nuncius (1610), tr. S. Drake
   Istoria e dimostrazioni intorno alle macchie solari (1613), tr. S. Drake
   Lettera a Madama Cristina (1615), tr. S. Drake
Discourse on Bodies in Water (Urbana, 1960)

Bodies in Water:
   Discorso . . . intorno alle cose, che stanno in su l'acqua . . . (1612), tr. Thomas Salusbury

Controversy:

The Controversy on the Comets of 1618 (Philadelphia, 1960)
> *Il Saggiatore* (1623), tr. S. Drake
>> (This volume also contains several other works by Galileo
>> and his opponent in the dispute, the Latin works having
>> been translated by Professor C. D. O'Malley.)

Dialogue:

Dialogue Concerning the Two Chief World Systems (Berkeley,
1953)
> *Dialogo . . . sopra i due massimi sistemi del mondo . . .*
> (1632), tr. S. Drake

Two New Sciences:

Dialogues Concerning Two New Sciences (N.Y., 1914, reprinted
v.p. and v.d.)
> *Discorsi e dimostrazioni matematiche intorno a due nuove
> scienze . . .* (1638), tr. H. Crew and A. De Salvio

In the appendix to the present work, I give my views on certain
controversial aspects of Galileo's trial and condemnation. I am
indebted to the American Council of Learned Societies and to the
Harvard Center for Italian Renaissance Studies for the opportunity to present these ideas before an international conference at
Florence in June 1962. To Dr. and Mrs. Kenneth Murdock I am
particularly grateful for my pleasant sojourn at Villa I Tatti.

I am grateful to Signor Fulvio Ognibene for suggestions concerning the translation, to Professor Francis Carmody for assistance with the Latin passages, and to Kathleen Johnson and Eliza-
beth Floyd for preparing the typescript for the press.

The present translation was completed in 1962. Since that time
a Hungarian translation has appeared and a second Italian edition
embodying some minor alterations has been published. It is fitting
that the year of Galileo's 400th birthday has been selected for
publication of this book, and that Professor Santillana has ap-
pended to it his comments on my views concerning the trial.

S. D.

Introduction

It is a striking fact that controversies over Galileo's character and his works, rather than dying out with time, have in fact become deeper and more serious since the beginning of the present century. The main source of this deepening interest lies in that marvelous tool of research for students of the history of scientific and philosophical thought, the National Edition of Galileo's works. This great publishing venture in twenty volumes (including one of index), appeared at Florence between the years 1890 and 1909 under the editorship of Antonio Favaro, one of the most diligent and devoted students of the life and writings of the great Pisan scientist.[1] Since that time, innumerable researchers have followed one after another; among these, some may be selected as fundamental labors that can still be considered today as sound points of departure for any rigorously critical investigation.

The most important themes on which modern Galilean research centers are essentially five: (1) the relations of Galileo to the Renaissance, and especially the relation of the technical and scientific problems he faced to the new structure which had been acquired gradually during the fifteenth and sixteenth centuries by the so-called mechanical arts in the broadest sense of this phrase; (2) the significance and limits of the originality attributable to Galileo's science when compared with that of the schools of Aristotle and William of Ockham; (3) the general philosophical assumptions of the methodological revolution brought about by Galileo, and the idealist or experimentalist nature of those assumptions; (4) the causes and the course of the battle undertaken by Galileo on behalf of the Copernican theory and its importance in the history of science and culture; (5) the presence in the thought and achievements of the great scientist of elements foreshadowing the philosophy of the Enlightenment.

Introduction

Among the eminent scholars who have contributed most to the clarification of one or more of the above themes, some foreign writers deserve special mention: Emil Wohlwill,[2] Leonardo Olschki,[3] Alexandre Koyré,[4] and (though we add this with many reservations) the Vatican astronomer Adolf Müller, S.J., whose learned volumes on Galileo[5] may be taken as testimony of the enduring grudge which the Jesuits hold against their ancient adversary. Among Italian writers I shall restrict myself at present to the mention of Vasco Ronchi, Antonio Banfi, and Giorgio de Santillana, authors of very engaging works which have much enriched Galilean literature.[6]

Confronted by so great a number of authoritative and recent researches, the reader may well ask the reason for still another book—the more so because, in view of its very modest format, it certainly cannot compete with the works already mentioned. I must reply in terms of two considerations. In the first place, I have a particular and specific informative purpose: that is, to introduce as speedily as possible to those readers who are not already specialists in Galilean questions the problems relating to the life and work of Galileo which are chiefly debated today. This interest in the more controversial aspects of the great scientist obviously obliges me to give special emphasis to some of his less well-known actions and ideas while relegating others, perhaps more widely known, to second place. However, I have sought to be objective in my exposition, the sole purpose of which will be to render more immediately understandable the historical and theoretical interest of Galileo's work.

Second, if the specialist in Galilean questions should notice here and there in the course of this volume some new interpretative clues, I freely confess that these also afford a justification for the whole undertaking. They arise, for the most part, from the particular methodological-illuministic orientation that I brought to my reading—otherwise objective and scrupulous—of the Galilean texts. It is evident that the place and manner in which I now present these clues will preclude my supporting them with all the proofs that would be necessary to secure their general acceptance. It will suffice for my purposes to set them forth as suggestions, hoping that in time they may bear fruit.

Introduction

By thus alternating references to old and new interpretations, one may see clearly the wonderful richness of Galileo's thought and the decisive significance of his battle in the history of modern culture. A realistic study of his personality, as human in its positive as in its negative side, cannot but be most instructive. His very errors, his weaknesses, and his illusions constitute precious lessons for anyone who would travel with full understanding the road Galileo opened.

L. G.

Chapter 1

Galileo's Youth

1. Galileo Galilei was born at Pisa on the fifteenth of February 1564. His parents were Vincenzio Galilei (1520–91), musician and merchant, and Julia Ammanati of Pescia (1538–1620).

Vincenzio and his ancestors were Florentines; indeed, the Galilei family had in times past been among the most noted families of that city. One of its members, Tommaso di Buonaiuto, had taken part in the democratic government of Florence which in 1343 succeeded that of the Duke of Athens. In the following century another member of the family, "magister Galilaeus de Galilaeis" (born 1370, died between 1446 and 1461), had been a famous doctor and magistrate. His tomb, still preserved in Santa Croce Cathedral at Florence, subsequently became the family tomb of the Galilei, near which Galileo himself was interred. A brother of the *magister* was Vincenzio's great-grandfather. In the sixteenth century the family must have declined somewhat, at least financially, and it was by reason of economic problems that Vincenzio was constrained to take up trade in addition to music.[1] For financial reasons also he moved to Pisa, where he was married in 1562, and where Galileo, his first child, was born.

Vincenzio Galilei was a highly cultured man of many lively interests. He was not only an accomplished lutenist and music theoretician (in which capacity he was active in the Academy or *Camerata* of the Bardi family), but was well informed in the classical languages and even in mathematics. Several of his works on music theory survive, among which it suffices to mention his *Fronimo*, his *Dialogue on ancient and modern music*, and his *Discourse concerning the work of Messer Gioseffo Zarlino of Cioggia*. In these he argued with great vivacity against the maestro Zarlino, whose pupil he had been, upholding the necessity of "rediscovering the ancient music"; that is, of returning to monodic melody as opposed to the contrapuntal polyphony of the Venetians. Along with a love for music, Galileo was to inherit from his father an independent character and very combative spirit.

Vincenzio had two other sons after Galileo, and four daughters, though of one son and two daughters all traces have been lost. The rest—Virginia (born 1573), Michelangelo (born 1575), and Livia (born 1587)—were destined to have a marked importance in Galileo's life. The obligations which he, with only too generous a spirit, undertook to provide for their ever-growing financial needs (and even more for those of his mother, a woman who was anything but tender and understanding) were not the least among the causes of his continual anxieties and his many changes of post.

The family of Vincenzio Galilei remained at Pisa until about 1574, returning then to Florence. Thus it was in those two cities that Galileo received his elementary education, which was strictly humanistic in character. He spent some time also in the monastery of Santa Maria di Vallombrosa, where he learned the elements of logic, but we are not sure whether he was there simply as a student or as a novice of the order.

In September 1581, Galileo was entered at the University of Pisa in the Faculty of Arts as a student of medicine. It is probable that behind the decision of Vincenzio Galilei to direct the young man's studies along this line lay a desire to have him emulate his famous fourteenth-century ancestor. But Galileo displayed no serious interest in medicine, and returned to Florence in 1585 without having been graduated; that is, without having received the title of "Doctor." Meanwhile, however, something had taken place which was to be decisive for the career of the future scientist.

During his return home for a vacation period in 1583, Galileo was able without his father's knowledge to arrange for a friend of the family, Ostilio Ricci, to introduce him to the study of mathematics. Though Galileo was no longer a child—he was in fact nineteen years of age—this science was entirely new to him, and he showed such enthusiasm toward it that Ricci was quite astonished. Accordingly he mentioned it to the father, asking his consent to a continuation of the lessons. Vincenzio agreed, provided that they should not be so intensive as to distract the youth

6

from the potentially more lucrative study of medicine. Before long, Galileo was able to carry on his mathematical researches by himself. Confronted by his extremely rapid progress, the father had to yield, and granted him the right to dedicate himself ever more intensively to the science he preferred.

2. Ostilio Ricci of Fermo had been a pupil of Nicolò Tartaglia, the celebrated algebrist who discovered the formula for the solution of cubic equations. Ricci lived in Florence, where he was professor at the Academy of Design, an artistic school dating from 1563. There he taught, among other things, various subjects of a technical and scientific character: mathematics, perspective, astronomy, mechanics, architecture, and anatomy.

In the school of Tartaglia, Ricci had studied mathematics in the spirit of engineering; that is, not as a general treatment of abstract concepts, but as a collection of researches linked to military science, architecture, and in general to practical affairs. Later he sought to give this same orientation to his own teaching, so that in his lectures mathematics ultimately assumed almost the aspect of an experimental science. Like his contemporaries, Ricci was a devoted student of the great Greek geometricians, and he had an open predilection for Archimedes, in whom the most perfect realization of the mathematical-experimental spirit is found. A similar motive had induced Tartaglia many years previously to publish Latin translations of several works of the great Syracusan. Devotion to Archimedes was to be one of the most precious legacies transmitted to Galileo by Ricci.

Galileo's own passion for mathematics never became detached from an interest in observation, measurement, and design; from the very beginning, mathematics appeared to him as a potent instrument for acquiring a knowledge of nature, a tool for drawing out her most intimate secrets, a key to the translation of natural processes into precisely reasoned propositions that were consistent and capable of rigorous verification.

The teaching of mathematics at the University of Pisa was almost entirely neglected at that time, for which reason (as we have noted) Galileo had to seek a teacher of mathematics at Florence among the friends of his father. But the same cannot

7

be said of physics. This was in fact taught at Pisa by a learned Aristotelian, Francesco Buonamico, professor of philosophy, a Florentine by birth. Although direct evidence is lacking, we may be sure that Galileo took the courses offered by Buonamico and was for a time under his influence. For proof of this it suffices to compare those fragments written by Galileo known usually only by the title of *Juvenilia* (which from all indications belong to the year 1584) with the book *De motu libri X* (*Ten books on motion*) published by Buonamico. The Galilean fragments reproduced with remarkable clarity the same arguments as those employed by the Aristotelian, and develop the same concepts. The science thus dealt with by both teacher and pupil had nothing to do with physics in the modern sense of the term. Rather, it was a sort of general cosmology in which they sought to find principles for the explanation of particular facts, a more or less successful synthesis between a teleological metaphysics and commonsense experience.

It is highly significant that the first impulse to abandon the ancient type of physics in favor of rigorous investigations restricted to well-defined groups of phenomena came to Galileo through mathematicians such as Ostilio Ricci. Probably he found himself for a while under the two conflicting influences, but in the end that of mathematics prevailed to the total abandonment of Aristotelian physics.

Galileo's first discovery in physics in the modern sense of that word occurred in 1583, the year in which he began the study of mathematics. This was his discovery that the beating of a pendulum takes place in equal times—a matter to which he was to return in his greatest scientific work, published in 1638. In his work on Galileo the Jesuit Father Adolf Müller asserted that the same discovery had already been made by the Arab astronomer Ibn Junis. Still, there is no question that in Europe it was virtually unknown, and that the young Galileo had never heard a hint of it from anyone. Now the young student's ability to contemplate the swinging of a lamp in the Cathedral at Pisa, and to draw from this a fact of such importance, shows that in his mind there was already developing an entirely new attitude: that spirit of observation which was to draw him with ever-growing enthusiasm to the type of restricted research which had been cultivated by the mathematicians of the school of Tartaglia. It is equally note-worthy that Galileo, having once established the isochronism of small oscillations, undertook at once (as his biographers attest) to apply this to the measurement of the pulse rate and other brief time intervals. This is a sure sign that he already felt an urge to transform scientific discoveries into practical principles useful to mankind. We shall see that this tendency remained with him, and was later to become one of the fundamental characteristics of his whole approach.

3. After returning to Florence in 1585, the young scientist passed four years with his family. He had no definite profession, but sought to enrich his knowledge in various fields as mathematician, philosopher, and literary man. He was in fruitful contact with the lively cultural groups that surrounded his father. Galileo's literary interests are thus described by Professor Antonio Banfi: "A love for and knowledge of the classics—Virgil, Ovid, and Seneca were his favorites—was united with an interest in the popular literature of the day. What Galileo sought in the latter (and what is essential to poetry in contrast with learning) is the fresh play of the imagination which, bursting forth from the complex and settled conventional reality, flourishes with satiric wit in the essays of Berni or in the comedies of Ruzzante, and frees the spirit from the weight and conventionality of daily life; or, creating a world of its own (as in the verse of Ariosto) im-parts life to dreamy images, to the innumerable myths in which humanity seeks and recognizes itself." [2]

To this period belong two lectures on the shape, place, and size of Dante's hell, delivered by Galileo before the Florentine Academy in 1588. The author's purpose was to defend the theories of Antonio Manetti concerning the topography of Dante's *Inferno*. Most interesting is the manner in which this defense turns into a series of precise geometrical problems, treated by Galileo with strict mathematical expertness and with perfect mastery of the text interpreted.

As to his activity in mathematics and physics, in 1586 he had invented a hydrostatic balance for the determination of the specific gravities of bodies, and had written on this subject a short but interesting work called *The Little Balance (La Bilancetta)*, which in a way constituted his scientific debut.[3] It was not printed during his lifetime, but was circulated among his friends and acquaintances, and later among his pupils. The influence of Archimedes is quite evident in this work both with regard to the problem treated and the method of solution. In this we may see indisputable proof that Ricci's teaching was bearing its first important fruit.

Another work of clearly Archimedean inspiration consisted of some theorems on the centers of gravity of solids, discovered by Galileo around 1586–87. These theorems were published only much later (in 1638) as an appendix to Galileo's greatest scientific work, the *Discourses and mathematical demonstrations concerning two new sciences*. They were, however, circulated in manuscript among interested students of such problems, and won for their author the sincere regard of authoritative mathematicians of his time. Among them we shall mention only the Marquis Guidobaldo del Monte (the man, according to Galileo's own words, who principally drew him into this type of research) and the German Jesuit Father Christopher Clavius (or Klau), who was deeply interested in the work and commenced a scientific correspondence about it with its author.

Meanwhile Galileo diligently sought to arrange his affairs so that he might prosecute his studies in serenity. He tutored in mathematics for a time at Florence and Siena, but he understood perfectly that only a regular teaching position could assure him of the financial independence he needed.[4] He made unsuccessful attempts at various universities, including that of Bologna, which passed over Galileo in favor of the mathematician Giovanni Antonio Magini (appointed on August 4, 1588). Finally he succeeded in 1589 in obtaining the chair of mathematics at the University of Pisa with a three-year contract. It was Ferdinand I, Grand Duke of Tuscany, who granted him this post on the recommendation of Francesco Cardinal del Monte, brother of Guidobaldo. Actually it was not a very important chair, and anything but well paid; Galileo received sixty scudi per year while Girolamo Mercuriale, professor of medicine, received two thousand scudi.[5] Yet it did give the young teacher a sure though small income, and at the same time it furnished him the means of demonstrating, for the first time in official circles, his own abilities as a scholar.

Thus Galileo was able to re-enter with the title of professor the same university he had left four years previously without even having completed the course of studies to which father had committed him. His personal honor was vindicated. On the twelfth of November 1589 he gave his inaugural lecture, and two days later began his regular course of lessons. The three years he spent at Pisa were to mark a noteworthy step in the development of his ideas.

4. In order to establish the exact progress made by Galileo during the three years he spent at Pisa as professor of mathematics, we should have to determine the development of his ideas in his two principal activities: astronomy and dynamics. The documents that have survived, however, do not afford so precise a determination.

As to astronomy, it is certain that he was occupied with it over the whole period under discussion. We know that the professor of mathematics was required to include in his program of courses either Euclid's geometry or the Ptolemaic system of astronomy. Now from 1589 to 1592, what was Galileo's personal conviction with regard to that system? The fact that he was careful to expound it in his lectures does not in itself suffice for us to conclude that he was personally convinced of its truth. We shall see in fact that at Padua he continued to explain this system with the same care even after he had begun privately to defend the truth of the Copernican system.

Because surviving documents are scarce, the opinions of Galilean scholars on this point are in conflict. Some (for example, Father Müller) maintain that in the years at Pisa he was a sincere follower of Ptolemy. On the other hand Emil Wohlwill and Sebastian Timpanaro [6] state positively that Galileo had already become a Copernican. The most plausible solution of this difficult question seems to me to be one which was given by Koyré, who assumes that Galileo's conversion to Copernicanism dates from those years, and closely connects this with his first studies of motion initiated at Pisa: "Doubtless it would be an exaggeration to pretend," he wrote, "that the work of Galileo sprang full-blown from his cosmological preoccupations. . . . It is nonetheless true that such preoccupations play a role of supreme importance in the thought and studies of Galileo, and that *from his youth, from the treatise and dialogue on movement that he drafted at Pisa*, we see him concerning himself with problems that take on their full and complete sense only as they relate to the Copernican conception of the universe." [7]

Without entering more deeply into the debate, it seems to me correct to assume that if in fact Galileo completed some notable steps toward Copernicanism during his three years at Pisa, these were on the whole determined by the maturation of his mechanical concepts. One must therefore first examine the concepts in order to make clear the progress of his thought.[8]

The mechanical conceptions which Galileo elaborated during his Pisan period are contained in various manuscrips which he preserved unpublished under the general title *De motu antiquiora* (*Older* [*studies*] *on motion.*)[9] The most important results of those researches were first published in abridged form among his collected works many years after his death.

Like all physicists of the time, Aristotelians or not, Galileo recognized the central importance of the problem of motion; that is, he assumed that the study of motion must be the starting point for any scientific treatment of natural phenomena. But the path he followed in the examination of motion lay completely outside the Aristotelian scheme of things.

What influence acting on the young Pisan professor induced him to abandon a scheme so widely accepted and so authoritative? To answer this question we must pause, if only briefly, to mention the work that constituted the most important reading done by Galileo in those years: the *Diversarum speculationum mathematicarum et physicarum liber* (*Book of various speculations on mathematics and physics*) by Giovanni Battista Benedetti.[10]

Of all the scientists of the generation immediately preceding Galileo, Benedetti was the most original and devoted adherent of the "impetus theory." The origin of this celebrated theory goes back to Philoponus, a sixth-century commentator on Aristotelian

12

Galileo's Youth

physics, it gained numerous learned defenders among scholars at the University of Paris in the fourteenth and fifteenth centuries, for which reason it is often known today by the name of "Parisian physics." In the sixteenth century it also achieved wide popularity in Italy, and was taken up by Tartaglia.

The criticism which this theory directed against Aristotelian mechanics centered on the explanation of so-called violent motion—as, for example, the motion of projectiles. Whereas Aristotle had pretended to find a cause for continued motion in the action of the medium through which the body moves (air, water, or the like), advocates of impetus theory sought this cause rather in an ill-defined entity called "impetus," placed in the bodies themselves by the act of impressing upon them their violent motion. Today, both explanations seem to us unacceptable, but that of the Parisian physicists undoubtedly fitted the known facts better than that of Aristotle. It suffices to reflect that according to the Aristotelian theory, violent motion would have been impossible in a vacuum.[11] Upholders of the impetus theory had recourse to the absurdity of this claim; and, the better to contradict Aristotle, they vigorously supported the possibility of a vacuum.

The reading of Benedetti's work played a decisive role in Galileo's development. It brought him to understand the consistency of the anti-Aristotelian Parisian arguments, and to deduce the absolute necessity of abandoning forever the schemes of Aristotle. It should also be noted (as Koyré remarks) that Benedetti was a Copernican, and hence it is possible that his influence was more than negligible in Galileo's development toward Copernicanism.

To two elements that were scarcely present in Benedetti's treatise, Galileo immediately gave a new and fundamental importance: the mathematical element and the empirical element. In Galileo there flourished on the one side the influence of Archimedes; on the other side was the spirit of the Renaissance technicians which made him eager to connect theory and practice inseparably, to link scientific explanation with empirical control. To put physics on a mathematical basis it was necessary above all to show the untenability of the vague concept of "impetus" and to demonstrate the necessity of constructing a new mechanics, freed

13

not only from the Aristotelian schemes but also from those of the Parisian physicists. In Galileo's *Older studies on motion,* this process of maturation was hardly begun, and the theory of impetus (though modified and filled in at various points) still constituted the groundwork of his early thought.

One thing worth emphasizing can be very useful to us in understanding the significance that Galileo's mathematization of physics was later to have. Galileo did not seek a mathematization analogous to that of the neo-Platonists, who claimed to find in numbers the essences of natural phenomena. What he proposed to achieve through mathematics was above all rigor of concepts and deductions: "The method which we shall follow in this treatise will be always to make what is said depend on what was said before. . . . My teachers of mathematics taught me this method." [12] Especially noteworthy is the plural, "my teachers of mathematics," which shows that Galileo meant to refer not only to Archimedes, but to any who had been his instructors in this discipline, including those who had taught him to study mathematics not as a general theory of abstract essences but as a workable instrument for the coherent and precise discussion of concrete problems.

5. Despite the scientific progress thus made by Galileo, one must not suppose that he dedicated all his time at Pisa to astronomical and mechanical researches. In no period of his life did he do so, least of all at Pisa, when the youthful exuberance of his powers encouraged him to broaden his rich personality through every sort of initiative.

Suffice it to record his biting attacks on the attitude and the academic costume of his colleagues at the university in an irreverent poetic lampoon "Against wearing the toga," composed at this time. After having demonstrated that the best thing is to go naked, Galileo declares himself resigned to the wearing of clothes, but not of the toga.[13]

His "Considerations on Tasso," or at least part of them, probably also belong to this period. The "Considerations," like his "Notes to Ariosto" (of uncertain date) consist of various annotations, sometimes inserted by Galileo in the margins of his copies

of Tasso's *Gerusalemma Liberata* and Ariosto's *Orlando Furioso,* and sometimes written on separate sheets interleaved in those two books. Certain it is that in the years under discussion, Galileo retained the lively interest in poetry which he had already displayed at Florence. He took part in the spirited debate of that time over the relative artistic merits of Ariosto and Tasso and was not afraid to express himself quite positively in favor of the former, emphasizing the fact that Ariosto's imagination and originality did not disturb the harmony of his poetic images. As Banfi well remarks, if Galileo "had the taste of his period for the fantastic and for bizarre whimsy, if he reproaches Tasso for lack of fantasy and for the slow monotony of his images and his verse, what he loves in Ariosto is not only the variety of the beautiful dreams, the rapid change of situations, and the lively elasticity of the rhythm, but the harmonious balance, the coherence of the images, the organic unity (even in variety) of the poetic fiction. The foundation of Galileo's taste, notwithstanding his fondness for the rich baroque elements, is and remains classic: the constructive clarity, the elegant and measured harmony, which effortlessly resolves in itself the play of complex intuition—this remains the fundamental criterion of his aesthetic judgment, as of his literary expression." [14]

To temper the carefree life begun at Pisa, however, important events soon intervened that profoundly affected Galileo's future. The first and most serious of these was the death of his father in 1591, which suddenly placed on his shoulders as eldest son the weight of a numerous family (mother, brothers, and sisters), putting him under the absolute necessity of improving his very modest income. Moreover, the academic world, often offended by Galileo's polemic temperament, showed itself daily more hostile toward him. He could foresee that no one would support a request on his part for an increase in salary. Nor should it be forgotten that Galileo's frankness in expressing his adverse judgment of a technical device invented by a member of the Medici family caused him to lose favor with the Grand Duke just when he most needed it. Thus he found himself at the beginning of 1592 not only deprived of hope for any improvement in his situation, but even threatened with loss of his post when his three-year contract expired that autumn.

Galileo Galilei

Confronted with the urgent necessity of seeking at any cost a new livelihood in some other university, Galileo turned once more to his eminent friend, Guidobaldo del Monte, who again promptly and generously intervened to assist him, recommending him warmly to the University of Padua, where the chair of mathematics had been left vacant in 1588 by the death of Giuseppe Moletti. Galileo made a trip to Venice about the first of September 1592, and presented himself personally to the authorities of the Venetian Republic, the source of financial support for the University of Padua. He was able to win such lively and immediate sympathy among them that on the twenty-sixth of the same month he obtained the desired position with a four-year contract, renewable for two additional years at the option of the Doge.

From a financial point of view, Galileo was not much better off than he had been at Pisa. The salary at Padua was only one hundred eighty florins per year,[15] but he could expect regular increases, and considerable ones, judging from the experience of his predecessor Moletti. Galileo requested and obtained permission from the Grand Duke at Florence to accept the position, and then moved at once to Padua, where he delivered his inaugural lecture on the seventh of December 1592.

Chapter 2

The Paduan Period

1. As Galileo himself wrote nostalgically to Fortunio Liceti many years later, the eighteen years he spent at Padua were without doubt the best of his life.

Even though his economic situation continued to be burdensome he quickly felt the good effects of his new position. The lively new surroundings stimulated serene optimism and enthusiastic faith in man's creative potentialities. It was an atmosphere characterized by sincere cordiality among colleagues and friends, and by extraordinary richness in cultural interests. Most fruitful of all was the broad freedom of thought guaranteed to all scholars by the Venetian Republic.

To illustrate the widespread cordiality among the professors of the University of Padua, nothing could be more appropriate than the relations between two open adversaries: Galileo and Cesare Cremonini, stalwart defender of the Paduan philosophic tradition of Averroist Aristotelianism.[1] From the very start these two men must have found themselves sharply in opposition on many theoretical matters of great importance; yet this did not hinder them from forming such a friendship that each had recourse to the other on occasions of serious personal difficulty. Reliable documents show that Cremonini offered his personal financial guarantee on Galileo's behalf when, in 1608, the latter requested a large salary advance (not the first) from the administration of the university. On other occasions, Galileo in turn came to the assistance of his colleague. It is also certain that during the trial opened against Cremonini by the Inquisition (an organization from which he was successfully defended by the Venetian government), investigations were extended to the person of Galileo himself.

Beyond the cultural circles of Padua, Galileo frequented also   17 those of Venice, where he was often to be found by reason of the proximity of the two cities. There he was able to establish relations with influential families of the Republic, and in particular with liberal young aristocrats, who appreciated to the highest degree his sharp and unprejudiced mind and his lively and scintillating conversation. One of the Venetian gentlemen most closely linked to Galileo was Giovanfrancesco Sagredo (1571–1620), who was later immortalized as the intelligent layman in Galileo's dialogues and as the owner of the palace on the Grand Canal in which those conferences were supposed to have taken place. At Venice, Galileo was also acquainted with Fra Paolo Sarpi and with Fra Fulgenzio Micanzio, who later succeeded Sarpi as adviser to the Republic on theological questions. Sarpi was regarded by his contemporaries as profoundly informed not only in political and theological matters but also in mathematics and astronomy. Galileo found in both these men powerful, competent, and loyal friends.

Nor were Galileo's activities in Venice limited to the highest circles in that city. He profited greatly during his visits there by frequenting the industry that gravitated toward its celebrated arsenal, and from this he drew much useful scientific material. Thus his great book, the *Two New Sciences*, begins as follows: "It seems to me that frequent visits to your famous Venetian arsenal open a large field for philosophizing on the part of speculative minds, especially with regard to the field in which mechanics is required. For every sort of instrument and machine is continually in use there by a large number of artisans, among whom, through observations made by their predecessors as well as those that they are continually making on their own account, there must be some who are real experts and capable of the most acute reasoning." [2]

Scientific interest in the work carried on by artisans and laborers was no longer a true novelty, for this had already acquired an important role in the "mathematical" investigations carried out by many scholars of the sixteenth century, particularly Tartaglia. In Galileo it stimulated a growing understanding, and ultimately it became the pivot of his methodological revolution.

18

The Paduan Period

Indeed, near the university he established a small shop. There he employed permanently an expert workman by the name of Marcantonio Mazzoleni, who lived with the family in the scientist's own house. In addition to the prosecution of new experimental researches, the shop was utilized also for the production of mathematical apparatus (surveying instruments, compasses, etc.), and this commerce assisted Galileo in making ends meet, often a difficult task for him.

We have already mentioned that after the death of Galileo's father, the maintenance of the family fell almost wholly on his shoulders. This burden continued to increase as rapidly as did his financial resources. In 1591 his sister Virginia was married to Benedetto Landucci, and it was Galileo who had to provide her dowry in a measure beyond his means. This obligation absorbed most of his salary for several years. In 1601 his sister Livia also wished to marry, and he obligated himself to pay a huge dowry to his new brother-in-law, Taddeo Galletti. In order to satisfy this debt he found himself constrained to request from the Venetian Republic an advance of two years' salary. His brother Michelangelo, who signed the dowry contract jointly with Galileo, not only failed to keep up his own share of the payments, but also required substantial aid himself. Endowed with noteworthy musical talent but incapable of settling down, he received two flattering offers of employment as a professional musician, the first time in Poland and the second in Bavaria. Both times it was Galileo who had to provide the expenses of travel. Michelangelo did not succeed in remaining in Poland very long, and returned poorer than before. In Munich he had hardly established himself when, instead of paying his debts to his brother-in-law and brother, he himself decided to marry Anna Chiara Bandinelli, and managed to spend every penny he had on a luxurious nuptial banquet. Many times in later years he resorted to Galileo for the maintenance of his numerous children.

Meanwhile, Galileo had founded a somewhat irregular family of his own with a Venetian woman named Marina Gamba, who came to settle in Padua (though not in Galileo's own house) and remained his affectionate companion for more than ten years. They had two daughters and a son, Virginia (1600), Livia

(1601), and Vincenzio (1606), and were not separated until Galileo left Padua to return to Florence in 1610. Shortly thereafter it appears that she married Giovanni Bartoluzzi, though the legal documents have not survived. The separation of Galileo from Marina Gamba seems to have been friendly, and when he departed for Florence the young Vincenzio, who was particularly in need of maternal care, remained with her for some time. Very cordial relations existed for several years between Galileo and Bartoluzzi.

In view of the financial demands on him, his initial salary (one hundred eighty florins per year) was far below his needs. It was increased on the occasion of each reappointment or renewal of the original contract with the university, advancing to three hundred twenty florins in 1598, five hundred twenty in 1606, and finally to one thousand florins per year in 1609. But even these increases were never sufficient for Galileo's needs, and he was obliged to rely to a considerably degree on private teaching. He transformed his own house into a sort of boarding school, where there were usually fifteen or twenty students to whom he gave lessons almost daily. These were young men of the best families who came to Padua from every part of Europe, attracted by the fame of the university or by the personal reputation of Galileo. In addition to this, he drew some income from the sale of mechanical instruments manufactured in his little shop, but for the most part sales hardly met the expenses of materials and payments to the craftsman.

It would be inaccurate to say that this state of affairs dampened Galileo's spirit; on the contrary, in those years he was particularly jovial, fond of good living, and full of self-confidence. Nevertheless, he must often have felt profoundly embittered. In all probability it was the constant awareness of his economic difficulties that kept him from founding a genuine family of his own, for many examples of marriages had demonstrated to him what troublesome consequences could stem from approaching family problems with too little forethought. But Galileo's tenacity in combating with renewed energy all the irritating pressures that tormented him is one of the most typical traits of his personality. In his own economic conflict may lie the

20

The Paduan Period

explanation of several aspects of his character, some of them quite appealing, as his generosity in aiding those who were struggling toward dignified work (first his brother, and later his pupils); some unattractive, such as his disregard for others when he sought to increase, by any means, his own prestige and consolidate his own position.[3]

His decision to seek still another move, breaking the many chains that held him in Padua, arose out of these financial struggles. It was in 1604 that he first began to entertain this idea, and started a series of negotiations to enter the service of Vincenzo Gonzaga, Duke of Mantua. But the Duke showed himself less generous than Galileo had hoped, and nothing came of it. Some years later, the Grand Duke of Tuscany offered Galileo means of definitively resolving his practical problems. This offer Galileo gladly accepted, though he did not hide from himself its many grave inconveniences.

In some of his letters, Galileo explained the reason for his decision. On the one hand, he felt the impossibility of continuously forgoing scientific research for several hours every day in order to give public and private lessons; on the other, he had to take into account the fact and a Republic such as Venice could never guarantee him a salary adequate to his needs without requiring from him something more than the mere prosecution of his own studies:

". . . My thought would truly be to get enough leisure and quiet so that I could bring to a conclusion, before my life, three great works that I have in hand in order that they might be published, perhaps with some credit to me and to him who would favor me in these undertakings. . . . Greater leisure than I have here, I do not believe I could have elsewhere so long as I am forced to derive the sustenance of my household from public and private teachings. . . . Nevertheless, the freedom that I have here does not suffice me, since I am required at anybody's request to consume many hours of the day, and often most of them. To obtain any salary from a Republic, however splendid and generous, without rendering public service, is not possible, since to draw benefits from the public it is necessary to satisfy the public, and not a particular individual; and so long as I am able to teach and serve, nobody in the Republic can exempt me from that duty and allow me the pay. In a word, I cannot hope for such benefits from anybody but an absolute ruler." [4] "But because giving private lessons and taking scholars as boarders constitutes something of an obstacle to me and impedes my studies, I should like to live completely free from the one and largely free of the other. Hence, if I am to return to my native land, I desire that the primary intention of His Highness shall be to give me ease and leisure to bring my works to a conclusion without my being occupied in teaching." [5]

To enter the service of a patron would deprive Galileo of many advantages which he enjoyed under the free Venetian Republic. Among the contemporary absolute rulers, however, the Tuscan Grand Duke Cosimo II would certainly be the one most disposed to respect Galileo's philosophic independence, for the Duke was linked to Galileo in true affection as a pupil, and as a youth had followed his lessons with particular enthusiasm. It was the consideration of this affection, coupled with the generous conditions offered him, that decided Galileo to take the crucial step. Knowing the subsequent development of events, we may judge this decision rash; but at that particular moment, and from Galileo's point of view, it was certainly the wisest and most rational course.

2. The eighteen years spent at Padua represent not only a relatively happy period in Galileo's life, especially in comparison with those which followed, but also a most important phase in his scientific development. Although none of his fundamental works date back to those years, some of his most significant discoveries certainly do; for example, the laws of naturally accelerated motion. But before passing on to his classical researches in mechanics, let us survey briefly Galileo's progress in other fields, particularly in astronomy.

At that time the university curriculum in mathematics usually included the explanation of both Euclid and Ptolemy. We need not be surprised that at Padua, as previously at Pisa, Galileo devoted several courses to the study of the Ptolemaic system. To that system he dedicated his *Treatise on the Sphere, or Cosmography*, written in 1597. It is a singular fact that in this he gave

22

The Paduan Period

no sign of any critical reservations concerning the Ptolemaic system, nor did he mention Copernicus, although it was in this very same year that Galileo uttered his earliest known private declarations in favor of Copernicanism. Critics have discussed at length the reasons for this inconsistency. It is all the more difficult to understand because in those years no real struggle against Copernicus had commenced among the Church authorities. Perhaps Galileo's behavior may be explained as an excess of prudence; or perhaps, more simply, by the fact that his professorial duty was to explain to his pupils the subjects established in the curriculum, rather than his own personal scientific opinions.[6]

Galileo's first private declarations in favor of Copernicanism occurred in two letters: one dated May 30, 1597, addressed to Jacopo Mazzoni, professor of philosophy at the University of Pisa (where Galileo had been a colleague of his) and for a while, at the college known as the Sapienza of Rome;[7] and the other dated August 4 of the same year, addressed to Johannes Kepler.[8] The first consisted of Galileo's defense of Copernicus against an objection raised in Mazzoni's recently published book, *De comparatione Aristotelis et Platonis* (*On comparing Aristotle and Plato*). The second is more important, both because it is more explicit as to Galileo's personal beliefs and because of the great scientific importance of the man to whom it was addressed.

Kepler had published at Tübingen in 1596 his first astronomical work, called *Prodromus dissertationum cosmographicarum continens mysterium cosmographicum de admirabili proportione orbium celestium deque causis coelorum numeri, magnitudinis, motumque periodicorum genuinis et propriis, demonstratum per quinque regularia corpora geometrica,*[9] of which a copy had been delivered to the mathematician of the University of Padua. In his letter of August 4, 1597, Galileo hastened to thank his German colleague for the gift just received, and while he confessed that he had hardly had time even to glance through the preface of the volume, he declared himself entirely in agreement with Kepler about the truth of the Copernican theory. He also went so far as to add that for several years he had accepted it, and had found explanations of many physical phenomena in confirmation of it (*quod in Copernici sententiam multis abhinc annis venerim, ac ex*   23

Galileo Galilei

tali positione multorum etiam naturalium effectuum causae sint a me adinventae, quae dubio procul per communem hypothesim inexplicabiles sunt).[10] In his reply of October 13, Kepler asked Galileo for a more complete opinion on the contents of the *Prodromus,* and encouraged him to publish the discoveries he had mentioned in favor of the truth of the Copernican theory. We do not know whether Galileo replied to this letter, since the surviving correspondence between the two scientists here suffers interruption for a long time—until 1610—which complicates the already difficult problem of their relations.[11]

Had Galileo really already inferred some proofs in support of the Copernican theory, as he asserted in his letter to Kepler, and what validity did they have? Why did he not accept the advice of the great German astronomer to publish them? Why did he not at least circulate them among those able to understand? These questions are usually raised by those scholars whom we may call "modern adversaries" of Galileo; for example, Father Müller. Indeed, they are even more serious when we consider the "proofs" that Galileo was to publish several years later. It is clear that nothing based on observations made with the telescope could have been possessed by him at the time. Hence nothing remains but certain indirect "proofs" based on mechanics, which were designed to resolve the commonsense objections against Copernicus. Did Galileo really intend to refer to these? Considering the level that had been reached in 1597 by Galileo's researches into the principles of dynamics, which was not yet very high, such "proofs" could have had little scientific value. Confronted with the dffiiculty of replying to these questions, one may consider the hypothesis that in his letter to Kepler, Galileo was referring to proofs that were desired rather than those he possessed.[12] Such behavior might be explained by his wish (understandable, if not excusable) to remain in good standing with the German scientist. Not even this unfavorable view can be proved in the present state of our documentation. Yet nothing can destroy the incontrovertible fact that from 1597 on, Galileo remained deeply interested in the Copernician doctrine and intuitively felt, with more or less scientific clarity, its profound truth.

24   The first public mention of Copernicanism by Galileo came

The Paduan Period

toward the end of 1604. In a letter dated September thirtieth of
that year, the friar Ilario Altobelli informed Galileo that he had
observed a new star in the heavens. This was also seen on the
tenth of October by the Milanese Baldessar Capra, a pupil of
Simon Mayr of Guntzenhausen [a German then residing at
Padua], and he brought it to the notice of Galileo through common acquaintances. The nova remained visible for eighteen
months, during which it gradually diminshed in magnitude. Because of the great interest attaching to the phenomenon, Galileo
made it the subject of three lectures which were attended by an
enormous audience, and it was on this occasion that he entered
publicly into the important controversy. Despite the fact that the
text of his lectures has not survived, it is known that according
to Galileo, the new star had to be considered a strong argument
in favor of the Copernican theory.[13] This shows that at least after
1604, Galileo tended to study Copernicanism not from a purely
mathematical point of view (and hence as merely hypothetical
within certain limits), but in relation to actual observation of the
heavens.

In the following year a discourse was published by the Aristotelian Antonio Lorenzini in reply to Galileo's arguments. Now, it
is an interesting fact that Galileo did not reply to Lorenzini's
pamphlet, while Baldessar Capra did, and Capra attacked not
only the Aristotelian, but Galileo as well. Not even this attack
moved Galileo to return to the subject directly. He confined himself to letting it be known that he was preparing a general treatise on the vexing problem. But this work was never written.[14]

How is this silence to be explained? The only possible reply
is that in drafting the treatise, Galileo became aware of the complexity of the problem and of the scientific insufficiency of the
theory he had set forth in his three famous lectures. He was certainly not a man to retreat when confronted with polemics—we
shall see how sharply he attacked Capra on another matter not
long afterward—and if he hesitated to reply in 1605 both to Capra
and to Lorenzini, he did so because he felt serious doubts about
the nature of the new star and about the possibility of using it to
demonstrate the truth of Copernicanism. He must have been practically certain of this theory, but not of the prooofs that he was

in a position to adduce in its favor. He preferred to wait patiently, seeking some new path that would lead to facts which were scientifically more persuasive. This path was opened to him by the discovery of the telescope.

3. What sort of experimental researches were carried out by Galileo in the little shop he had set up in his own house at Padua? Primarily, he manufactured there various mathematical instruments. The most famous of these was an original type of calculating ruler, the "geometric and military compass," based on the principle of proportional magnitudes. It was not a new invention in an absolute sense; instruments of the sort had already been in use for some years by mathematicians of the time. For example, one had been constructed by Guidobaldo del Monte; but Galileo hit upon his instrument independently, about 1597, and was able to give it a particularly useful form. For several years he felt no need to publish a specific explanation of this invention, but was content to explain its use orally to his private pupils, especially those who were studying mathematics with a view to its application to military science.[15] And as a matter of fact the compass was so useful for rapid calculations that it was widely employed prior to the appearance of logarithmic tables.

It was only in 1606 that Galileo published a little book on the subject under the title *The Operations of the Geometrical and Military Compass*, dedicated to the Grand Duke Cosimo II de' Medici. The fact that it was written in Italian shows that Galileo thought of it as directed to his students and not to scientists. Nevertheless, this publication was beneficial to him, because it helped to bring him to the attention of the Venetian government and enabled him to obtain more easily a renewal of his contract with a substantial increase in salary.

A few months later another book on the same instrument came out, written in Latin by Baldessar Capra; this bore the title *Usus et fabrica circini cuiusdam proportionis* (*Use and construction of a certain proportional compass*). Capra now claimed the invention for himself and his teacher, Simon Mayr. This question of priority had no great significance, strictly speaking, since it concerned only an invention of a practical nature, and not an authentic scientific discovery. But Capra's attack, obviously linked with the polemic he had previously opened against Galileo, was unquestionably intended to undermine the reputation of the Pisan with the academic authorities at Padua.

This time Galileo's reaction was immediate and violent. On April 9, 1607, he filed legal action against Capra, accusing him of plagiarism, and quickly obtained his public condemnation by the Regents of the University of Padua. Nor was he content with this victory, for he published next a harshly polemic *Defense against the calumnies and impostures of Baldessar Capra*. Although the subject did not really deserve so lengthy a debate, Galileo's persistence is easily explained by his desire to re-establish his own reputation and to nurse his wounded pride. Clearly we are dealing with an episode of little intrinsic importance, but it is one which Galileo's biographers have always enlarged upon because of its symptomatic value in evaluating his character.

In addition to his mathematical instruments, Galileo was much interested in magnets during those years. Magnetic phenomena had, in fact, become very popular through publication of the important work of William Gilbert, *De Magnete* (1600). Kings and princes themselves sought to procure good samples of lodestone, and became very excited over their power. During the seventeenth and eighteenth centuries it became the fashion in the courts of Europe to collect physical apparatus—optical, mechanical, electrical, and the like—which had some particular scientific or aesthetic value.

The theories of the English scientist left Galileo somewhat perplexed, as he found among them a large residue of magical notions, not worked out in a clear scientific form. Later he undertook to refute any application of the concept of attraction to the explanation of the tides, and did his best to give a purely mechanical theory of that phenomenon. Meanwhile, the fashioning of magnets struck him as a very interesting problem, particularly the construction of "armatures" to increase the magnetic power of lodestones. It appears that in this matter he obtained some striking results, and it is certain that he devoted much time to it. One of his motives may have been to do something to please the Grand Duke Cosimo, who was extremely fond of magnets. He also negotiated the purchase of a particularly strong lodestone for Cosimo from his Venetian friend Gianfrancesco Sagredo.[16]

At this time (shortly after 1600) Galileo also occupied himself with the phenomena of heat, inventing an apparatus for the measurement of temperature. From a modern point of view it had many defects, because the level of the liquid in the unsealed apparatus depended in reality not only on temperature but also on atmospheric pressure. For this reason, Favaro justly remarked that Galileo's device ought to be called a thermobaroscope, and not a proper thermometer. But defective or not, the invention is interesting because it shows the variety of the phenomena studied by Galileo, as well as his growing familiarity with the importance of instruments of measurement in physics.

It was in 1609 that Galileo manufactured in his little shop the first models of his famous telescope. The new invention represented the crowning achievement of his practical abilities, acquired over long years of painstaking and intelligent manual labor. From it was to stem the most glorious phase of his scientific career.

4. Among all the activities undertaken by Galileo during his eighteen years at Padua, by far his most fruitful investigations from the scientific point of view were those concerning the phenomena of mechanics. These were not, however, published at that time. The results he obtained during this period were destined instead to constitute the opening wedge for the theories developed in his last great work (1638).

In 1598 Galileo had devoted an entire course of lectures to this subject, taking his clue from the *Mechanical Problems* of Aristotle. It is probable that the completion of his own *Treatise on Mechanics* dates from these same years, though it was first published in 1634 at Paris, in a French translation by Father Marin Mersenne. The Italian text was not printed until 1649, seven years after Galileo's death.

From various evidence, and above all from the correspondence of Galileo, it is known that he began to apply himself to mechanical researches with particular attention and notable success between 1602 and 1609. In a letter to Fra Paolo Sarpi, dated

The Paduan Period

October 16, 1604, a formulation of his famous law of free fall appears for the first time:

"Reconsidering the phenomena of motion, in which I totally lacked any indubitable principle that could be put down as an axiom for the demonstration of the events I have observed, I hit upon a proposition which contains much of the natural and evident. This being assumed, I can then demonstrate the rest; that is, that the spaces passed over in natural motion are in proportion to the squares of the times, and consequently the spaces passed over in equal times are as the odd numbers beginning from one; and other things. Now the principle is this: that the body in natural motion increases its speed in the same proportion as its departure from the origin of its motion" (that is, grows in direct proportion to the distance from the initial point of fall).[17]

In order to grasp the great scientific significance of Galileo's new mechanics, its principal point of departure from the mechanics of Aristotle must be understood. Aristotle assumed the existence of two "natural" motions—one downward, belonging to earth and water; the other upward, belonging to air and fire. For Galileo, on the other hand, there existed only a single "natural" motion—downward motion. According to him, every body is heavy, and therefore tends naturally (as an effect of its heaviness) to fall toward the center of the earth. If some bodies on the contrary ascend, it is only because they are surrounded by a medium which, exceeding them in specific gravity, drives them upward according to the principle discovered by Archimedes. But such things (even air or fire), if they were not immersed in a medium of greater specific gravity, would exhibit their natural tendency to move downward. Herein lies the importance of the law of free fall of heavy bodies: it is valid for *all* bodies, and acquires a genuinely *universal* character. It was not without reason that Galileo used the expression "natural motion" to designate only the motion of freely falling heavy bodies.

The Archimedean character of his conception is further evidence for the influence of the ancient Syracusan thinker upon the originator of modern mechanics. In one thing, however, Galileo clearly surpassed the science of Archimedes: whereas the latter had applied mathematics only to static phenomena, Galilean science succeeded in applying it also to dynamics. And the most remarkable thing, in the eyes of Galileo and his contemporaries, was that the new mechanics revealed the existence of an *arithmetical* regularity in the fall of heavy bodies: "The spaces passed over in equal times are as the odd numbers beginning from one." Who can deny the fascination of such a law, in which the scientists of the seventeenth century could hear the echo of the most ancient Pythagorean ideas?

The various steps taken by Galileo in arriving at that perfect rational systematization of the laws of falling bodies which became the greatest treasure of his *Two New Sciences* need not detain us. Suffice it to mention that in his *Older studies on motion* Galileo still believed that the motion of fall was accelerated only in the initial instants. From the moment in which the body had reached its own "proper speed" (a speed supposed to be proportional to the relative weight of the body), he believed its speed would have to remain constant. The abandonment of this concept required great powers of scientific penetration; it necessitated a renunciation of the ancient principles according to which every body that falls freely to the earth possesses a particular speed of its own, proportional to its weight.

In his letter to Fra Paolo Sarpi, Galileo showed that he had already arrived at a correct formulation of the law that determines the kind of relationship existing between the spaces traversed and the time elapsed in naturally accelerated motion. But he was still in error about the "natural and evident" principle from which he thought he could deduce this law, for his principle affirmed the existence of a simple direct proportion between the speed of the body and its distance from the initial point of fall, whereas in reality no such proportionality exists. Only later was Galileo to succeed in discovering the correct principle, from which in fact his laws of naturally accelerated motion are deducible. The principle is that in free fall, the speed of the body increases in direct proportion not to the spaces, but to the times (or to the interval of time elapsed between the instant in question and that in which the movement began). The complete formulation was eventually given by Galileo himself in the following words: "Equable or uniformly accelerated motion I call that to which,

30

commencing from rest, equal velocities are added in equal times." [18]

In the *Two New Sciences*, Galileo also added an important refinement of his rule. Enlarging upon an argument previously used by Benedetti, he showed that were it not for the resistance of the medium, "the difference in heaviness, however great" would not have "any part whatever in varying the speed of the moving bodies, so that all would move with equal speed." That is, the acceleration of gravity is equal for all bodies, even those of differing substances and different weights.

Another result of great importance which Galileo acquired in his researches on mechanics relates to the so-called principle of virtual velocities. This had already been discovered by Guidobaldo del Monte as it applied to the study of the level and of pulleys. In such machines, he declared, two weights are in equilibrium whenever the products obtained by multiplying each weight by its respective velocity when moved are equal (but in contrary directions).[19] Galileo had the merit of giving to this principle a new generality, extending it to the study of the inclined plane and all its derivative machines. Ultimately the principle thus appeared as a common property of all machines, and as the sure road to the determination of their conditions of equilibrium. This important concept stands at the base of Galileo's *Treatise on Mechanics*.

It would seem appropriate next to deal briefly with the principle of inertia, tackling the difficult problem whether or not Galileo ever succeeded in grasping this in all its generality. Until fairly recently it was usual to credit him with expounding the inertial principle, but not necessarily to maintain that it was an entirely new idea. Some recent critics, on the contrary, contend that not Galileo but Descartes was truly the first to arrive at the principle in question. Since this very complex problem is interwoven with the entire work of Galileo, its consideration had better be postponed to a later chapter.

5. We have seen how great was the variety of Galileo's scientific interests. Now, to what degree did they extend also to mathematics? Here it is necessary to make a clear distinction between   31

Galileo Galilei

pure and applied mathematics. Galileo never had any serious interest in pure mathematics, and for that reason contributed nothing to it that is comparable with what he did for the other branches of science. Even his highly ingenious considerations on infinitesimals arose from physical rather than mathematical interests.[20] But matters are very different with regard to applied mathematics, and not only because Galileo enjoyed occupying himself with mathematical instruments, but also (and more important) because he gave a precise mathematical character to his most important physical investigations—those in mechanics.

Yet Galileo himself had no clear intuition of the profound difference between pure and applied mathematics. Rather, when he devoted his best energies to the latter, he was not even aware of the existence of another kind of mathematics, rigorously theoretical. In this regard he remained perennially under the influence of Tartaglia's preferences; throughout his life he regarded mathematics as a science that was essentially directed to the study of nature, a means of rendering precise and coherent our investigations of natural phenomena.

This interpretation of mathematics is very important in the evaluation of the "Platonism" which many scholars believe they have discovered in Galileo's thought. There is no doubt that such Platonism, if any exists, is linked to the importance which Galileo attributed to mathematics in the study of nature. But the mathematics to which Galileo referred bore very little resemblance to the noble theoretical science whose praises Plato sang when he held mathematics to be capable of elevating our minds to the ideal world. Galileo's mathematics resembled a good deal more the geometry of surveyors and the arithmetic of accountants, which were scorned by the Athenian philosopher. Though for two centuries immediately before Galileo, Italy had been the active center of a trend toward Platonic mathematicizing, the parting of the ways between this and the road opened by Galileo is very clear. Indeed, the best means for bringing into focus the difference between Kepler and Galileo consists precisely in taking the viewpoint that the former was still closely tied to Renaissance Platonism, with its mystico-magical interpretation of numbers, while the latter moved on an entirely different track.

32

The Paduan Period

Certain specific characteristics of the alleged Galilean Platonism have been elaborated by able scholars.[21] Olschki, for instance, held that the link between Galileo and Plato was more a sentimental than a truly scientific and doctrinal relationship; that is, Galileo was influenced more by the literary style of Plato than by his actual theories. The Platonic legacy of Marsilio Ficino had passed to the philosophers of southern Italy, and not into the cultural heritage of Florence, which was dominated by the practical spirit of Machiavelli, and it was there that Galileo grew up. Koyré, the most unyielding proponent of Galileo's Platonism, was obliged to acknowledge that: "There exist, in the history of philosophy, many Platos and many Platonisms. Two different types are conspicuous: the Platonism—or rather neo-Platonism—of the Florentine Academy, which is a mixture of mysticism, numerology, and magic; and the Platonism of the mathematicians, of a Tartaglia or a Galileo, which Platonism is mathematicism and nothing more." [22]

The Platonic character of Galilean science can be readily admitted if Platonism is merely to be identified with mathematicism. But this admission seems to me not so easy when it is claimed, as by Koyré, that mathematicism must be taken as the absolute line of demarcation between Platonism and Aristotelianism. We shall see, in fact, as we proceed, that it was not so for Galileo. As his ideas gradually matured, he sought with ever-increasing clarity to interpret mathematics as a particular instrument of logic in the Aristotelian sense of that word, and not as something contrasted with logic.

In supporting a Galilean Platonism, Koyré really meant to assert that only by a Platonic conception was Galileo able to justify the mathematization of the real world. Now here is precisely the most difficult problem, and it lies in the following two questions: (a) Did Galileo ever really seek a *justification* for his own physical science, or at any rate seek to justify it with *full knowledge* of its philosophical implications? and (b) did he *seek* such a justification in Platonism (or principally in Platonism), or did he not rather simply *assume* that he had found it in an operationalist view of mathematics? [23]

Galileo Galilei

These are questions of the utmost importance, to which we must often return. In my opinion, in order to answer them it is first necessary to take into account all Galileo's scientific researches, and not just his mechanical investigations.

Chapter 3

The First Fortunate
Astronomical Observations

1. The most important device by far to emerge from Galileo's little shop was the telescope. Like the "geometric compass," this was not a truly new invention, and Galileo was certainly at fault in presenting it as one, obscuring as well as he could the suggestions received from others.[1] However, that does not substantially detract from his merit, for it was with him, and only with him, that the telescope gained entrance into science and brought about a development of decisive importance.

Since the end of the thirteenth century, spectacle-makers had worked glass into the form of lenses to correct defective vision. But for centuries lenses failed to receive serious consideration from official science, which was unable to explain their functioning. Not until the close of the sixteenth and the beginning of the seventeenth century did things begin to change, largely through the efforts of Giovanni Baptista della Porta and Johannes Kepler.[2] Porta examined this curious phenomenon in the seventeenth book (dedicated exclusively to optical matters) of his expanded *Magia naturalis* (*Natural Magic*) in 1589, and returned to the subject in his *De refractione* (*On Refraction*) in 1593. In 1604, Kepler published an interesting volume which dealt with the phenomena of refraction under the title *Ad Vitellionem paralipomena* (*Supplement to Vitellio;* i.e., to the treatise on perspective written by Witelo in the thirteenth century). Here Kepler gave for the first time a precise explanation of the properties of lenses. From these publications it appears that both Porta and Kepler were in a position to arrive at the construction of the telescope. The fact remains that neither did so, nor can we give any weight to Porta's reproach against Galileo that his "pretended invention" could be found in the pages of the *Natural Magic.*[3]

What had happened with single lenses was more or less repeated

Galileo Galilei

with the telescope. It is said to have been first constructed by an Italian in 1590, and copied in the final years of the sixteenth century by ordinary Dutch spectacle-makers [4] who worked without the slightest reference to theoretical considerations. These able inventors sought to present their discovery to princes and governments in the autumn of 1608, pointing out its special advantage for military purposes, but with little success even from a commercial point of view. Scholars remained oblivious to the invention; not even Porta or Kepler heard about it.

It was only toward the middle of 1609 that news of the curious device reached the ears of Galileo; perhaps a model even came into his hands.[5] Certainly he was quick to display an active interest in it, and in August of that year he worked to construct one with notable improvements. Repeated experiments satisfied him that the new apparatus had remarkable enlarging power; like the first inventors, he sensed that it had useful application in practical fields. With a disregard for the rights of others that is really perplexing, he therefore decided to offer it as his own to the Venetian Republic in order to obtain the maximum personal profit from it. The presentation took place on the twenty-fifth of August 1609 and aroused great enthusiasm among the representatives of the Venetian government, especially the Procurator Antonio Priuli, who was one of the Regents of the University of Padua. Galileo received an offer of lifetime renewal of his contract (which was to expire the following year), with an increase in salary to one thousand florins per year. The event aroused murmurs among his adversaries, especially when it became known that the invention was by no means original. But the astronomical observations made shortly afterward incontestably demonstrated to Galileo himself, as well as to both friends and enemies, that the instinctive common faith in the telescope had not been misplaced.

Later, describing his invention, Galileo wrote in one place that he had arrived at it on the basis of profound considerations of perspective, and in another that he had drawn it from the doctrine of refraction. Modern critics will grant neither claim. Up to 1609, Galileo had not been occupied in optical researches; hence it is impossible that he could have employed any exact reasoning with regard to the laws of refraction. His construction (or rather reconstruction) of the telescope was the result either of pure trial and error or at best of brief and exclusively qualitative reasoning. It was, in a word, the result of a process which more resembled the empirical practices of those simple spectacle-makers than the scientific approach that might have been pursued by a Porta or a Kepler.[6] Jean Tarde interrogated Galileo in November 1614 concerning the construction of a telescope in such a way as to achieve a previously assigned enlargement. According to Tarde's diary, he received only the reply that this science was not yet well understood. Galileo did mention Kepler's *Dioptrics* of 1611 (where the complete theory of the telescope was explained), but told Tarde that the book was so obscure that perhaps not even its own author had understood it. Clearly Galileo had not found time, in the five years that had elapsed, to go deeply into geometric optics. So much the less could he have known about the subject in 1609.[7]

Should we add a word of censure? Surely we have the right to do so. But then we have an equal right to reproach Kepler for not having invented the telescope first (or at least first among the scientists), since he was doubtless better informed concerning the laws of optics than his fellows.[8] The curious thing is that in his *Dioptrics*, Kepler not only gave the correct theory of the Galilean telescope with concave eyepiece, but also that of the much more efficient[9] instrument with convex eyepiece, known today as the Keplerian telescope; yet he made not the slightest attempt actually to construct it. This was done about 1615 by the Jesuit Father Christopher Scheiner, who described it in a book published in 1630.

The truth is that in the history of human thought it makes no sense to hurl reproaches. The task of history is not to blame one scientist for failing to make discoveries that fell to another. Its task is to establish with precision the contributions of each, and their lives and researches. In the particular case of Galileo and Kepler, the recognition that to a high degree each had positive qualities not possessed by the other should help us to understand the striking difference in the cultural impact of the two men.

Vasco Ronchi, in his book *Galileo e il cannocchiale* (*Galileo*   37

Galileo Galilei

and the Telescope), recognized explicitly that neither the invention of the telescope by craftsmen in Holland nor its reinvention by Galileo "constitute episodes deserving of great admiration from the standpoint of theory." The special interest of the telescope, he explained, "lies in the process by which the world of science, which at first did not even want to know about this novelty, in the end came to recognize it as a real treasure"; and it was precisely here that "the potent intervention of Galileo leaps into importance."

Within this process there should be distinguished two separate steps: that in which Galileo personally gave his entire confidence to the telescope, and that in which he succeeded in spreading this faith among his contemporaries. We must pause briefly to consider the first of these steps in order to be able to explain more fully the second, which coincides with the period of polemics following the lucky astronomical discoveries that Galileo made by means of the telescope.[10]

Because Galileo had no rigorous scientific knowledge of the laws of refraction, he could not establish his own faith in the telescope on a sound theoretical base. His faith was at first something instinctive, more the product of enthusiasm than of reflection. Later on it became a faith founded on facts; that is, on repeated demonstrations that objects appeared identical whether observed at a distance through the telescope or close at hand with the naked eye.

Ronchi declared that Galileo was not the first to turn the telescope upon the heavens, but that he was the first to grasp the enormous interest of the things thus seen. And he understood at once that these things fitted in perfectly with the Copernican theory, whereas they contradicted the old astronomy. Galileo had believed for years in the truth of Copernicanism, but he had never been able to demonstrate it, despite his excessively optimistic statements to friends and colleagues. Should direct proof be at last sought here? The more this conviction took root in his mind, the clearer to him became the importance of the new instrument.

In Galileo's own mind, faith in the reliability of the telescope and recognition of its importance were not two separate acts, one

following upon the other; rather, they were two aspects of the

same process, though it was long, laborious, and filled with obstacles. On the twenty-fourth of May 1610, he wrote that he had
tested the telescope "a hundred thousand times on a hundred
thousand stars and other objects." [11] It was the observation of
these "other objects" that had supplied him with proof that the
device was reliable, while the observations of the stars proved its
importance. Twelve months later—the twelfth of May 1611—
faced with the persistent indifference of others to his marvelous
apparatus (and by that time he had a right to consider it "his"),
he was to explain in still greater detail to Piero Dini the slow
and gradual formation of that faith: "nor can it be doubted that
I, over a period of two years now, have tested my instrument (or
rather dozens of my instruments) by hundreds and thousands of
experiments involving thousands and thousands of objects, near
and far, large and small, bright and dark; hence I do not see
how it can enter the mind of anyone that I have simple-mindedly
remained deceived in my observations." [12]

Kepler quickly expressed his complete and influential acceptance of Galileo's astronomical discoveries. He praised the Italian
for having had the courage, "all doubt put aside," to observe the
heavens through the telescope. But Galileo's abandonment of all
doubt was not a sudden act of faith (as Ronchi himself seems to
consider it) ; it was the crown of long research, tightly linked
to experience.

Modern commentators who see in Galileo only a mathematician
and Platonist ought to reflect seriously on the process through
which he arrived at trust in his telescope. They should remember
that it remained throughout Galileo's life the center of his philosophical astronomical research, and in this field he never shifted
his faith to a mathematical basis. For if it is true that his experiments concerning mechanical phenomena always had the character of syntheses between mathematics and experiment (syntheses
in which mathematics often had the upper hand, so that some have
interpreted his experiments as purely theoretical), it is also true
that in the case of the telescope it was experience and not mathematics that led Galileo to a serene faith in the reliability of his
device. Are we to conclude from this that the two aspects of
Galileo's scientific activity—as observer of the skies and as   39

founder of modern mechanics—are somehow discordant? Or should we not admit instead that the usual attempts to sum up those activities are a bit oversimplified?

2. Galileo devoted the latter part of the summer of 1609 to the construction of new and better telescopes. Among other things, he had to consider the importance of devising a usable mounting, in order to record precisely its various positions. Not long afterward, he began the celebrated celestial observations which he prosecuted with great intensity to the end of that year. By the first of January 1610 he was in a position to announce some astonishing results: that the moon was a body quite similar to the earth, with even higher mountains, and that the Milky Way appeared to be "a congeries of very minute stars." Immediately thereafter he discovered first three, and then four, satellites of Jupiter.

Realizing the revolutionary importance of such observations with regard to the system of the world, Galileo hastened to Venice on January 30 with the partly completed manuscript of a little book that would carry the exciting news to the scientists of the whole world. On the twelfth of March the *Starry Messenger* (*Sidereus Nuncius*) appeared at Venice, written in Latin, and addressed to the world of science. A week later Galileo sent a copy to Cosimo II de' Medici, with the gift of a "very good" telescope and a promise to send him another, still better. But his most conspicuous tribute was the name he gave to the four moons of Jupiter: the "Medicean planets," after the family of the Grand Duke.

What induced Galileo to pay Cosimo such an honor? The main motive was clearly personal. For several years Galileo had been growing tired of his post at Padua. There, despite repeated increases in salary, his pay was still too small for his economic needs and those of his burdensome family, and thus he was constrained to spend too much of his time teaching, to the detriment of pure scientific research. For that reason he had begun some very delicate negotiations to obtain from his former pupil, now Grand Duke of Tuscany, a way of life that could finally free him from his financial worries and the duty of teaching. The greater the homage, the more favorable was likely to be the disposition of the Grand Duke toward his distinguished former teacher. In addition to this economic motive, there was a quite different kind of reason, hardly less important. Galileo was well aware of the hostility that his discoveries would have to face in the scientific world, and he sought by every means to obtain universal recognition of their truth as quickly as possible. The most appropriate means, at that time, was to gain for the discoveries in question the patronage of the ruling class and of the Church. Hence the device of linking the fate of Jupiter's satellites by name with that of the powerful Medici family, and the presentation of "exquisite" telescopes first to Cosimo II, and shortly afterward to the chief monarchs and princes of all Europe.

Cosimo showed himself most grateful for the dedication of these stars to the House of Medici, and presented to their discoverer a valuable gold chain and medal. Before long, in a letter dated the fifth of June, Belissario Vinta (as secretary to the Grand Duke) advised Galileo that Cosimo had decided to employ him as "Chief Mathematician of the University of Pisa and Philosopher of the Grand Duke, without obligation to teach and reside at the University or in the city of Pisa, and with a salary of one thousand Florentine scudi per annum" to begin upon his arrival at Florence. Galileo accepted, and the official appointment was signed on the tenth of July.[13]

Galileo's move from Padua to Florence took place at the beginning of September, and marked his lasting separation from the mother of his children. He desired to solve all his practical and domestic affairs as quickly as possible, that he might dedicate himself completely to the great scientific questions that were opening before him.

His hurried departure much displeased the Venetian rulers, especially in view of the fact that less than a year had elapsed since the renewal of his professorial contract in a manner intended to link him for life to the University of Padua. They did nothing to detain him, but they showed themselves gravely offended.[14] One of them wrote to Sagredo suggesting that he break the friendship which had bound him for years to the Pisan scientist.

Meanwhile, Galileo continued his astronomical researches at a sweeping pace. Shortly before his departure from Padua, he observed sunspots, which had been mentioned in a general way in antiquity; Virgil, for instance, seems to have spoken of this phenomenon in his *Georgics*. It seems, however, that Galileo did not fully recognize their importance at once, and contented himself with showing them to some of his friends, among whom were Fra Paolo Sarpi and Fra Fulgenzio Micanzio.[15] About the same time he noticed the strange appearance of Saturn, most distant of the known planets, which to his telescope appeared as a central star with two small adjoining stars. Not long after his arrival at Florence he was able to commence observations of Venus and soon detected its phases, analogous to those of the moon. Since he did not have time publish a full account of these discoveries, but wished to assure himself of priority regarding them, he made use of a device common at that time: he communicated anagrams containing the news, to Kepler in the case of Saturn, and to Giuliano de' Medici in the case of Venus. The first of these anagrams was SMAJSMRMJLMEPOETALEVNJPVNENVGTTQVJRAS, which Kepler deciphered as *Salve umbistineum geminatum Martia proles*, mistakenly thinking it referred to two newly discovered satellites of Mars. Galileo eventually revealed the true reading: *Altissimum planetam tergeminum observavi*, "I have observed the most distant planet to be three-bodied." The second anagram was cast by Galileo into a mock Latin sentence, *Haec immatura a me iam frustra leguntur o. y.* ("These are at present too young to be read by me o. y."), which when recast gave the message: *Cynthiae figuras aemulatur mater amorum*: "The mother of love imitates Cynthia's shapes"; that is, Venus has the changing forms of the moon.

Astonishment at such great novelties spread through the entire cultured world of the time, and the fame of the great scientist quickly reached even the most distant countries. Evidence of this is supplied by a letter sent to Galileo on the eighth of March 1612 by a Polish nobleman (Christopher, Duke of Zbaraz): "Your brilliant Medicean stars have penetrated all the way to the frigid Muscovite zone. A friend of mine has sent your little book to me from Italy, doing worthy homage to so rare a mind. Ptolemy himself lacked the advantage of possessing all these teachings; our own age, in comparison with that of antiquity, will be celebrated by all. . . . I am very glad that your name will be consecrated to immortality, and honored and admired by everyone." [16]

3. As Galileo had foreseen, the publication of the *Starry Messenger* aroused not only applause and admiration, but also doubts and harsh criticism. Various sources correctly accused him of not being the true inventor of the telescope. Some were men of science, such as Porta and Kepler; others were technicians. Though these accusations were true, they did not detract from Galileo's merit. Indeed, the very number and variety of persons who laid claim to invention of the telescope almost before the ink was dry in Galileo's book demonstrated clearly both the interest aroused by the *Starry Messenger* and the fact that it had convinced very wide circles of the importance of the new device. One writer even claimed he had beaten Galileo by several days in the discovery of the satellites of Jupiter. This was that same Simon Mayr who was mentioned earlier in connection with the famous polemic on the military and geometric compass. Even if it had been true, the fact would not deprive Galileo of credit for having made the discovery independently, for having immediately grasped its revolutionary importance, and for having been the first to diffuse this startling discovery through the whole scientific world.[17]

Of still greater interest are the objections of some who denied the validity of the discoveries made by means of the telescope. The most intransigent adversary of this instrument (though indeed the least dangerous) was the Aristotelian Cesare Cremonini, the former colleague and intimate friend of Galileo at the University of Padua. He persisted so stubbornly in developing the theory of the heavens according to the ancient schemes that he did not even feel the need to take issue with Galileo over his revolutionary discoveries, nor did he attempt to look through the telescope. A letter sent to Galileo on the twenty-ninth of July 1611 by Paolo Gualdo (an acquaintance of both the friendly adversaries) recounted the outcome of a visit to Cremonini during which Gualdo brought up the subject of a book *Disputatio de coelo* (*Discourse on the Heavens*) which Cremonini was about to publish (and indeed did publish in 1613): "Not long ago I was at Dr. Cremonini's house, and commencing to discuss you, I said to him, jokingly, 43

Galileo Galilei

'Signor Galileo is anxious to know what is coming out in your book.' He replied, 'He has no reason for anxiety, because I make no mention whatever of these observations of his.' I answered, 'Probably it is enough for you to hold the exact opposite of what he does.' 'Oh, yes indeed, since I do not want to endorse things of which I have no knowledge whatever, and have not seen.' 'That,' I said, 'is what has annoyed Signor Galileo—that you have not wanted to see them.' He replied, 'I believe that no one but Galileo has seen them; and besides, looking through those spectacles gives me a headache. Enough; I do not want to know any more about it.' " The extract ends with a celebrated reproach which shows simultaneously the philosophical limitations and the political objectivity of the Aristotelian: "Thereafter he burst out, 'Oh, how much better Signor Galileo would have done not to enter into these capricious ideas, and not to leave the freedom of Padua!' " [18]

But the real center of the most severe criticisms directed against the *Starry Messenger* was not Padua; it was Bologna. The ringleader there was the same Giovanni Antonio Magini who had been preferred over Galileo in 1588 for the chair of mathematics at the University of Bologna. It was probably he who suggested the publication at Bologna in 1610 of Martin Horky's celebrated libel, *Brevissima peregrinatio contra Nuncium Sidereum (A very brief excursion against the Starry Messenger).*

Galileo was aware of the danger from his colleague at Bologna and, wishing to overcome this opposition, he went to meet him in person in April 1610. With him he took his own telescope, in order that Magini might see for himself the marvelous discoveries. But the outcome was bad, not only by reason of the ill-will of Magini and his friends, but also because of the actual difficulty of observation.[19] Horky (not, indeed, the most reliable witness) described the unfortunate visit in a letter to Kepler: "Galileo Galilei, Paduan mathematician, came to us at Bologna, bringing his telescope with which he saw four feigned planets. I never slept on the twenty-fourth or twenty-fifth of April, day or night, but I tested this instrument of Galileo's in a thousand ways, both on things here below and on those above. Below, it works wonderfully; in the sky it deceives one, as some fixed stars are seen double. I have as witnesses most excellent men and noble doctors . . . and all have admitted the instrument to deceive. Galileo fell speechless, and on the twenty-sixth . . . departed sadly from the distinguished Doctor Magini." [20]

Father Clavius, celebrated professor of mathematics at the Collegio Romano, also believed at first that Galileo's new discoveries were only an illusion of the lenses. On the tenth of October 1610 Cigoli wrote, among other things, ". . . concerning the four stars, Clavius told a friend of mine that he laughed at them, and that it would be necessary first to build them into some glasses and then to show them, and that Galileo was welcome to his opinion and that he would hold on to his own." [21] By December, however, Clavius had made some careful telescopic observations and was obliged to recognize that Galileo had been right. In due course, Magini also altered his beliefs.

Besides objections based on the poor functioning of the lenses then in use, Galileo had also to overcome some others of a completely different sort. These, which were certainly no less dangerous, were linked to the belief (shared by most scholars of the time) that only direct vision had the power to grasp actual reality. Such men were guided not by a lack of faith in experience, but by an excess of faith in the senses.

To overcome this latter type of objection required philosophical arguments to expose the absurdity of making our eyes the absolute criterion of real existence. Galileo wrote: "Besides, who would wish to say that the light of the Medicean planets does not arrive on the earth? Are we to make our eyes the measure of the expansion of all lights, so that wherever the images of luminous objects do not make themselves sensible to us, it should be affirmed that light does not arrive from them? Perhaps such stars, that remain hidden from our weak vision, are seen by eagles or lynxes." [22] From this recognition of the possibility of visual perception more acute than that of mankind, he went on (and this time the step was easy) to the assumption that an instrument like the telescope may *not distort, but strengthen* our capacity to perceive. Today, doubts of this kind may seem infantile; to appreciate Galileo's achievement, it is necessary to take into account that they constituted extremely grave difficulties in his time. Often   45 the development of science meets its most perilous obstacles precisely in certain prejudices which, once they have been overcome, appear to be banalities pure and simple.

Kepler himself had many reservations, the more so when he felt very strong pressure on all sides to speak out against the Galilean discoveries. His first comments were sent to Galileo on the nineteenth of April 1610, and later published at Prague and Florence under the title *Dissertatio cum Nuncio Sidereo* (*A Conversation with the Starry Messenger*). In this he showed himself firmly, if only generally, convinced of the importance of the news communicated in Galileo's celebrated booklet. He did not conceal his own distaste for some glossing over on the part of the Italian scientist, and in particular reproached him for not having mentioned the names of those who had anticipated the invention of the telescope, at least in theory; above all, those of Porta and himself.

But as soon as Kepler had in his own hands a good telescope, sent by Galileo to the Elector of Cologne, he began immediately to carry out accurate celestial observations. These lasted from the thirtieth of August to the ninth of September, and Kepler took care above all else to establish the existence of the Medicean planets. When he was certain of the scientific reliability of the Galilean discoveries, he so stated immediately in the *Narratio de observatis a se quattuor Jovis satellibus erronibus* (*Narrative of personal observations of the four wandering satellites of Jupiter*), which he published at Frankfurt in 1611. It included some epigrams by Thomas Seggeth which contained the celebrated exclamation: *Vicisti Galilaee.*[23] The text of Kepler's *Narratio* ends with these significant words: "To you indeed, gentle reader, by this sharing, such as it is, some scanty and hasty observations with the public, I recommended that either you follow my faith and that of my testimonies, all doubts laid aside, and henceforth know the naked truth; or look forth from a good instrument, which in the present matters brings down to you an eyewitness." [24]

Kepler and the mathematicians of the Collegio Romano were universally recognized as the chief scientific authorities of the age, and Galileo knew that only their agreement would vanquish once and for all the objections to his discoveries. As to Kepler, the

The First Fortunate Astronomical Observations

Narratio of 1611 was undoubtedly sufficient for the purpose. As to the others, however, it was clearly not sufficient to have a private letter from Father Clavius, like that which he sent to Galileo in December 1610; it would be necessary to obtain something further, something on the subject that could be given publicity. And it was to this end that Galileo decided, shortly after he arrived at Florence, to ask permission from the Grand Duke to undertake as soon as possible a scientific journey to Rome. Because of the great enthusiasm of the moment, he foresaw correctly that by the persuasive force of his words and his telescope, it would be easy enough for him to gain full and complete assent to the great astronomical novelties—and not only from the Jesuits, but from the top hierarchy of the Church as well.

The trip was in fact made in the early months of 1611, and Galileo arrived at Rome on the first of April. From the beginning his visit assumed the proportions of a triumph. He was immediately received with the greatest courtesy by various cardinals and then by Pope Paul V himself, who, as the height of benevolence, would not permit Galileo to remain kneeling during the audience as prescribed in the ceremonial then in use.

Great honors were also paid to him by [Marquis, later] Prince Federico Cesi, one of the most influential personages of the Roman scientific world. It was he who had founded the Academy of the Lincei in 1603, and he now proceeded promptly to enroll in it its most distinguished member. From that time on, Galileo's most important letters carried the signature: Galileo Galilei Linceo.[25] His reception by the Jesuit fathers was also of the best, and took place in an atmosphere of frank scientific discussion. In a letter to Belissario Vinta, the Tuscan secretary of state, Galileo related that: ". . . The next day I was with the Jesuit fathers, and spoke at length with Father Clavius and two very learned mathematicians, and with his pupils. . . . I found that the said fathers, having finally learned the truth of the new Medicean planets, have for two months made almost continual observations of them, which are still going on; and we have compared them with my own, to which they correspond most accurately." [26]

As a matter of fact, the Jesuits agreed with Galileo's astronomical observations, but not with his interpretation of them. Nevertheless, the visit was a noteworthy success, and for the moment Galileo could not have hoped for more from them. Official confirmation was given to Galileo's discoveries by the powerful fathers in a solemn meeting held in the Collegio Romano in May 1611 in his presence. At this meeting, Father Odo van Maelcote read the address, which was entitled *Nuncius sidereus Collegii Romani (The Starry Messenger of the Roman College)*.

In order to understand Jesuit resistance to Galileo's interpretation of the new astronomical discoveries, it is necessary to note that although these fathers undoubtedly represented at that moment the religious order which was most open-minded toward the exact sciences, they were nevertheless the most loyal custodians of Catholic orthodoxy. They intended therefore to use their scientific competence to one end above all, that of preventing any conflict between modern science and dogma. After all, the most authoritative living representative of the spirit of the Counter-Reformation was the Jesuit Robert Cardinal Bellarmine (1542–1621), who had for ten years been professor of disputation at the Collegio Romano and was later the Pope's own theologian, adviser to the Holy Office, and examiner of bishops.

During these very days when Galileo commenced to enjoy his first successes at Rome, Cardinal Bellarmine was hastening to send to the mathematicians of the Collegio Romano detailed questions concerning their opinions of the new astronomical discoveries. He received a reply, signed by Christopher Clavius and three other fathers, which set forth with great care their points of agreement and dissent. As a matter of fact, Bellarmine himself had observed the sky through the telescope; what was clearly worrying him now was the atmosphere of excessive novelty which seemed to emanate from this instrument. He did not succeed in hiding his own suspicions with respect either to the discoveries themselves or their too-dynamic discoverer. What influence might these singular developments in science have upon the general conception of the universe, and thus indirectly upon the sacred principles of traditional theology?

Anticipating the reply that the future would give to this question, the Congregation of the Holy Office decided, on the six-

The First Fortunate Astronomical Observations

teenth of May 1611, with Cardinal Bellarmine present, to obtain secret and precise information as to whether the name of Galileo was involved in the trial then going on against Cremonini, a trial in which the Aristotelian was to be victoriously defended by the authority of the Venetian Republic: *videatur an in processu Doct. Caesaris Cremonini sit nominatus Galilaeus, Philosophiae et Mathematicae Professor.*[27]

4. Father Müller maintains with regard to the new things set forth in the *Starry Messenger* that Galileo must be considered more as a "lucky finder" than as an authentic discoverer worthy of credit.[28] They were, he continues, "purely matters of time and often only of days." [29] In particular, he asserts that the discovery of the moons of Jupiter could not be ascribed solely to the Italian; he says they had been seen at almost the same time by the German Simon Mayr. Father Müller recognized in Galileo principally one distinction, that "of having brought these objects to general attention through publication of his *Starry Messenger.*"

This is not the place to go into the question whether or not Mayr did discover the Medicean planets simultaneously with and independently of Galileo.[30] Nevertheless, Müller's general thesis seems to me to call for at least brief discussion, if only to make clear its points of agreement and disagreement with the view defended here.

That the discoveries of Galileo were "purely matters of time and often only of days" seems to me a perfectly acceptable statement. But practically the same thing may be said about all scientific discoveries, not only those of an experimental nature, but also those which are essentially theoretical. One need only think of the invention of the infinitesimal calculus, which constitutes one of Newton's principal claims to fame. Today everyone knows that this had its direct antecedents in the studies of Cavalieri, Torricelli, Fermat, Pascal, and Barrow; so that if we want to be strict about it, it would be better to say that the calculus was the fruit of a century rather than of a man. Moreover, the calculus was rediscovered by Leibniz shortly after and independently of Newton, and each was able to claim in good faith that he had been the true originator of this new and important branch of mathematics. The fact is that even inventions of the greatest genius are never the fruit of one isolated individual, but always of a scholar who lives and works in a specific culture. This does not detract from the fact that it has indeed been this scholar and not some other whose achievement it is, for which reason a special merit belongs to him, separate from the general merit belonging to the culture in which he grew up.

Müller affirms further that "nothing could have been more natural than to turn the new optical instrument on the heavenly bodies." [31] Unless we can divest ourselves of the modern scientific spirit, we cannot understand the difficulties of an action that is today so automatic. But if we reflect for a moment on the disputes raised by Galileo's announcements, it becomes clear that his actions, which with the passage of time have become so "natural," must have required no little boldness in the man who first managed to perform them. To believe in the telescope when it is turned toward the sky means to believe in the existence of that which it enables us to perceive, even though in principle there is no way to verify that existence by direct vision. Who can deny that this faith implied a veritable methodological revolution?

Thus Vasco Ronchi insists too much on the "faith" that must have guided Galileo in the bold act of pointing the telescope toward the sky. According to Ronchi, this act was motivated more by Galileo's enthusiastic temperament than by any precise scientific reasoning on his part. Müller, on the other hand, advances the opposite thesis; he would remove all difficulty from the same action and present it as perfectly natural.

I maintain that historical truth is to be found in an intermediate position; that is, in the recognition that in order to carry out the act in question, Galileo had in fact to overcome some serious difficulties—serious from the psychological point of view—and that he overcame them not by an appeal to faith, nor by means of his own enthusiastic spirit, but rather through serious and well-weighed reasoning. It was not mathematical reasoning, such as Kepler (who knew the laws of optics) might have used. Nevertheless it was an equally rational act, at least from Galileo's point of view, because it was based upon thousands of observations of terrestrial objects, with respect to which the accuracy of the telescope could be experimentally tested, and upon the extension of this concept to cases in which such verification became impossible.

5. It will be good now to examine some philosophical and methodological implications of the attitude Galileo displayed toward the telescope; that is, his conviction that it did not distort, but fortified, the direct perception of reality. There is implicit here a profound alteration of ancient empiricism. In order to assume the existence of stars which, like the Medicean planets, are not seen by our eyes, it is necessary to assume—in accordance with ancient rationalism—that our eyes are not perfect (nor are our other senses). It is also necessary to assume, however, that this imperfection is not a sufficient reason for condemning our senses and appealing instead to some entirely different source of knowledge. Galileo's new attitude was to become characteristic of modern experimental science: faced by the imperfection of our senses, the scientist has the task not of condemning sensory knowledge, but of creating means to render it gradually more perfect.

Galileo often affirmed in letters of this period that mankind has two instruments for knowing: "sensory experience" and "rigorous demonstration." Yet this does not mean that he saw an actual duality in these instruments, or that he assumed some type of antithesis between experience and reason. On the contrary, he saw in them a profound dynamic unity: experience and reason are, in his view, capable of ever-increasing perfection, and each is constantly necessary to the other in order to realize its gradual perfection. In modern terms, Galileo would say that every scientific research is always in process of development; mankind has the task of pushing it ahead by means of all available techniques, empirical or rational.

There may indeed be reason to believe that a certain indirect influence was exercised on the birth of this conception by Galileo's own critique directed against the Aristotelian (though not exclusively Aristotelian) concept of perfection as an absolute quality of things. During these years, Galileo developed this critique with particular attention to geometric forms; later he was to repeat it with reference to numbers, in an open attack on the 51

Galileo Galilei

Pythagoreans. Both times the operationalist orientation of Galileo's reasoning is clear: the word *perfection* signifies nothing if considered in isolation, but it acquires a very precise import if referred to a "means-end" process, where the means may be called more or less perfect according as they turn out to be more or less appropriate for achieving the end.

The subject that furnished Galileo with the occasion to unfold his interesting critique of the concept of absolute perfection was the examination of one of the most characteristic objections raised by the Peripatetics against the mountainous character of the moon. Here was a typical example of an *a priori* objection: the moon *cannot* be mountainous because that would deprive it of the spherical form which belongs to all of the heavenly bodies as an absolutely perfect form. Galileo's reply courageously confronted the assumed "ultimate" on which the entire argument about the sphericity of the heavenly bodies was based: "The reasoning," he wrote, "is trite enough among the Peripatetic schools, but I think that its main strength consists only in its being an inveterate idea in the minds of men, and not in its propositions being either demonstrated or necessary; indeed, I believe that they are very shaky and uncertain. In the first place I do not see how it is possible to assert that the spherical form is absolutely more or less perfect than the others. One can say this only with respect to some particular thing—thus, for example, for a body that must be able to rotate in every direction, the spherical form is most perfect; and for that reason the eyes and the ends of the thigh bones have been made by nature perfectly spherical. On the other hand, for a body that must remain stable and motionless, this shape would be the most impractical of all; and anyone who in the construction of a wall should make use of spherical stones would do very badly, because angular stones are the most perfect. . . ." [32]

The methodological importance of this reply requires no stress. Galileo will not allow the ascription of perfection "absolutely," but only "with respect to something"; in this way, perfection is made to come down from the absolute plane of metaphysics to the technical plane of science, and may then acquire an internal dynamic quality which was formerly precluded. Thus understood, the perfection or imperfection of an object, and in particular of an instrument, is no longer judged in generalities but only relative to a well-determined use. It is, therefore, possible for an instrument to be perfect with respect to a given purpose, and yet to be strengthened and made more perfect with respect to some other end.

Applying this concept to those particular instruments which we call our senses, we may conclude that it is permissible to assume that they have a decisive value from the viewpoint of certain kinds of knowledge, without thereby denying the necessity of correcting and strengthening them when other kinds of knowledge are in question. What is denied is the acceptance of any instrument of knowledge as perfect, for that would limit all research to a quest for new means to improve the knowledge already in our possession.

6. Galileo's polemic against absolute perfection takes its place among the weapons in his critical arsenal because it is a part of his general resistance against every attempt to introduce unverifiable concepts into science. For Galileo, the superiority of relative over absolute perfection depends on the fact that the former can be verified by testing whether the given means serves the end relative to which it is judged perfect, whereas absolute perfection evades every test.

It was in the discussion of a new and subtle stratagem dreamed up by the Peripatetics for the purpose of denying the mountains of the moon that Galileo expressed with particular clarity his condemnation of every surreptitious introduction of unverifiable entities into science, though in a less explicit form the same condemnation figures frequently in his works, sometimes on the most significant pages in them. The stratagem in question was devised by Father Clavius for the purpose of reconciling the results of the new celestial telescopic observations with the old Aristotelian theory of the perfect sphericity of the moon. He based it on the postulate that the valleys and mountains of the moon were covered by a crystalline substance which was absolutely transparent, and this was distributed in such a way as to give the moon a perfectly smooth surface. No doubt this argument was invincible, at least in appearance; for by postulating the absolute transparency, and therefore the invisibility, of this crystalline substance, it follows that since it cannot be seen, nothing can be proved against its existence.

Now how did Galileo behave when confronted with this last refuge of the Aristotelians? His reply is as brief as it is efficacious: "Really, this is a beautiful flight of the imagination. . . . The only thing lacking in it is that it is neither demonstrated nor demonstrable." [33] The meaning of his sarcasm is this: Since it is neither demonstrated nor demonstrable, the hypothesis of Father Clavius lack the rights of citizenship in science; it is only a beautiful fancy and nothing more.

We find ourselves thus gradually led from the critique of the absolute value of direct vision to a critique of the concept of absolute perfection, and from that to a decisive refutation that goes to the root of all pseudo-scientific fantasies which turn out to be "neither demonstrated nor demonstrable." It is a position that cannot fail to astonish us by its remarkable modernity.

We need only scan the letters written by Galileo in this period to see how rich they were in acute methodological remarks of the same sort. This very richness constitutes one of the principal fascinations inherent in the numerous and lively disputes in which he engaged. Only the bold objectivity and pointedness that permeate all the arguments used by Galileo against his various critics can explain the extraordinary formative power those arguments had over scientists of the seventeenth century, and the exceptional interest that grew up around the Galilean discoveries. The fact is that the scientific campaign conducted by Galileo was based not only on new discoveries, but also, and chiefly, on the new methodological maturity which they revealed.

Chapter 4

The Ambitious Program

1. When Galileo left Padua for Florence in September 1610, his young son Vincenzio remained for a time with Marina Gamba. His elder daughter, Virginia, had already left Padua some time before, returning with her paternal grandmother to Florence at the conclusion of a visit by the latter to Galileo; the younger daughter, Livia, accompanied her father to Florence. At first the girls lived with his mother there, but this arrangement was destined not to last because of the elderly woman's character, and he could think of no other solution except that of putting them in a convent. Accordingly, toward the end of 1613, they went to the Convent of San Matteo in Arcetri, in the hills above Florence. Because of their youth (they were then thirteen and twelve years of age), they did not at this time joint the convent as nuns, but as soon as they reached the age of sixteen, in 1616 and 1617, respectively, the two girls assumed the vows. Virginia took the name of Sister Maria Celeste, and Livia became Sister Arcangela.

Various reasons have been offered to explain Galileo's behavior toward his daughters, for if not unquestionably cruel, it certainly disregarded their wishes. There is no denying the fact that even though the older girl accepted in a spirit of resignation the life imposed upon her by her father, and indeed revealed a true religious vocation, the younger daughter suffered much from it, and developed a complaining and unpleasant character. A sort of general justification for Galileo's action may be found in the customs of the day—sad indeed, but well known—and another, more personal, in the fact that the girls were illegitimate and hence could scarcely hope to find husbands within social strata commensurate with the high position occupied by their father.

Beneath it all, however, lay Galileo's desire to find for them a mode of life which would not entail new responsibilities for him 55 in the future, and would relieve him of all worry on the subject forever. We may succeed rather easily in understanding this desire, especially when we consider what he had gone through in the past with respect to members of his own family, as well as the great social and cultural problems that were taking shape then in his mind, but it is impossible to overlook the fact that the desire masked a paplpable and profound egoism in him. It frequently is the case that even the greatest men show in their personal characters a side unworthy of their greatness.

In this period (1611 to 1615), Galileo's strictly scientific production revolved around two special problems: those of floating bodies, and those of the sunspots. In both instances he became involved, not voluntarily, but because he was driven to it by spoken or written attacks.

Galileo had hardly returned from his triumphant visit to Rome when he took part in a dispute among some more or less friendly philosophers and scientists concerning the properties of cold. The argument led to a discussion of floating bodies and the possible explanations of this phenomenon. Galileo explained and defended the law of Archimedes, while others defended the theory of Aristotle. The discussion was resumed a few days later at another meeting, to which Lodovico delle Colombe, a Florentine man of letters and avowed opponent of Copernicus, had been invited to support the Aristotelian party. The debate widened and became more interesting as it went along, and in the end it was repeated at the table of the Grand Duke Cosimo II on an occasion when members of the ruling family and some distinguished guests took part in it. Maffeo Cardinal Barberini (the future Pope Urban VIII) took sides with Galileo, while Federico Cardinal Gonzaga upheld the Aristotelians. Cosimo himself proposed that the disputants reduce their arguments to writing.

Thus was born Galileo's *Discourse Concerning Bodies Placed in Water,* which was published in May 1612 and dedicated to the Grand Duke. In the opening pages of this book, Galileo mentioned his further researches on the satellites of Jupiter, his discoveries concerning Venus and Saturn, and his observations of sunspots. The book had a great success, and a second edition was brought out before the end of the year. On the other hand, it called forth heated replies on the part of several of Galileo's adversaries. Special importance attaches to a booklet by Colombe entitled *Apologetic Discourse Concerning Galileo's Discourse,* published at Florence in 1612. Against this and another similar attack, a *Reply to the Oppositions* was eventually published in 1615, also at Florence. Although this book appeared over the name of Galileo's former pupil, Benedetto Castelli, it was inspired, corrected, and to a large extent actually written by Galileo himself.

Likewise Galileo's essay on sunspots had a definitely polemic nature. His observations of the sun may go back to 1610, but at that time he neither published nor wrote on the discovery of the celebrated spots, and at most he discussed them with some friends at Venice. They were shown in the following year to various persons at Rome, but still nothing was written about them. Only a few months later, the phenomenon began to arouse the liveliest interest on the part of the German Jesuit Father Christopher Scheiner, professor of mathematics and Hebrew at the University of Ingolstadt.[1] It is not a simple matter to determine whether Scheiner was led to his observations of sunspots by suggestions emanating from his Roman colleagues or whether (as is more probable) he hit on them by himself. But it is certainly a fact that in November and December 1611 he sent three important letters on the subject to Mark Welser, a magistrate and leading citizen of Augsburg. Welser was intimately linked with the Jesuits and was in fact one of their bankers. He published the letters on the fifth of January 1612, concealing the name of their true author under the pseudonym Apelles.

A copy of this interesting publication was immediately sent by Welser to Galileo. Although he may have been offended, he had no reason to feel himself robbed of a discovery of his own, since up to that time he had written nothing concerning the matter, nor had he made sunspots the object of precise studies.[2] In any event Galileo's reply was not long in coming, and it also took the form of a series of letters. The three letters of "Apelles" and the three of Galileo, all addressed to Mark Welser, were published in 1613 under the auspices of the Lincean Academy under the title, *History and Demonstrations Concerning Sunspots and*

Their Phenomena. . . . The book was dedicated to the Florentine nobleman Filippo Salviati.[3]

The dispute lasted for many years and was equally spirited on both sides. But while Galileo confronted many other problems, Father Scheiner occupied himself especially with solar observations, so that he eventually became the greater expert on this matter. In 1630 he was to publish a basic treatise on sunspots entitled *Rosa Ursina.*[4]

Both the book on floating bodies and that on sunspots had an obviously occasional nature. During this period, Galileo neither published nor began to write anything of a more systematic nature, such as that "Treatise on the System of the World" which he had promised his readers some years earlier in the *Starry Messenger.* Considering that he was at last free from all teaching tasks and family worries, the question is why he did not take advantage of this liberty to compose the promised treatise, to resume and complete the remarkable mechanical researches he had begun at Padua, or to develop his investigations of lenses. Why was it that he never found time to read Kepler's fundamental works on optics and astronomy? Clearly he must have been less interested in these than in something else.

The fact is that all the evidence we have proves that Galileo's interest at this time was moving away from pure scientific research to active cultural propaganda. As the years passed, he became more and more convinced that one thing above all was necessary: to spread belief in Copernicanism more and more widely, and in this way to inculcate the spirit of modern science in the greatest possible number of persons. This propagandist spirit underlies the *Discourse on Bodies in Water* and emerges still more clearly in the *Letters on Sunspots.* It was to become the dominant note in some celebrated letters, not published but circulated among his friends, in which he sought to demonstrate the compatibility of the Copernican theory with Catholic dogma. These were the letter to Benedetto Castelli of December 21, 1613, two letters to Monsignor Piero Dini dated February 16 and March 23, 1615, and the *Letter to Madam Christina* which he wrote at various intervals and completed in the latter half of 1615.

The Ambitious Program

2. In order to comprehend the value which Galileo attached to the defense and propagation of the Copernican theory, we must first understand the new significance which he gave to that theory.

Some previous thinkers—for example, Giordano Bruno [5]— had already given to Copernicanism a meaning much broader than the predominantly astronomical signification which it had originally possessed. That is, these men interpreted adherence to this system as a sharp break with the entire medieval Aristotelian universe, and as the beginning of a new conception of reality. Although something analogous may be said of Galileo, his position differed sharply in several respects.

Bruno tended to broaden the Copernican theory in a purely philosophical or metaphysical direction, in which precise scientific consequences were lacking. He made the heliocentric system the point of departure for a philosophy of nature that was rich in new ideas but poor in rigorous thinking. His reasoning was full of allegories, references to magic, and broad generalizations that were quite unverifiable; Bruno's arguments shattered the old Aristotelian physics only to replace it with still less rigorous schemes. It did not inaugurate a new type of research methodologically different from that which he criticized.

Galileo gave to Bruno's program a completely different direction. For him, the Copernican conception possessed the unique property of being a point of convergence for all new scientific research—mathematical, astronomical, and mechanical. Its acceptance required the adoption of the methodology that makes such sciences possible; to reject Copernicanism meant adherence instead to all the old prejudices. The philosophical importance of the Copernican theory, in his opinion, was not that it opened the way to some new metaphysics, but that it rendered impossible any loyalty to the old metaphysical spirit.

Keeping in mind these differences between the two great thinkers, it becomes easy to understand why Galileo never felt a need to mention Bruno by name. Kepler reproached him for this neglect in his own day, and many scholars still reproach him for it— scholars who love to linger over the analogies between these two developments of Copernicanism, and to dwell upon some almost identical arguments that are to be found in the works of Bruno

59

and Galileo.[6] Galileo saw perfectly clearly the basic antithesis between the nature of scientific research, for which he was fighting, and that of philosophy applied to natural phenomena, for which Bruno had battled. It made no difference to Galileo whether this philosophy was new or old; any mention whatever that might tend to confuse the two standpoints must have appeared to him to imperil seriously the outcome of his own cultural battle, and was therefore to be avoided at all costs.[7]

At a distance of several centuries, it may seem that Galileo's behavior in regard to Bruno is to be judged ungenerous at best. Would it not have been finer if he had had the courage to extol the prisoner who had been burned for his ideas little more than a decade before? Should he not have dared to recognize frankly that which Bruno's program and his own had in common? (That is, their mutual desire to consider the Copernican theory as more than astronomical, as a truth pregnant with the broadest implications.) Without discussing here whether Galileo's silence concerning Bruno contained an element of timidity (and we shall see that in certain circumstances Galileo behaved with outstanding courage, though in others he was extremely prudent), we may at least say that some very serious theoretical considerations existed to justify his action. To what end, indeed, should he have broken this silence when, however fine it might have been as an act of bravery, this would certainly have given rise to the worst confusion?

The problem of the relations of Bruno and Galileo may today be viewed as part of the wider problem of interpretation of the Renaissance as a whole. It is a chapter in the debate between an idealist intepretation, which finds the culmination of that grandiose movement of thought in the philosophy of Bruno, and the anti-idealist interpretation, which instead identifies this culmination with the science of Galileo. Without attempting to go into the various arguments in favor of either side, it is nevertheless true that the antithesis between these two interpretations which is everywhere apparent simply confirms the existence of a similar antithesis between the two thinkers who are taken as the respective symbols and standard-bearers of the opposing conceptions.

The Ambitious Program

3. The profound disparity between Bruno and Galileo ultimately finds its decisive counterpart in the position of the latter with respect to the Catholic Church.

Students of Galileo and of his two trials generally pause to examine the political, theological, and philosophical reasons that may be used to explain the behavior of the Vatican authorities toward the valorous scientist. On the other hand, they usually pass over as secondary in importance the motives that impelled Galileo to act as he did, and confine themselves to commenting on his imprudence or his thoughtlessness. Some, it is true, have also been concerned to seek justification for Galileo's behavior, and believed that they found it in a supposed anticlericalism that is assumed to have guided his actions. But this explanation is unacceptable, both because it is merely verbal (that is, because one would then have to explain his anticlericalism), and because it does not correspond to the historical realities.

Unlike Bruno, Galileo never raised the question of renovating the philosophical and theological heritage of the Church. Born in a Catholic country, he was a practicing Catholic, but the religious problem as such did not trouble him in the least. He showed no interest at all in proofs of the existence of God or in controversies between one Christian faith and another. That which did interest him in the highest degree, that which aroused his sincere admiration, was the organizational power of the Catholic Church. One must not forget that for a number of years Catholicism had been rapidly reinvigorating itself, and had already regained a good deal of ground against the Protestant churches.

When he named Jupiter's moons the Medicean planets, Galileo proposed to connect them in some way to the fortunes of the potent ruling family of Tuscany. This action was part of his general plan to obtain for the new science the favor and support of all the powerful men of the world, from temporal princes to the Church itself. Galileo considered science not as a private activity of individual scholars but as a matter of public interest that was destined to permeate all society. For this reason he believed that, in order to achieve full development, it needed sustenance and aid from all who occupied positions of command in society. From this belief arose Galileo's particular interest in the Catholic Church; this interest was the more active and sincere, the more evident the organizational power of that great institution became, and the more widespread its influence, especially in the cultural sphere. Thence arose Galileo's conviction that he must try by every means to convert the Church to the cause of science, in order to prevent any rupture between the two that might dangerously retard the development of scientific research.

This, then, is why the problem of the relations between Copernicanism and dogma assumed the highest importance in Galileo's eyes. Copernicanism was for him the crucial turning-point between the old science and the new, while dogma constituted the central pivot of all Catholic cultural organization. Hence there was no other choice: either agreement must be found between the Copernican theory and Catholic dogma, or Church support for the new science would be lost, with great damage to the cause of scientific progress.

In these circumstances, the question arose who was to take upon himself the task of fighting for and obtaining so difficult and so important an agreement. Galileo had no doubts on this score. He considered himself the person best qualified to do it because of the world-wide fame recently gained by his *Starry Messenger,* because of the protection assured to him through the powerful and devoutly Catholic Medici family, and because of his many close personal friendships within the upper hierarchy of the Church. He took up the task for which he felt he was destined with all the enthusiasm of which he was capable. He threw himself into the project, giving it all his energy; soon he had to sacrifice every other activity, even strictly scientific research itself. For about two decades after 1611, pure science ceased to be his main interest. An ambitious project, which in modern terms we may call one of cultural politics, took its place. It was his program to capture for the new science (that is, for Copernicanism) the support of the Catholic Church.

This view of Galileo's behavior from 1611 explains his actions not only up to 1616 (that is, until the first serious setback of his program), but also in the ensuing years, when he found himself forced to change the tactics (though not the strategy) of his great battle. It was only after his second and definitive defeat in 1633 that Galileo had to give up the struggle for this program and resume the purely scientific work in mechanics which he had begun during the Paduan period.

4. Let us now return to the *Discourse on Bodies in Water* and the *Letters on Sunspots.*

The first of these books combines a lively but calm critique of the Aristotelian explanation of floating with a full and profound exposition of the Archimedean explanation of the same phenomenon. According to the Stagirite and his followers, floating is caused by the presence in floating bodies of the element of air, which naturally rises, and by the flat shape of such bodies, which impedes their descent. Archimedes, on the other hand, invoked the difference in the specific gravity of floating bodies and that of water. Of special interest is the examination carried out very acutely by Galileo of the experiments customarily adduced by Aristotelians against Archimedes. Of these, the most significant are drawn from the *Ten Books on Motion* by the philosopher Francesco Buonamico, one of Galileo's professors at Pisa. As Banfi has put it, these "pretended experiments . . . are no more than rough observations without distinction between the mere data and the complex causal relationships. The experiments which Galileo proposes, on the other hand, are designed to lend themselves to the phenomenon in its various states, simplifying it and permitting the illustration of its essential underlying relations." [8]

From the Galilean point of view, the hardest case to explain was the floating of thin metal chips and similar things which have a specific gravity greater than that of water. This appears to contradict the principle of Archimedes. We know now that in reality these bodies do not float, but rest upon the surface of the water because they do not break the film that is formed there as a result of forces of cohesion. Strictly speaking, Galileo did not succeed in giving an exact scientific explanation of the exceptional case in question, but to that end he introduced a very penetrating and interesting hypothesis; namely, that what floats in this case is not the metal chip itself, but a combination of that chip and a layer of air: "the adversaries' chip floats when it is coupled with such a quantity of air as forms, together with it, a body less heavy than that quantity of water which would fill the place occupied by such a combination in the water." [9] It was his merit to perceive that here he was dealing with a special phenomenon, where the exceptional behavior was rooted in the special situation, and that the exception could not be invoked to overthrow general laws, like that of Archimedes, which rest upon a firm experimental foundation.

The interest of the *Discourse,* apart from its content, resides in its methodological observations; these show how rapidly a clear consciousness of the difference between the inexact and purely qualitative experience utilized by the Aristotelians, and the experimentation of the new physics, was developing in Galileo's mind.

A significant observation concerning language not found in the *Discourse* occurs in the *Reply* published in 1615 by Castelli, which is known to be chiefly Galileo's own work. This observation sought to distinguish inaccurate and ambiguous common speech from precise and rigorous scientific language, where every term appears always with the same meaning "most clearly explained"; that precision stands in sharp contrast with the varied and alternating meanings of the same term as used in ordinary language. "Here Signor Colombe begins to enter into an infinite sea of confusion, created by his failure to understand a simple term most clearly explained by Signor Galileo and used a thousand times in the *Discourse;* and this disorder has its root in his not having considered the fact that since there are many different languages in the world, each containing thousands of names arbitrarily imposed by men, Signor Galileo had also every right to introduce a word of his own by first explaining distinctly its meaning." [10] This passage reveals Galileo's awareness of both the conventional nature of scientific definitions and the rigor that this very conventionality enables us to introduce into our reasoning. Clearly he was fully aware of the difference between common language and scientific language; by writing in the colloquial tongue, he did not intend to indulge the ordinary imprecisions of common speech. On the contrary, he proposed to educate the common man to the rigor that is indispensable to science.

As to the *Letters on Sunspots*, it is useless to explore further the problem of priority of discovery. Since this was a question on which each contestant felt he was defending his personal honor, both Father Scheiner and Galileo treated it with a spitefulness beneath the scientific dignity of either man. The dispute went on for years. Galileo was much to blame; indeed, he let himself be dominated far too much, in controversies of this sort, by his restless and proud spirit. Yet without any doubt the faults of his stubborn and vindictive opponent were far more serious. In fact, it is probable that Father Scheiner himself was among the chief instigators of Galileo's trial in 1633—a fault so much the graver when it is considered that, as an able astronomer, Scheiner understood better than other men the arguments in favor of Copernicanism.

Putting aside the personal aspect of this affair, it suffices to note the most characteristic point on which the original dispute between the two scientists turned; that is, the interpretation of sunspots. Father Scheiner took them to be stars rotating about the sun at some distance from it. The advantage of this theory (which he later abandoned) was principally that it connected the cause of the spots with something outside the sun itself, and in that way it preserved the "perfection" attributed to that celestial body by ancient astronomy. Galileo answered this by remarking that the spots, when carefully observed, do not show the sort of constancy which ought to characterize even a complex system of stars. By the irregularity of their formation and dissolution, sunspots are more like clouds than heavenly bodies. This in turn suggests that they exist in a fluid material not external to the sun, but situated on its surface, or at the very most that they belong to its atmosphere. In the fact that the spots evidently turn on the surface of the sun, Galileo discerned a direct proof of the sun's rotation on its own axis, and this seemed to him to be a valid proof of the Copernican system; for he, like Kepler, was convinced of the existence of some relation between the rotation of the sun and the revolutions of the planets around it.[11] Hence   65 a manifestation of the former, through the movement of the spots, seemed to afford a direct verification of the latter.

Though Galileo's conclusions about sunspots were important, the path he followed in arriving at them was still more so. As Banfi wrote, his procedure furnished "a maximum of concrete certainty to the inductive procedure" and made the work a true "model of method." It is useful to add that this methodological perfection is reflected not only in the rigor of the inductions, but also in the terminological critique. This is an aspect of major interest, though it is usually ignored by Galilean scholars. We may illustrate it by a direct quotation of one of the most significant passages of the work, which concerns the Galilean critique of the theory by which Scheiner had attempted to explain the spots as stars: "For reasons of this kind, the sunspots might also be called stars, but essentially they have properties that differ not a little from those of the true stars"; [12] that is, of "stars" in the usual sense of the word. It is true that, considered in the abstract, such terminological freedom cannot be condemned in itself, but it can damage effective reasoning by leading us to indicate with the same name objects that differ in actual behavior: "I make so little difficulty about names, since I also know that anyone may impose these in his own way, that I do not care if they are called stars. . . . But these solar stars will be different from any other stars." [13] Galileo concludes that if we want to fit names to things, then sunspots will be analogous not to stars, but to clouds or smoke on earth.

Galileo's full realization of the conventional but not arbitrary character of scientific terms shows that he must have meditated long over this particularly subtle aspect of methodology.

5. The problem of language also underlies the famed Galilean letters which were designed to show the compatibility between the Copernican truth and Catholic dogma.

Today as in the seventeenth century, no one can doubt the existence of obvious contradictions between the doctrines of Copernicus and some very clear scriptural passages, as for example the words of Joshua when he ordered the sun to stand still.[14] Galileo knew this, but he also knew that anyone who wished to be simultaneously a scientist and a Catholic must be in a position to assume as true both the Copernican doctrines and the biblical passages. It was therefore necessary to demonstrate the possibility of doing this. Galileo thought that he had such a demonstration, and he did all he could to expound it to his friends, to the authorities of the state, and to the highest ecclesiastical officials.[15] He was convinced that only by spreading his own conviction could he succeed in his program of capturing support for the new science from the Catholic Church.

This, however, was not a matter of finding some compromise between Copernicanism and dogma. As we shall see, Galileo looked with lively disdain upon any attempt of that sort, and it was for that reason that he felt it his duty to combat relentlessly the system of Tycho Brahe, which stood midway between the ancient and the new astronomy.[16] Still less was it his task to attempt any correction of dogma, which would have placed the new science beyond the bounds of orthodoxy and would thus have automatically lost it the support of the Church. Nor was it a matter of bringing back the Averroist theory of the duality of truth, since that would constitute either a mere cloak for a denial of the truth of dogma or an open violation of the fundamental principles of logic.

The way out of all these difficulties, Galileo suggested, require recognition of the existence of two languages, radically different from one another: ordinary language with all its imprecisions and inconsistencies, and scientific language with its rigor and exactness. God in his infinite wisdom, being familiar with both, understood very well when dictating the Sacred Scriptures that, in order to make the Bible comprehensible to its intended audience, it would be necessary to employ ordinary language as the only one understood by the common man. This entailed writing that the sun turned round the earth. But in science we must make use of the second kind of language, rigorous and exact, which is characteristic of scientific reasoning; hence we need not accept as scientifically valid the statement in question, despite the fact that it is found in the Bible.

Galileo concludes that truth is one, but there are two languages for its expression. The renunciation in scientific research of the language used by God in the Bible does not signify a renunciation of the Bible, a wish to correct it, or a doubt as to its authority. It simply means that we must proceed from one kind of discourse to another, in this case to the one employed by God not when he wanted to reveal himself to men, but when he wrote the great book of nature. This observation is important. "Since, then, in many passages the Scriptures are not only capable, but even needful, of expositions differing from the apparent significations of the words, it seems to me that in physical disputes they should be reserved for the last place. For both the Holy Scriptures and nature proceed from the Divine Word, the former as the saying of the Holy Spirit and the latter as the most observant executrix of God's orders; and since it is needful in the Scriptures, in order to accommodate these to the understanding of ordinary people, to say many things which appear different (as to the meaning of the words) from absolute truth, while on the other hand nature is inexorable and immutable and cares nothing about having her hidden reasons explained to the understanding of man, so long as she never oversteps the bounds of the laws imposed on her, it seems that none of the physical effects that are either placed before our eyes by sensible experience or are the conclusions of necessary demonstrations should ever on any account be placed in doubt by passages of the Scriptures which seem to have a different verbal import. . . . This being the case, and it being even more evident that two truths can never contradict one another, it is the office of wise expositors to labor to find the true senses of the sacred passages in accordance with those physical conclusions which have first been made certain and sure to us by manifest sense or necessary demonstrations." [17]

Galileo's solution is thus so simple (perhaps so simple-minded) that it can hardly fail to leave us perplexed. The very fact that the ecclesiastical authorities of his time would not let themselves be persuaded by it strengthens our own perplexity. However, we shall limit ourselves to those objections that can be drawn from Galileo's own subsequent development of his basic propositions. The first and most important such development consists in changing the distinction between two types of language into a distinction between two types of discipline: on the one hand, ethics and religion; on the other, physics.

The Ambitious Program

In the first of these fields, Galileo concedes without debate that their object "transcends all human reasoning," by which it is clear that he means scientific reasoning. He concedes as an obvious consequence that the truth of such disciplines "cannot be made credible to us by any other science nor by any other means than by the mouth of the Holy Spirit." These truths are indeed of interest to every man, he says, since they bear upon the salvation of our souls; therefore the Holy Spirit was obliged to express itself in ordinary language, which is the only one that everyone understands.

In the second field, however, Galileo maintains that man possesses, as a gift from God himself, certain faculties naturally suited for the discovery of truth with scientific rigor. Especially for that reason, he therefore raises the following question, rather a leading question: Why should God, not content with the natural means he had supplied to men, add a supernatural means, and thus reveal that same truth to him through the Sacred Scriptures? Galileo had no doubt as to the answer. It appeared to him impossible that God wished to carry out so superfluous an act, or that "that same God who endowed us with senses, with reason, and with intellect wished us to put off their use, giving us by other means the information we could acquire through them." [18] This would be still more absurd when one considers that physical entities can supply us with this information in a perfectly rigorous language, while the Sacred Scriptures would furnish it only with all the imprecisions of ordinary language.

But here a great difficulty arises, which even Galileo seems not to have taken fully into account: Who can deny that the reason and intellect with which we are endowed, if not the senses, may sooner or later turn out to be able to handle with scientific rigor those truths which concern the moral disciplines? It is true that Galileo says repeatedly and clearly that one needs complete freedom from the Bible only for scientific knowledge and concerning "debates over physical problems," but what guarantee could he offer to the Church that others who would follow the path he had opened would not require an analogous liberty for debates on moral or religious problems? What guarantee could he offer that the method of scientific research, once it emerged victorious in the field of physics, would not seek to extend itself also into ethics and religion? From their point of view, the theologians were perfectly right; they foresaw and feared a situation so dangerous to them. Nor does it matter whether the danger was immediate or remote.

While on the one hand, as Galileo's adversaries well knew, he seemed to recognize the equal right of the two languages, on the other he entertained no doubt whatever concerning the incontestable superiority of the scientific language of rigorous research over that of everyday life and of the Bible. The foundation of his thought was this: when a question has been dissected by scientific reasoning, any wish to refute the results thus arrived at by invoking statements from ordinary language loses all sense, and it makes no difference whether such statements are made by men in everyday life or by the Holy Spirit in the Bible. Confronted with truths demonstrated by science, ordinary language has absolutely nothing to say against them. A single example sufficed. In the past, some objections had been raised against the Medicean planets on the basis of Holy Writ: "Now that everyone has seen these planets, I should like to know what new interpretations these same antagonists employ in expounding the Scriptures." [19]

Thus, according to Galileo's conception, scientific reasoning possesses an intrinsic value which is incontestable, and which does not have to be supported on any authority extraneous to itself. But ordinary reasoning has a limited value; on any given problem, when its propositions are discordant with those of science, there is no way out but to use the latter as the basis for interpreting the former. This held for the Medicean planets, and in the same way it held for Copernicanism. Narrow-minded theologians who wanted to limit science on the basis of biblical reasoning would do nothing but cast discredit upon the Bible itself.

Several years later, on the eve of his departure for Rome at the summons of the Holy Office, Galileo was to repeat once more this same worry of his (in a letter to Elia Diodati dated January 15, 1633): "If Fromond or others have established that to say the earth moves is heresy, and if [later] demonstrations, observations, and necessary experiences show it to move, in what predica-

ment will they have placed the Church itself?" [20] All these energetic declarations help us to understand that the autonomy of
scientific thought defended by Galileo was really very broad;
in fact, he required the recognition not only of the liberty of
science to reject the dictates of some other form of knowledge,
but also of its task of giving the unique and definite criterion of
truth to all other forms of knowledge. What sense is there, he
asked, in denying this autonomy when scientific reasoning is based
not on mere whims, but on verifiable facts, possessing a force that
no man can bend to his will? "If the earth moves *de facto*, we
cannot change nature and have it not move." [21]

6. Galileo's attitude foreshadows that of the Enlightenment. It
reveals a completely illuministic faith in human reason which,
by scientific research, can clear up the most deceitful misunder-
standings, overcome all the ancient prejudices, strip from nature
every secret. In the *Dialogue* this faith in the invincibility of
science was to be expressed in the following effective words: "As
to science itself, it can only improve." [22]

The rationality to which Galileo constantly appealed is not
static, but dynamic; it is an activity which unfolds itself in doubt,
in debate, in research; it is the spur that drives every man to
love truth and feel joy when he succeeds in freeing himself from
error: "As to philosophers, if they are true philosophers (that is,
lovers of truth), they should not be irritated; but, finding out
that they have been mistaken, they must thank whoever shows
them the truth." [23]

The foreshadowing of the Enlightenment in Galileo's rationalism is still more evident in one function which he explicitly
attributed to the scientist—that of raising from ignorance the
greatest possible number of persons. In other words, science is
not a matter of restricting the liberating function of reason to
some specialists, but of projecting it to all men in order to
awaken them, stimulate them, render them ever more conscious.[24]

But is there not a deep contradiction between this tendency to
give the greatest possible breadth to the liberating function of
science and the necessity of differentiating ever more clearly between ordinary language and that of science? Or is this contradic- 71

tion not more apparent than real? What Galileo proposed is not, in fact, the *popularization* of science in the sense of lowering its level and defiling its rational rigor, but the *diffusion* of science by reducing its reasoning to "clarity intelligible by many, where it is now very difficult." For him, clarity did not mean lack of precision and coherence; on the contrary, it meant exactness of ideas, definiteness of relations, and thus intimate perspicuity. In other words, for Galileo rigor and abstruseness are not equivalents. Abstruse knowledge cannot be truly scientific: rigorous knowledge, through its very rigor, is so limpid that anyone may easily penetrate all its reasons and most recondite assumptions.

Thus the mission of enlightenment is not something that Galileo wished to impose upon science from the outside; it is a task which he considered inseparable from all true science because it originates in the structure of scientific knowledge itself. Whereas the old metaphysics was encased in incomprehensible formulas which prevented its spread beyond the universities and its application to concrete exigencies of life, the new science is a fertile seed which knows no bounds, and which tends by an inner energy to pervade the world and transform it.

Hence the necessity for the new scientific words to be written in colloquial language (which does not mean inexact language) and in a nonacademic form: its expansive force must not be hindered by completely extrinsic obstacles.[25] It follows that the scientist shall not hide from the theologian his boldest theoretical developments, but shall openly face the problem of the relations between science and dogma, with faith in the light that can be brought into this field also by sincere and unprejudiced investigation.

It is not difficult to understand the close ties between the particular type of faith mentioned in the last few lines and the Galilean program to win support from the Church for the new science. It was precisely his faith in the enlightening force of reason which in 1615–16 was to delude Galileo into thinking, right up to the last moment, that with his conciliatory program he could triumph over all the labors of the obscurantists. Only concrete events could accomplish the difficult task of crushing his hopes.

Chapter 5

The First Discomfiture

1. The "trial" of 1616 constituted for Galileo a serious discomfiture; it forced him to alter some very important aspects of
his program of conciliation between the Catholic Church and
Copernicanism. The preparations for this great battle and the
significance of its unfortunate outcome must now concern us,
with only minimal attention to the events of the "trial" itself.[1]

Few of his fellow scientists approved Galileo's ambitious program. Kepler, for example, judged it useless and imprudent; in
his view, the only possible task for supporters of the Copernican theory was that of stripping it to its fundamental scientific
basis and thus pleading its cause strictly in learned circles,
scrupulously avoiding the involvement of anyone in this debate
who was not a specialist in astronomical research. Confirmation
of Kepler's attitude, so different from that of Galileo, appears in
a letter he wrote some years later (1619) in which the anti-
Galilean points are evident:

"Some, through their imprudent behavior, have brought things
to such a point that the reading of the work of Copernicus, which
remained absolutely free for eighty years, is now prohibited until
that work is corrected. Nevertheless, I am assured by well-in-
formed authorities and superiors, both ecclesiastical and civil,
that this action is not meant to place obstacles in the way of
astronomical speculation." [2]

It is clear from these words that Kepler's only preoccupation
was with freedom of research on the part of specialists. Galileo,
on the other hand, had in mind a much broader and more complex
problem: that of bringing to modern science, at the moment of
its laborious birth, the authoritative support of the powerful
Church organization.

The only place in which the Galilean program encountered   73 wide acceptance (as well as violent opposition) was among churchmen, of whom one part, the more cultured and open-minded, actively sought to reconcile Catholicism with the newborn scientific culture. Galileo counted a good many friends among monsignors, bishops, and cardinals; and even if they did not basically understand (as he did) the intimate linkage between the new science and Copernicanism, they were nevertheless aware of the fact that herein lay one of the crucial turning points in the culture of the epoch. Hence they felt it worthwhile to use every effort to induce the Church to adopt an enlightened and modern position on this subject. They pointed out that Copernicus himself had been a loyal Catholic and even a worthy canon. They recalled that à Spanish Augustinian friar, Diego de Zuñiga, had recently maintained (in his *Commentary on the Book of Job*) that belief in the motion of the earth was more consistent with the Holy Scriptures than the contrary view.[3]

The official spokesman for this current of thought was a Carmelite friar, Paolo Antonio Foscarini, who published at Naples in 1615 a "Letter" to the General of his order "on the opinion of the Pythagoreans and of Copernicus, in which there are brought into accord and agreement the passages of Holy Scripture and the theological propositions that have been previously adduced against that opinion." Galileo saw Foscarini's work while completing the draft of his own famous *Letter to Madam Christina of Lorraine.*

2. Of great importance were the attitudes of the two most influential religious orders of that period—the Jesuits and the Dominicans—toward this delicate problem.

At the beginning of the seventeenth century, the Jesuit order was the most influential depository of the loftiest culture within the Church, and had initiated into its ranks some eminent scholars in mathematics, physics, and astronomy. This deep interest in the scientific disciplines, however, did not imply any genuine open-mindedness toward modernity. Rather, it constituted an intelligent attempt by the Jesuits to place all new researches on the rails of orthodoxy, and to derive from them some advantage that would give luster to the great authority of the Church.

This preoccupation with reconciling the new sciences to orthodoxy at any cost often revealed itself in attempts to give them a philosophical interpretation in agreement with the teachings of Aristotle. We have had a particularly instructive example of this in Father Clavius' subtle device for reconciling the sphericity of the moon with the discovery of its mountainous character. At that time, Aristotelianism was unanimously judged by the greatest theologians to be the metaphysics best suited to provide a firm base for Catholic dogma; hence agreement with Aristotle implied secure orthodoxy.

It is easy, therefore, to understand the vacillation of the Jesuits up to 1616 with regard to the Copernican controversy. They did not hide their open-mindedness toward this very important astronomical theory; at the same time, however, they hesitated to declare themselves definitely favorable to it because of its obvious and absolute irreconcilability with any form of Aristotelianism. This hesitation is clearly visible in the reply sent by Cardinal Bellarmine (the greatest theologian of the Jesuit order) to the Carmelite Foscarini, who had requested the cardinal's opinion of his famous little tract (the *Letter* of which we have spoken above). Bellarmine wrote:

"1. I say that it appears to me that your Reverence and Signor Galileo did prudently to content yourselves with speaking hypothetically and not positively, as I have always believed Copernicus did. For to say that assuming the earth moves and the sun stands still saves all the appearances better than eccentrics and epicycles is to speak well. This has no danger in it, and it suffices for mathematicians. But to wish to affirm that the sun is really fixed in the center of the heavens and merely turns upon itself without traveling from east to west, and that the earth is situated in the third sphere and revolves very swiftly around the sun, is a very dangerous thing, not only because it irritates all the theologians and scholastic philosophers, but also because it injures our holy faith and makes the sacred Scripture false. . . .

"2. I say that, as you know, the Council [of Trent] would prohibit expounding the Bible contrary to the common agreement 75 of the holy Fathers. And if your Reverence would read not only all their works but the commentaries of modern writers on Genesis, Psalms, Ecclesiastes, and Joshua, you would find that all agree in expounding literally that the sun is in the heavens and travels swiftly around the earth. . . .

"3. I say that if there were a true demonstration that the sun was in the center of the universe and the earth in the third sphere, and that the sun did not go around the earth but the earth went around the sun, then it would be necessary to use careful consideration in explaining the Scriptures that seemed contrary, and we should rather have to say that we do not understand them than say that something is false which had been proven. But I do not think there is any such demonstration, since none has been shown to me. To demonstrate that the appearances are saved by assuming the sun at the center and the earth in the heavens is not the same thing as to demonstrate that in fact the sun is in the center and the earth in the heavens. I believe that the first demonstration may exist, but I have very grave doubts about the second; and in case of doubt one may not abandon the Holy Scriptures as expounded by the holy Fathers. I add that the words *The sun also riseth, and the sun goeth down, and hasteth to the place where he ariseth* were written by Solomon, who not only spoke by divine inspiration, but was a man wise above all others, and learned in the human sciences and in the knowledge of all created things, which wisdom he had from God; so it is not very likely that he would affirm something that was contrary to demonstrated truth, or truth that might be demonstrated. . . ." [4]

Thus, after much hesitation, the Jesuits finally decided to stay outside the pro-Copernican current in order that they might not contribute to the abandonment of the Aristotelian conception. After 1616, the general tendency among the Jesuits was to adhere to the astronomical system of Tycho Brahe, which differed markedly from those of Aristotle and Ptolemy, but seemed to be reconcilable with the principles of the Aristotelian–Thomistic metaphysics.

The attitude of the Dominicans was quite different. Faithful to the metaphysics of St. Thomas Aquinas as well as to everything he had thought about every scientific and philosophical problem, they looked with deep suspicion upon every innovation, even though it might be purely astronomical. Hence they particularly opposed Galileo, who tended to look upon Copernicanism as the great turning point not only of astronomy, but also of modern science. In other words, during the years in question the Dominicans constituted the rear guard for the ultraconservative and reactionary elements of Catholicism. It was no accident that Galileo's earliest, most ignorant, and most obstinate religious adversaries belonged to this order.

Yet curiously the positions of these two orders with respect to Galileo were completely reversed between the trials of 1616 and 1633. In the first trial, the accusation came from the Dominicans, and Galileo received at least indirect if not complete support from the Jesuits. In the second, the accusation was inspired by the Jesuits and included charges against some Dominicans who had authorized publication of Galileo's *Dialogue Concerning the Two Chief World Systems.*

3. The two Dominicans who instigated the first official move against Galileo were Nicolò Lorini and Tommaso Caccini.

Lorini opened a general but concealed attack against Galileo at the end of October 1612. A few days later, perhaps intimidated because he had dared to go so far against so powerful a personage, Lorini hastened to address to Galileo a letter in which he assured him that he had not meant to "discourse against anyone on philosophical matters," least of all against him. He made it clear that he had said only "a few words" to explain that "the opinion of Ipernicus, or whatever he is called, appears to oppose the Divine Scripture." In view of this immediate retraction, Galileo was not upset by the preacher's words, and merely laughed with his friends at the gauche ignorance thus revealed.

The second attack was pronounced by Caccini in the Church of Santa Maria Novella nearly two years later, on the fourth Sunday of Advent in 1614. This time the accusation was more particular; Caccini felt it his duty to announce publicly to the faithful the dangers of mathematics, a diabolic art and one that fostered heresies. His attack was closed rhetorically with the celebrated words (Acts 1:11): *Viri galilaei, quid statis adspicientes in* 77

Galileo Galilei

coelum? ("Ye men of Galilee, why stand ye gazing up into heaven?"). Thus the two angels had told the inhabitants of Galilee not to remain with their eyes fixed on the sky, because Jesus, whose ascent they had witnessed, could no longer be seen. Caccini punningly applied these words to the Galileists, presenting the statement as a direct divine order not to persist in diabolical observations of the stars.[5]

A few weeks later, the Dominican Nicolò Lorini sent to Cardinal Millini of the Holy Office a copy of Galileo's incriminating letter to Benedetto Castelli, denouncing the philosophical and theological dangers contained in it: "Since, besides the common duty of every good Christian, there is an infinite obligation on the part of all the brothers of St. Dominic as those whose patron saint has made them the black and white dogs of the Holy Office,[6] and in particular all theologians and preachers, behold how I, the least of all and the most devoted and special servant of your Excellency, there having fallen into my hands a certain writing here current in the hands of everyone, done by those who call themselves 'Galileists,' affirming that the earth moves and the heavens stand still, following in this the position of Copernicus, in which letter (in the opinion of all our Fathers at this most religious Convent of St. Mark) there are many propositions *that appear to us suspect or rash*—as saying that certain modes of expression in the Holy Scripture are inconsistent, and that in disputes over physical effects the Scripture should be put in the last place . . . for this reason [I] have resolved to send the letter to your Excellency, so that you, being filled with the most holy zeal, and because of the position that you hold, which requires you and your most illustrious colleagues to be alert concerning such matters, may, if it appears to you that this stands in need of correction, set in motion those measures which you may judge to be necessary, in order that *parvus error in principio non sit magnus in fine* (a small initial error may not become a large one in the end)." [7]

An inquiry was immediately opened under great secrecy. The Archbishop of Pisa and the Inquisitor of that city were charged with the duty of "dextrously" obtaining the original of Galileo's

letter to Castelli; meanwhile, the copy sent by Lorini was turned over to a competent adviser on such topics. The reply was rather reassuring; for, apart from certain improper expressions (for example, where it was said that in the Sacred Scripture many propositions are found that are *false* as to the strict sense of the words), the letter did not deviate from the standards of good Catholic language (*a semitis tamen catholicae locutionis non deviat*). In all probability the proceedings would have gone no further, especially in view of the many supporters Galileo had among the highest ecclesiastical hierarchy. But this rapid conclusion was not to be; on the twentieth of March, Father Caccini presented himself voluntarily to the Holy Office to testify against Galileo. He asserted, among other things, that Father Ferdinando Ximenes (regent of Santa Maria Novella in Florence) had repeated to him that he had heard from some "Galileists" the following serious affirmations: God is not substance, but accident; God is sensitive "because in him are divinatory senses"; miracles said to have been performed by saints are not true miracles.

Accordingly the witnesses cited by Caccini (Father Ximenes and one Giannozzo Attavanti, parson of the Church of St. Ippolito in Castelfiorentine) were examined in due course, though in no great hurry. Both depositions were rather favorable to Galileo, and in substance gave the lie to the accusations of Caccini. Attavanti was particularly clear: "I have never heard Signor Galileo say things repugnant to the Holy Scripture or to our holy Catholic faith; but concerning philosophical or mathematical matters, I have heard Signor Galileo say according to the doctrine of Copernicus that the earth moves on its center and in its orbit, and that the sun likewise moves about its center, but has no other progressive motion, as in some of his letters published at Rome under the title *On the sunspots,* to which I refer in their entirety." As to the other affirmations (that God is not substance, but accident, etc.), it turned out that these had to do purely and simply with dialectic exercises of the friars and had no bearing on any doctrines upheld by Galileo. The examination concluded with a general declaration by Attavanti in support of the scientist's religious faith: "I hold him to be a very good Catholic, and otherwise he would not remain with these noble rulers [his Medicean employers]." [8]

Galileo Galilei

At the session of the Holy Office held on the twenty-fifth of November 1615, the depositions of the two witnesses were read. It was decided to take no further action at the moment, but to examine Galileo's book on sunspots (cited by Attavanti) in order to have all the data regarding the troublesome matter. Father Caccini must have heard that the testimony had not led to the result he desired, for he presented himself personally to Galileo, who had meanwhile come to Rome. He made his excuses somewhat as Father Lorini had done three years before. Galileo described the visit in a letter to Curzio Picchena, an officer of the court of Cosimo II: "Yesterday that very person came to find me at home, who first from the pulpit there, and later here and elsewhere, has spoken and intrigued so gravely against me. He was with me more than four hours, and in the first half-hour when we were alone, he tried with all submission to excuse the things he had done there, offering to give me any satisfaction; then he tried to make me believe that he had not been the instigator of the other rumor here." [9]

Meanwhile, however, the controversy had broadened to assume the character of an internal battle between two factions within the Church: the uncompromising reactionaries, and the ardent advocates of complete open-mindedness toward modern culture. It was a rough battle, even if partly concealed. Eventually the liberal party was defeated, and in its discomfiture, the Galileist group also suffered.

4. The struggle was so complex that we shall mention only the part Galileo took in it. He doubtless deserves credit for understanding better than anyone else the importance of the stakes and the significance which victory would certainly have in the future development of European culture.

Although in 1612 he had not taken Lorini's denunciation seriously, in 1615 he realized well enough that this time the enemy maneuvers were dangerous and went far beyond his own person. He sought at once to interest some of the most potent and highly cultured princes of the Church in the delicate affair, and to alert the many friends he counted in Roman circles, who were often too ingenuous and optimistic. A significant letter, sent to him on

The First Discomfiture

the twenty-eighth of February 1615 by Monsignor Giovanni Ciampoli [10] shows how difficult it was even for this ardent Galilean to understand basically the seriousness of the issue opened up by the two Dominican friars. "I am so devoted a servitor of your Excellency that I almost feel accused of suspicion of instability when you ask if I continue to love you. . . . To me it seems impossible to have dealt with you and not to love you; even your adversaries have said that you enchant people, and I surely believe that a noble heart cannot use more effective magic than knowledge and the force of eloquence. . . . But to be more specific, I shall say in a few words, *ne tantos mihi finge metus* (do not create for me so many fears). Those great evils surely are not current, as I find here neither prelates nor cardinals, even among those who usually know about such things, who have heard a word about them. . . . I had news about three weeks ago concerning that sermon [Caccini's], but did not know what it was, and though *non omnia metuenda* (not everything is to be feared), I recalled only that *nihil spernendum* (nothing is to be despised). Although it was two hours into the night, I did not wish to delay, but went at once to find Cardinal Barberini, who holds much affection for you and salutes you. . . . Be certain then that what I do not do for you, I would not do for any man living, especially concerning an injustice so inconsistent with the fame of so talented a person, so deserving from men of letters and from all his friends. . . . It is indeed true that one must always remember that *acres esse viros, cum dura proelia gente* (men are bitter, like people in hard battle) in these matters in which the friars usually do not wish to lose. But that salutary little phrase about submitting yourself ever to the Holy Mother Church, etc., can never be too often repeated. . . ." [11]

Great hopes were aroused among Galileo's friends by the publication, precisely at this time, of the famous *Letter* by the Carmelite Foscarini. Later, however, they had to recognize that even though this supported their cause, in the end it complicated matters; it unleashed the passions of the adversaries, who spoke with increased vehemence, and it aggravated the suspicions of the authorities at the Vatican.

Galileo wanted to go immediately to Rome for the purpose of

explaining personally the scientific arguments for Copernicanism. We know that he set great store by his personal prestige and the efficacy of his own words, which had been decisive in 1611. But he was detained at Florence by illness, and had to put off the journey for several months. His worry was well expressed in a letter to his friend Monsignor Piero Dini dated May fifteenth: ". . . how can all my labors fail to be in vain if those Peripatetics who must be persuaded show themselves incapable of understanding even the simplest and easiest arguments? . . . Yet I should not despair of overcoming even this difficulty if I were in a position to use my tongue in place of my pen; and if I ever get well, so that I can come there, I shall do so, with the hope at least of showing my great affection for the Holy Church, and my zeal that nothing shall happen on this point, through the stings of a multitude of malign persons who understand nothing, which could produce a decision that is not entirely good." [12]

Restricted to pressing his cause by means of correspondence, Galileo wrote his famed letters to Dini and to Madame Christina. Early in December, he was at last able to proceed to Rome. Though still not entirely recovered, he was full of confidence, both because of the intrinsic value of the theory he went to defend and the powerful support he had obtained. The Grand Duke himself had written warmly in recommendation to several high church officials and ordered his Roman ambassador, Piero Guicciardini, to lodge Galileo in some "honorable and comfortable" rooms of the embassy (the magnificent Trinità dei Monti) and to "provide for him suitable food, a secretary, a servant, and a mule." Galileo's enthusiasm for his mission appears clearly in letters overflowing with confidence and the spirit of battle, which he sent reguarly to the minister Picchena: "I hope to be able to leave here with my own reputation not only completely vindicated, but thrice augmented, for I shall have brought to a conclusion an enterprise of no little moment which has been under study for several months by persons excelling in doctrine and in authority." [13]

". . . All these activities, in Rome as it is, and by an alien here, turn out to be long and laborious. But . . . my confident hope to bring a great undertaking to an end, and the fact that I have already made a strong impression upon those with whom the final determination rests, enable me to tolerate patiently every labor." [14]

"Continuing . . . to give you an account of my progress, I tell you that my mission is entirely completed as to the part which concerns my own person, as has been freely and openly indicated to me by all those eminent men who are handling these matters." [15]

The last of these letters has a particular interest, both because it was written only three weeks before the day on which the Holy Office condemned Copernicanism and because of the very solemn tone Galileo took, a few lines after the passage quoted above, when he passed from the personal question (which he believed already resolved) to the heart of the problem: "But to my own cause there is linked a matter that concerns not only me but all the men who, for the past eighty years, either with printed books or private writings or with public lectures and speeches or even in private debates, would have adhered or did adhere to a certain doctrine and opinion not unknown to your Excellency, concerning the determination of which I am now debating here in order that the deliberations may be just and the best possible. Therefore, as one who can perhaps be of some aid to the side which relies upon knowledge of the truth that is given to us by the sciences which are my specialty, I cannot and must not neglect that assistance which is afforded to me by my conscience as a zealous Christian and Catholic." [16] In other words: I, Galileo, at this decisive moment in the history of thought, feel myself called, as a Catholic and as a scientist, to the highest duty of aiding Catholicism to assume a just and unimpeachable position with respect to the great Copernican movement; strengthened by eighty years of life, it is ready now to consummate its proper directive function in modern world culture.

5. What was Galileo's behavior in Rome? Did it turn out to be useful or harmful to the causes close to his heart?

All witnesses agree that the great scientist held to his purpose with all the energy at his disposal, and with full knowledge of the stakes. His action was frank, open, without reticence. To

make clear the reasoning behind the new theory, he courageously
attended the most challenging meetings, at which he knew he
would encounter the ablest and most aggressive adversaries. Wherever he went, he made "stupendous discourses," always with
vivacity on the defense as in the attack, always rich in arguments
both old and new. It was in a conversation with Maffeo Cardinal
Barberini that he revealed for the first time his famous argument
based on the tides, to which he was to dedicate the final "day"
of his *Dialogue*. This argument was considered decisive by Galileo, though it was scientifically erroneous.[17]

Thus canon Antonio Querengo wrote to inform Alessandro
Cardinal d'Este (then at Modena) of Galileo's campaign: "Your
Eminence would take great pleasure in Galileo if you could hear
him discourse, as he does often among fifteen or twenty who attack
him cruelly, now at one house and now at another. But he is
fortified in such a way as to laugh at them all, and although he
does not convince people of his new opinion, he nevertheless
vanquishes most of the arguments by which his opponents seek
to crush him. Monday, in particular . . . he gave marvelous
proofs, and what pleased me extremely was that before replying
to the opposing arguments he amplified and strengthened them
with new supports of apparently great magnitude, in order, when
he demolished them, to make the adversaries look even more
ridiculous." [18]

One thing, however, Galileo did not take sufficiently into account: that this dispute was no mere matter of overcoming the
bitter opposition of monks who "did not usually wish to lose,"
for behind them stood a Church which feared any deep and considerable renovation. It is true that in the Church there were
many high prelates with a taste for letters and the arts, but they
were disinclined to pursue this interest to the extent of a serious
effort to liberate letters and science from the restrictions imposed
by the ancient culture of the religious orders. Deceived by his
mistaken judgment of the real orientation of the Church, Galileo
became the victim of a naive optimism very similar to that of
which he himself had tried to forewarn his friends at Rome some
months earlier, when he was first aware of his personal danger.

The Florentine ambassador, Guicciardini, clearly perceived this

The First Discomfiture

error. Accustomed to the devious intrigues that were the order of the day at the Vatican court, he foresaw from the beginning that all debates would prove useless and that the Copernican cause could hope for nothing but a rout. In this connection it is highly significant that he sent a letter to the minister Picchena shortly before Galileo's arrival at Rome which revealed the antipathy of the hardened diplomat toward the deluded scientist who thought he could bring his new ideas into the capital of the Counter-Reformation. "I hear that Galileo is coming. . . . When I first came here [in 1611] he was here, and spent some days in this house. His views, and something else too, did not please the advisers and cardinals of the Holy Office. Among others, Bellarmine told me that . . . if he was here too long, nothing less could be done than to arrive at some judgment concerning his affairs. . . . I do not know if he has changed his views or his temper, but I know very well that some Dominicans who play a great part in the Holy Office, as well as others, are ill-disposed toward him, and this is no place to come to argue about the moon, nor, in this age, to support or import any new doctrines. . . ." [19]

Events demonstrated only too well that it was Guicciardini and not Galileo who grasped the real situation. The chief cause of Galileo's defeat may perhaps be sought in the action of the Jesuits. At first they seemed disposed to support Galileo; in fact, on the sixteenth of May, Monsignor Dini had written to his friend: "I hear that many Jesuits are secretly of the same opinion, though they remain silent." But they preferred to stand apart, concerned lest the triumph of the Copernican system bring excessive discredit on Aristotelian philosophy. Probably this indirect responsibility on their part did not escape Galileo, which would explain the progressive sharpening of his antagonism toward them after 1616. However that may be, and without seeking to determine whether the responsibility for the events should be attributed to the Dominican offensive or the Jesuit retreat, the judgment pronounced by the Holy Office could not have been worse. Some (and in a sense Galileo was among them) pretended to see in it the fruits of a compromise; for example, there was the fact that no work of Galileo's appeared among the condemned books. But in reality it was an utter rout for the Pisan scientist, a discomfiture which, though it did not touch him personally in any explicit way, struck a heavy blow at his whole program.

6. On the nineteenth of February, the Holy Office sent to its theologians two propositions which contained the core of the whole question:

(1) "That the sun is the center of the universe, and consequently is not moved by any local motion;

(2) "That the earth is not the center of the universe nor is it motionless, but moves as a whole, and also with the diurnal motion."

On the twenty-fourth of the same month the theologians unanimously proclaimed the first proposition to be foolish and philosophically absurd, and to be formally heretical insofar as it expressly contradicted many passages in the Holy Scripture in a literal sense and according to the common expositions of the Church fathers and the doctors in theology. As to the second proposition, without calling it heretical, they declared it to be liable to the same philosophical censure as the first, and from a theological point of view to be at least erroneous in faith. This judgment was brought to the attention of the general congregation of the Holy Office on the following day.

Banfi remarked that "the two propositions, whose actual terms will be sought in vain among the works of Galileo or Copernicus, and which are no more than an amplification of Caccini's accusation, obviously do not express even approximately the scientific framework of the Copernican theory, with its complex demonstrations, as presented by Galileo. What is expressed, in metaphysical and scholastic terms (and hence unsuitably) are two conclusions related to biblical texts wrenched out of context . . . which constituted therewith a unique doctrine in the general explanatory system of celestial motions. Moreover, the mode of expression, particularly in the second case, lacks coherence and precision; and in the first proposition the idea of 'entire motionlessness' of the sun contradicts Galileo's own opinion." [20] Yet despite these formal defects, despite the imperfect agreement between the two propositions in question and the Copernican system, their condemnation represented beyond any doubt a general condemnation of Copernicanism. Proof of this was to appear within a few days.

The judgment of the Holy Office was duly transmitted to the Congregation of the Index, and on the third of March this body passed a decree (made public on the fifth) dividing its condemnation into three parts: (1) the books of Copernicus and of Diego de Zuñiga were simply "suspended" until corrected (*donec corrigantur*); (2) Father Foscarini's book suffered complete condemnation and prohibition (*omnino prohibendum atque damnandum*); (3) all other books that taught the same doctrine, though not condemned, were prohibited (*aliosque omnes libros, pariter idem docentes, prohibendos*).[21]

As to Galileo's works, they were not specifically listed in the condemnation. That his famous letters to Castelli, Dini, and Madame Christina should be disregarded is easily explained; those were private and unpublished documents. The question why his *Letters on Sunspots* should have also been left alone offers some difficulties, the more so because this work had been considered by the Holy Office in its session of November 25, 1615. Official silence on this point reveals the desire not to offend the great scientist, protected as he was by the powerful and Catholic Medici family.[22]

7. The decision of the Holy Office was communicated to Galileo, the person most directly involved in the trial, in a modified form during the brief interval between the original determination and the passage of the decree of the Congregation of the Index.

On the twenty-fifth of February, Pope Paul V ordered Cardinal Bellarmine to call Galileo before him and admonish him to abandon the censured opinions. The Pope's order went on to say that if Galileo refused to obey, the Father Commissary of the Holy Office was to instruct him officially, before a notary and witnesses, to refrain completely from teaching or defending this doctrine, or dealing with it (*et si recusaverit parere, P. Commissarius, coram notario et testibus, facial illi praeceptum ut omnino abstineat huiusmodi doctrinam et opinionem docere aut defendere,*   87

Galileo Galilei

seu de ea tractare) ; finally, if he refused to consent, he was to be imprisoned (*si vero non acquieverit, carceretur.*) [23]

In obedience to the instructions, Bellarmine called Galileo before him on the twenty-sixth of February, in the presence of the Father Commissary General of the Holy Office (at least as recorded in the minute of the meeting), and admonished him to abandon the condemned doctrine, only to pass on immediately (*successive ac incontinenti*) to the second phase of the procedure. This consisted in the order given to Galileo by the Father Commissary in the name of the Pope and the entire Congregation of the Holy Office to abandon completely the false doctrine, and not to hold, teach, or defend it in any way, orally or in writing (*. . . supradictus P. Commissarius . . . ordinavit ut supradictam opinionem . . . omnino relinquat, nec eam de caetero, quovis modo, teneat, doceat aut defendat, verbo aut scriptis*). The minute adds that Galileo consented (*acquievit*) and promised to obey, which explains why he was not imprisoned.[24]

I have said above, "at least as recorded in the minute of the meeting," because this constitutes one of the most controversial points of the whole affair. It is a point of the greatest importance, for the contents of this minute became the pivot of the charge brought against Galileo in the trial of 1633. There are two grounds of controversy over the minute of which we are speaking.

The first concerns the actual content of the minute. Why on earth does this say that the procedure went on immediately from the simple admonition to the specific precept? Various circumstances lead us to exclude the possibility that Galileo refused to obey the admonition; hence there was nothing to authorize the Father Commissary to proceed from the first to the second phase of the instruction. Was this a mere excess of zeal? Was it an abuse of discretion on the part of Bellarmine or the Father Commissary? Also, it seems strange that the Commissary specified in his precept the words *quovis modo* (in any manner), which made Galileo's situation worse in the eyes of his contemporaries: it implied a prohibition from dealing with the question even hypothetically.

The second cause of trouble is the outward form of the document containing the minute. It does not have the signatures of those present, as required in an official document, and seems rather to be a simple memorandum. Some critics have inquired whether the document may not be apocryphal. Is it not possible that it was added in 1633 to the papers of the trial of 1616, simply because of its convenience to the new judges, who wished to aggravate the personal position of the accused? Clearly this suspicion, if upheld, would throw complete discredit upon the trial of 1633.

Any detailed analysis of this problem is outside our present purpose. Yet the conjecture that this document was added in 1633 is today rejected by the majority of critics; ultraviolet examination of the writing has proved that it originated at the same date as the pages preceding and following it in the records of the entire proceeding. Thus the fabrication of the document cannot be placed in 1633. This does not mean, however, that most critics are inclined to accept its contents as genuine. On the contrary, as Santillana asserts, the suspicion that the minute does not correspond to the truth "has today become, outside of Italy, a certainty, even among ecclesiastical writers."

In the interest of objectivity, I shall summarize here two accounts of this document put forth by serious modern scholars, Morpurgo Tagliabue and Santillana, who may be considered opponents in the matter. Their difference of opinion demonstrates the complexity of the question.

Morpurgo Tagliabue is one of the few persons today who still consider the document an authentic minute, rejecting not only the hypothesis that it is false, but also that it is a mere "notary's draft." His argument is juridical: the very incongruity of the document—that is, its failure to coincide with the order of Pope Paul V—makes us accept it as true. A simple draft of a minute, precisely because it would be prepared for the eventuality of Galileo's refusal to agree, would not have failed to mention this refusal. All that is left to consider is a breach of procedure, or an abuse of initiative by the Commissary. The fact that the sentence of the Holy Office in 1633, in its preliminary summary, reports this document without either noticing or explaining its incongruity, and even makes it the chief point in the charge 89 against Galileo, permits us to believe that such procedural defects were of no concern under juridical customs of the time.

Santillana, on the other hand, is convinced that the document is a forgery prepared in 1616 at the initiative of the Father Commissary, who was particularly enraged against Galileo. This is the kernel of his argument: The Commissary, Father Seghizzi, was not in accord with Cardinal Bellarmine concerning the way of handling the matter. Nor did he hide the fact. As the ambassador, Guicciardini, had written to Florence, "I know that there are here at the Holy Office and elsewhere certain Dominicans who are ill-disposed toward Galileo. . . . One of these days we shall hear that he has fallen over a steep precipice." The Commissary must have been annoyed by the friendly manner in which the audience was conducted by the Cardinal, since this precluded his intervention. He therefore decided against entering the minute in the form of Bellarmine's instructions, returned to his office, and had a secretary draft a minute in line with his own wishes— a minute which could not be considered literally a forgery, since it was not signed, but which might come in handy in some unforeseen event. Indeed, such an act, if it occurred, would offer a classic instance of that religious hatred which shrinks from no stratagem.

Again without entering into details, it must be granted that Santillana's hypothesis turns out to be very efficacious for explaining the ensuing developments in the relations between Galileo and the Holy Office. Suffice it to add that no one has yet succeeded in establishing conclusively whether the treatment of Galileo—that is, his having been called before Cardinal Bellarmine to receive personally the decision of the Holy Office—was adopted because of some special regard for him or because of the desire to bind him more than anyone else to the result of the deliberations. Actually, the treatment adopted lends itself equally well to either interpretation.

8. No more is necessary here to illustrate the many ambiguities and contradictions that characterize the whole development of this trial. The two propositions condemned by the Holy Office were not drawn textually from the works to which the judges meant

to refer expressly or by implication, and furthermore, the decree of the Index treats the authors of the various works mentioned with quite different degrees of severity. The facts compel reflection on the uncertainties and internal contradictions of the Church; despite having chosen the path of intransigent dogmatism, it sought to give supporters of "modernism" the impression that something had been conceded to them also.

Curiously, the "modernists" felt no desire to expose the equivocation. On the contrary, they tried to broaden and deepen it; this ambiguity alone allowed them to maintain publicly that they had not been completely routed. This appears clearly in a letter written by Galileo on the sixth of March to the minister Picchena, in which he tried to minimize his own discomfiture to such a degree as to present it as a minor victory: ". . . as the result has shown, his [Father Caccini's] opinion has not met with a corresponding view on the part of the Holy Church, which has decided nothing more than that this doctrine [i.e., the Copernican theory] is not in agreement with the Holy Scriptures, wherefore the only books prohibited are those which have expressly tried to maintain it to be not discordant with the Bible; and there are no such books, except a letter of a Carmelite Father printed last year, which alone is prohibited. Diego de Zuñiga . . . is suspended until corrected. In the work of Copernicus himself some ten lines of the preface to Pope Paul III will be removed, where he says that it does not appear to him that this doctrine is repugnant to scripture. . . . No mention is made of other authors. I, as may be seen from the nature of the affair, have no interest in it, nor should I have occupied myself about it . . . had my enemies not interjected me into it." [25]

Was Galileo sincere when he wrote these words? There is some doubt that he was entirely sincere, in view of his suppression of details unfavorable to him. But probably he was not entirely insincere either. The one thing certain is that despite the sharp opposition of ambassador Guicciarni, Galileo still remained at Rome three months after publication of the decree of the Congregation of the Index, in order to see personally just how severely the Church intended to apply the decision of the Holy Office, as well as to try to rescue something through his powerful friends. He even managed to see the Pope himself, who granted him a "most benign audience" and assured him of his personal favor, but did not hint at any concession on the principle in question. Despite these benevolences, however, Galileo's personal position began to appear gradually more shaky. Some news of his audience with Bellarmine had leaked out, and rumors went around that he had abjured his beliefs in front of the Cardinal. It was even added that his coming to Rome had not been voluntary, but that he had been called by the Holy Office.

To put an end to this talk, Galileo decided to ask Bellarmine himself for some explicit statement that would enable him to counter such accusations. This was given to him on the twenty-sixth of May, to his great satisfaction, for he saw in it a final proof of the prestige he still retained in the eyes of the top hierarchy of the Church. The document reads as follows: "We, Robert Cardinal Bellarmine, having heard that Signor Galileo Galilei is calumniated or imputed to have abjured in our hand, and even of having been given salutary penance for this; and inquiries having been made as to the truth, we say that the said Signor Galilei has not abjured any opinion or doctrine of his in our hand nor in that of anyone else at Rome, much less anywhere else, to our knowledge; nor has he received penance of any sort; but he has only been told the decision made by His Holiness and published by the Holy Congregation of the Index, in which it is declared that the doctrine attributed to Copernicus, that the earth moves round the sun and that the sun is fixed in the center of the universe without moving from west to east, is contrary to the Holy Scriptures, and therefore cannot be defended or held. And in witness of this we have written and signed this with our own hand." [26]

Backed by this statement, Galileo finally decided to leave Rome for Florence on the fourth of June. Two other cardinals, Alessandro Orsini and Francesco Maria del Monte, provided him with letters addressed to the Grand Duke Cosimo II, informing Galileo's patron that his servant had acquired the "highest reputation" with the College of Cardinals during his stay at Rome, and that on this occasion they had had an opportunity to learn "more intimately of his virtues."

The First Discomfiture

If these unparalleled courtesies had the effect of lessening Galileo's bitterness, in the end (as may be easily understood) they merely rooted more deeply in his mind the ambiguity of the decision. And this can only be a source of regret when we think of the still deeper bitterness the same ambiguity was to cause Galileo in the second trial. He was destined to encounter atrocious misfortunes because of excessive reliance upon the benevolence of the Church toward him, and especially upon the effectiveness of the document given to him by the powerful Cardinal Bellarmine, which he was to present fruitlessly to the judges inquisitors during the trial in 1633.

Yet if it is true, as Morpurgo Tagliabue wrote, that in the "contradictions and distinctions and compromises originating in the first trial . . . lies the origin of the future complications of Galileo's second trial," it is also true that it was the ambiguity rooted in Galileo's heart which kept him from realizing his full discomfiture in the first great test of 1616, and hence enabled him to find the fortitude to attempt another test. It was the prepparation for this final battle which stimulated Galileo to write one of the most remarkable classics in all scientific and philosophical literature: the *Dialogue Concerning the Two Chief World Systems.*

Chapter 6

The Years of Silence

1. Upon his return to Florence in June 1616, Galileo retired to his villa at Bellosguardo and applied all his energies to the prosecution of precise astronomical observations. Meanwhile he was making final arrangements for the care of his children. His two daughters took their vows in the Convent of San Matteo at Arcetri in October of the years 1616 and 1617, respectively; his son Vincenzio was legitimized in 1619. During the months of May and June 1618 Galileo made a pilgrimage to Loreto, stopping with the Duke Francesco Maria della Rovere at Urbino on his return.

Early in 1616 Francesco Ingoli, recently appointed secretary of the *Propaganda Fide*,[1] had addressed to Galileo a long refutation of the Copernican system in the form of a letter. Entitled *De situ et quiete Terrae contra Copernici systema disputatio (Discussion of the location and immobility of the earth against the system of the Copernicans)*, it was based upon arguments drawn from Aristotle, Ptolemy, and Tycho Brahe. Since there had not been time for Galileo to refute Ingoli's "proofs" before discussion was banned in February, he was obliged to bide his time in silence and leave any reply to some more auspicious occasion. No doubt this was a difficult decision for a man of so fiery a character, but it was clear enough even to him that silence constituted the best armor while he awaited the return of serenity to his spirit.

There were signs, moreover, which convinced Galileo that something was about to change in the highest circles of the Vatican. Hence it was best to wait patiently and to exert every effort to regain full favor among the rulers of the Church. The correctness of these tactics was revealed by an event of no great intrinsic importance which was nevertheless highly symptomatic. In August 1620, Maffeo Cardinal Barberini spontaneously paid Galileo

The Years of Silence

homage in the form of a poetic composition in his honor called *Adulatio perniciosa (Dangerous admiration)*. The tone of the letter accompanying it is more than enough to show us that the cardinal intended henceforth to remember not the faults of the great scientist, but only his merits. Barberini wrote:

"Illustrious Sir:

"The esteem I have always felt toward you and toward the excellences combined in you has supplied material for the composition that is enclosed; and if it is lacking in any respect, you must see in it only the affectionate intention that it shall shine from the mere presence of your name. So, without prolonging my excuses, which I omit in my confidence in you, I pray that you may be gratified by this small demonstration of the good will I bear you. And greeting you with all my heart, I wish you every contentment from our Lord God." [2]

Despite Galileo's prudent silence, there is no doubt that he persisted in his deeply rooted Copernican faith. His state of mind shines clearly through the delicate irony that everywhere pervades his letter to Archduke Leopold of Austria, dated May 23, 1618.[3] Ostensibly this letter merely contained the usual obsequious expressions accompanying some gifts (two telescopes and other things) sent by the scientist to the powerful ruler. It is a singular fact, however, that among these gifts were included a copy of the *Letters on Sunspots* (a work, as we have seen, that openly supported Copernicanism) and a copy of Galileo's *Discourse on the ebb and flow of the seas* which had been composed for Cardinal Orsini early in January 1616, expounding the proof that Galileo considered most decisive in support of Copernicus. Clearly these two writings, especially the second, had in no way lost their original value in Galileo's eyes despite the edict of 1616. How are we to justify an act so lacking in respect for the Holy Office? Here is Galileo's significant reply: "Now, since I know how necessary it is to obey and believe in the decisions of the superiors, as men who are led by higher knowledge which my humble mind cannot attain by itself, I regard this present essay which I am sending to you—founded on the earth's mobility, and being one of the physical arguments which I produced in confirmation of that mobility—I repute this, I say, as a bit of poetry, or a dream; and as such Your Highness is to receive it. Yet since poets sometimes prize this or that fantasy of theirs, I likewise have some esteem for this vanity of mine; and since I wrote it for and permitted it to be seen by that worthy cardinal named above (and some few others), I have since then allowed copies to go into the hands of other great gentlemen; and I have done so in order that if others, outside our Church, may perhaps wish to attribute to themselves this capricious idea of mine . . . there may remain the testimony of persons great beyond all exception that I was the first to imagine this chimera. . . ." [4]

There was only one exception, but a serious one, to Galileo's quietist tactics during these years; it had to do with the potent Jesuit order. The ambiguous and spineless action of the Jesuits in the course of his campaign must have deeply wounded Galileo, and he now sought a chance to revenge himself upon them. Such an opportunity was offered by a debate on the nature of comets which arose among European scientists late in 1618.

Here it is advisable to mention briefly the astronomical observations to which Galileo dedicated most of his energies upon his return from his unhappy visit to Rome. Patiently he continued his observations of the satellites of Jupiter, the most celebrated discovery he had made. In this way he hoped to arrive at an exact measurement of their periods, not only because of the obvious scientific interest of that measurement, but also for a very practical purpose which deserves emphasis as typical of his outlook, committed as he was to the technical orientation of science inherited from the "mathematicians" of the sixteenth century.

Galileo was convinced (a conviction to which he clung all his life) that an exact knowledge of the periods of the satellites would afford a secure method for the practical determination of the longitude of any point on the earth's surface. He believed that this method, applicable also at sea, would allow ships to distinguish the various positions occupied at all points along their assigned courses.

To accomplish this, one would have first to observe telescopically the eclipses, occultations, and conjunctions of Jupiter's satellites, and then apply a process analogous to one which had already been used with some success in the calculation of longitudes on the basis of observations of eclipses of the sun. The advantage of using the satellites of Jupiter rather than the sun, as Galileo pointed out, lay in the fact that eclipses of the satellites take place very frequently, whereas those of the sun are quite rare. But as Ferdinando Flora, speaking as an expert in astronomy, notes: "Though the method is theoretically perfect, it was inapplicable at sea, both because of the difficulties of telescopic observation due to the rolling and pitching of the ship, and because of the lack of any chronometers. . . . Even today, the Galilean method requires astronomical knowledge and special learning on the part of the observer . . . and has never been employed." [5]

Although Galileo's conviction on this point was largely illusory, it is of great interest both historically and for an understanding of his personality. It shows in him the constant and active impulse to connect theory with practice. Driven by this impulse, he could not conceive that his greatest astronomical discovery should remain without practical application and should draw its importance only from its consequences in the field of philosophy. He felt that on the contrary this discovery ought to demonstrate its utility in one of the most difficult and urgent problems of the period, the calculation of longitudes. This in turn was connected with the problem of shipping routes, which was fundamental for dominion over the seas.

Accordingly Galileo entered into negotiations with the Grand Duke Cosimo II and subsequently (through Cosimo's ambassador to Madrid) with the King of Spain himself, seeking a test of the applicability of his idea. But the technicians of the Spanish government felt (intuitively rather than through any full understanding) that it involved difficulties sufficient to destroy its practical use, and hence these negotiations were defeated. Similar dealings were again undertaken, toward the end of Galileo's life, with the Dutch government, which sent a representative to Italy to secure a complete explanation of the subject. But by that time Galileo was becoming blind, and with the loss of his sight went any possibility of his verifying the workability of the proposed method. Thus he went to his grave under the illusion that he carried with him a precious secret which he had offered to his contemporaries repeatedly but in vain.

2. In the autumn of 1618, three comets appeared in the heavens, and this extraordinary astronomical event stimulated debate not only among the populace (who drew ominous auguries from such things), but among leading scientists throughout Europe. Galileo recognized immediately the exceptional interest of the phenomena, though he was unable to observe them personally because he was confined to bed by a grave rheumatic condition. But this unfortunate circumstance did not prevent him from taking part, at first indirectly and later directly, in the scientific debate which raged among the learned over the general nature of comets.

Two theories came chiefly under discussion: that of Aristotle, in which comets were conceived of as atmospheric phenomena rising to the sphere of fire [6] where they were ignited and dragged into circular rotation by the upper motion of the heavens; and that of Tycho Brahe, who, after making careful observations of the comet of 1577 and comparisons between the parallaxes of comets and of the moon, had declared them to be bodies located beyond the lunar heaven, and hence far above the sphere of fire.

The first of these theories was intended principally to preserve the supposed perfection of the heavens, while the second constituted a partial return to the ancient Pythagorean hypothesis of the stellar nature of comets. Tycho accepted from that theory only the location of comets in the highest heavens, and said nothing about the stellar or nonstellar nature of these bodies. Moreover, he sided with the Aristotelians in conceding that they were subjected to motions of circular form.

The Jesuit astronomers after 1616 had abandoned every concession to Copernicanism and tended to embrace and defend the astronomical system of Tycho. In one aspect this system represented something quite modern, for it was based upon the most exact observations. Yet it did not constitute a revolutionary break with the old conceptions, because it still assumed the immobility of the earth. On the whole, it was natural for the Jesuits to become open supporters of the Tychonic theory, with regard to comets as well as planetary motions. That they did so is clear from a learned dissertation on the subject given at Rome by the Jesuit Father Horatio Grassi of Savona, professor of mathematics at the Collegio Romano.[7] Grassi's discourse was published anon-

The Years of Silence

ymously in 1619 with the title *Disputatio astronomica de tribus cometis anni MDCXVIII* (*Astronomical discussion of the three comets of the year 1618*). It was a work of flowery and rhetorical style, which really added nothing scientifically relevant to the theory of Tycho. Banfi remarked that the only novelty introduced by Grassi was "an attempt to reconcile the new hypothesis with Aristotelian metaphysical principles insofar as it employed the distinction between celestial and elemental matter and movements." That very attempt confirmed the character of compromise, so odious to Galileo, in the Tychonic system as elaborated by the Jesuits, and this led him to open a sharp and general polemic against the kind of scientific reasoning used by the professors of the Collegio Romano.

As a first step, Galileo had his pupil and friend Mario Guiducci read before the Florentine Academy a *Discourse on Comets* in which Grassi's [or rather, Tycho's] opinion was declared to be "idle and false." This *Discourse*, inspired and mostly written by Galileo, attacked the Jesuit's position by showing that it could be sustained only if comets were real bodies, and not phenomena similar to rainbows and haloes, in which case they would be pure and simple optical effects of solar reflections in masses of vapor elevated high above the earth.[8] The connections between this suggestion and the old theory of Aristotle is undeniable, but the reasons for its defense by Guiducci (that is, by Galileo) were anything but Aristotelian.

Guiducci's *Discourse* was published at Florence in June 1619, and Grassi's reply appeared in the same year under the title *Libra Astronomica ac Philosophica* (*The Astronomical and Philosophical Balance*). The author concealed himself under the name of Lotario Sarsi Sigensano, a slightly defective anagram of Oratio Grassi Savonensi. The title *Libra* (balance) was meant to indicate that the statements of the *Discourse* must be carefully weighed before being accepted, and was at the same time a pun on the name of the celestial sign in which the author asserted that the comet first appeared. Sarsi (that is, Grassi) entered directly into argument against Galileo without stopping to debate with Guiducci, as shown by the subtitle: [*Libra. . . .*] *qua Galilaei Galilaei opiniones de cometis a Mario Guiducio in florentina Academia*

expositae, atque in lucem nuper editae, examinantur [9] (*Balance
. . . on which are weighed the opinions of Galileo Galilei regarding
comets, presented in the Florentine Academy by Mario
Guiducci and recently published*).

Thus Galileo found himself dragged directly into the debate
and constrained to reply in person. There were, in fact, two
replies: one (published at Florence in 1620), quite moderate and
obsequious, was addressed by Guiducci in the form of a letter to
the Jesuit Father Tarquinio Galluzzi of the Collegio Romano;
the other, very long and polemic in tone, was by Galileo. It also
was written in the form of a letter, and was addressed to the
Reverend Signor Don Virginio Cesarini, Lincean Academician
and Lord Chamberlain to the Pope. This letter took almost three
years to write; it was sent to Cesarini in October 1622, and
published with a dedication to the new pope in 1623.

Taking up Sarsi's metaphor, Galileo gave to his reply the title
Saggiatore (assayer), suggesting that in this delicate problem one
should not use just any balance (*libra*), but rather only the very
precise balance of an assayer of gold. To this he added (and his
words give an idea of the bitterness of the polemic) that as a
matter of fact, the comet had first appeared not in the sign of
Libra, but in that of Scorpio, wherefore Sarsi might more truth-
fully have called his work the *Astronomical and Philosophical
Scorpion*—"a constellation," he went on to say, "which our sover-
eign poet Dante called the

> . . . *figura del freddo animale che colla coda percuote le gente;* [10]

> (figure of the chilly animal which pricks and stings people
> with its tail)

and truly there is no lack of stings here for me. Much worse ones,
too, than those of scorpions; for the latter, as friends of mankind,
do not injure unless first offended and provoked, whereas this
fellow would bite me, who never so much as thought of offending
him. But as luck will have it, I know the antidote and speedy
remedy for such stings, and I shall crush the scorpion and rub
him on the wounds where the venom will be reabsorbed by its
proper body and leave me free and sound." [11]

The Years of Silence

22663

Sarsi, or Grassi, returned to the fray and published a book in 1626 entitled *Ratio ponderum librae et simbellae* (*A reckoning of weights for the balance and the coin-scale*) dedicated to Francesco Cardinal Boncompagni. The Jesuit's style remained apparently serene and peaceful, but in reality it was full of venom; Galileo had good reason to make this marginal note on the first page of his copy:

Simula il viso pace, ma vendetta
chiama il cor dentro, e ad altro non attende.[12]

(His countenance feigns peace, but 'vengeance'
  Cries his heart within, nor will he hear aught else.)

3. *Il Saggiatore—The Assayer, in which with a delicate and precise scale will be weighed the things contained in* The Astronomical and Philosophical Balance *of Lothario Sarsi of Siguenza* —is a stupendous masterpiece of polemic literature. If we were to judge it solely from the viewpoint of astronomical science, however, we should be obliged to admit frankly that it is erroneous. Santillana attempted to rescue some part of Galileo's hypothesis concerning the nature of comets, and to that end he remarked that "in fact, the connection that he inferred between the comets' tails and the sun's beams turned out to be substantially right." [13] But obviously this concerns a particular point which has no weight in an evaluation of the general theory. In order to justify Galileo's stubborn incomprehension of Tycho's merits. Wohlwill maintained some years ago that the Tychonic theory, universally recognized as one of the most important advances in astronomy, did not in fact possess the significance in the seventeenth century that we are in a position to attribute to it today.[14] But he was unable to adduce in support of this justification any proof other than a general appeal to the contradictions in the history of thought. Against his position stands the fact that Kepler understood very well the value of Tycho's astronomy, though he adhered to that of Copernicus, and that the difference of opinion between Kepler and Galileo concerning Tycho's system lay at the root of a serious disagreement between them.[15]

On the whole it seems fair to recognize, with Olschki, that the theory of comets does not constitute the true kernel of the argument unfolded in the *Assayer*, but merely its point of departure.[16] More careful examination shows that Galileo did not even attempt to develop a satisfactory theory of these phenomena.[17] Indeed, to judge a work like the *Assayer* from a strictly astronomical viewpoint (that is, by the tenability of Galileo's theory of comets) would be to miss its most telling and fruitful point. This point is to be found in its wealth of problems, its innumerable special investigations in which Galileo's exceptional acumen as an observer shines forth, and in its biting polemic arguments, which are often transformed into ingenious indications of new themes for scientific research. The evolution of the feud between Galileo and Grassi cannot be understood if one stops at the hypothesis advanced by Galileo, without considering the manner in which he supported it. In this respect, it has been correctly said that "Of the two contestants, so different in ability, Grassi defends a thesis closer to the truth with arguments that are often trifling, while Galileo suggests an erroneous hypothesis and sustains it with the mind of a scientist who searches directly in 'the great book of nature' to discover her laws, and will not be content with inadequate and confused argumentation." [18]

A multitude of themes dealt with in the *Assayer* reveal its rich variety and the consequent impossibility of considering it purely and simply as an astronomical treatise on the nature of comets. Several discussions turn on the problem of the magnification produced by the telescope, with special reference to the case in which it renders visible stars that are completely invisible to the naked eye. (The difficulty of this case hinges on the fact that where nothing is seen with the naked eye, the ordinary definition of "magnification" loses its sense.) Among the most significant pages, both from the standpoint of their scientific penetration and from that of their unusual stylistic brilliance, some are devoted to the demonstration that heat is not produced by the simple motion of bodies, but by an attrition suffered in movement. Other pages examine more or less fully curious phenomena drawn from almost every branch of physics then known; for example, the relation between the pitch of sounds emitted by an organ and the lengths of the pipes emitting them, the adherence of surfaces to one another and in particular that of air to water and of water to the surface of bodies, and the nontransparence of luminous bodies.

Intermingled with the description of various experiments, there are also some interesting (though combative) autobiographical remarks and many valuable methodological considerations. Among the latter are subtle critiques of the supposed nobility and perfection of certain geometric figures and penetrating comments on the indeterminacy of certain words used in ordinary language such as *near* and *far, large* and *small*: ". . . he would err who should say, 'Everything in the world is either large or small,' in which proposition there is neither truth nor falsity, nor is there in saying 'Objects are either near or far.' From indeterminacy of this sort, it comes about that the same things may be called close or distant, great or small; the closer may be called distant, and the farther close; the larger may be called small, and the smaller large." [19] Again, there are some particularly characteristic considerations in which the superiority of proofs based on direct experience over those based only on the testimony of others is insistently hammered home:

"Adducing further witnesses serves no purpose, Signor Sarsi. . . . You take your stand upon the authority of many poets, and against the experiments which we produce. I reply by saying that if those poets were to be present at our experiments, they would change their opinion. . . ." [20] "I cannot help wondering that Sarsi still wishes to persist in proving to me by means of witnesses that which I can see at any time by means of experiment." [21] "Sarsi continues in the style in which he began, trying to establish by the stories of others what actually exists and may be seen every day by experiment." [22] Of special significance because of its modernity is the advice never to be content with old solutions transmitted to us in traditional wisdom, but continually and boldly to seek other solutions, if only as working hypotheses: ". . . Signor Mario's and my primary purpose . . . is to set forth those questions which have appeared to us to throw doubt upon the opinions previously held, and to propose some new considerations. Let us examine and consider whether there is anything that can   103 give us light in any way and can pave the road for the discovery of truth. . . ." [23]

For the rest, the form and appearance of the book show that it is not an independent treatise. It is presented merely as a commentary which follows Sarsi's *Libra*, page by page, in the tradition of commentaries by medieval writers, and takes from Sarsi the clues for its varied and bold reflections. Nor is its form without a certain irony, both because the method to which Galileo descended was already so antiquated, and because he elaborately pretended to do homage to Sarsi by treating the *Libra* as if it were an authoritative text worthy of commentary.

Then is the *Assayer* a fragmentary work, lacking internal unity? On the contrary, it possesses unity, if for no other reason than that it is pervaded by the vibrant personality of Galileo, ever-present in the biting polemic style, in his perspicacity as an acute observer, and in his strength as a bold cultural innovator. What is certain is that the *Assayer* is not a scientific treatise, but rather a fascinating document of cultural propaganda, of the destruction of old methods, of open denunciation of that spirit of compromise which was concealed under the pseudo-modernity of the Jesuit dialectic. It was not without reason that Olschki attempted to draw an analogy between the polemic which Galileo developed here and that which Pascal was to develop in his famous *Provincial Letters* against another aspect of the Jesuit culture.[24] But, although the remark is important, the analogy can be supported only within narrow limits. Nothing would be more misleading than to confuse Pascal's Jansenism with Galileo's foreshadowing of the philosophy of the Enlightenment.

4. Because of the difficulty of the subject, those pages of the *Assayer* which deal with specifically philosophical questions require separate examination. In the main there are two such questions. One is raised in a few lines near the beginning of the book, and concerns the language in which the great book of nature is written.[25] The other is developed at some length near the end, and concerns the distinction between two kinds of qualities attributed to bodies.[26]

The Years of Silence

The latter is considerably simpler, and will be discussed first. The distinction in question was later formulated by several other philosophers, sometimes with arguments similar to those of Galileo and sometimes rather differently. John Locke characterized it as a distinction between primary and secondary qualities. "I say," writes Galileo, "that upon conceiving of a material or corporeal substance, I immediately feel the need to conceive simultaneously that it is bounded, and has this or that shape; that it is in this place or that at any given time; that it moves or stays still; that it does or does not touch another body; and that it is one, few, or many. I cannot separate it from these conditions by any stretch of my imagination. But that it must be white or red, bitter or sweet, noisy or silent, of sweet or foul odor, my mind feels no compulsion to understand as necessary accompaniments. Indeed, without the senses to guide us, reason or imagination alone would perhaps never arrive at such qualities. For that reason I think that tastes, odors, colors, and so forth are no more than mere names so far as pertains to the subject wherein they reside, and that they have their habitation only in the sensorium. Thus if the living creature were removed, all these qualities would be removed and annihilated. . . . I do not believe that for exciting in us tastes, odors, and sounds there are required in external bodies anything but sizes, shapes, numbers, and slow or fast movement; and I think that if ears, tongues, and noses were taken away, shapes and numbers and motions would remain, but not odors or tastes or sounds. These, I believe, are nothing but names apart from the living animal—just as tickling and titillation are nothing but names when armpits and the skin around the nose are absent." [27]

The clarity and importance of these Galilean pages must be evident, because they indubitably opened the way which has since been traveled by modern science. Until quite recently (in accordance with Galileo) physics and physiology assumed that any explanation of secondary qualities, unquestioningly recognized as subjective, must lie in a precise determination of the processes by which these spring from the primary qualities of physical stimulation by the object on the physiological apparatus of the perceiving subject. Even today, when through our improved critical knowledge we are more disposed to identify the concept of "explanation" of sounds, colors, tastes, etc., with that of their "reduction" to primary qualities, we must still admit that such a reduction represents a step of overwhelming importance in the explanation of secondary qualities.

Yet the enormous scientific importance of the distinction made by Galileo notwithstanding, there is really nothing to show that he himself recognized all its philosophical implications. It was as a scientist rather than as a philosopher that he elaborated the distinction; that is, he did so for practical rather than theoretical reasons. He boldly made the point because it was useful to his researches, and within limits where its usefulness was apparent, but he did not analyze its assumptions with regard to knowledge in general, because such an analysis lay outside his interests.

If there is any real rationale for the difference maintained by Galileo between objective and subjective qualities, it is found in the opening lines of the passage last cited, and consists solely of the impossibility that any physical material or substance can be conceived without its numerical, geometrical, and mechanical properties. Even here, Galileo did not examine fundamentally whether this was a logical or an intuitive impossibility; nor, in the latter case, whether it was to be referred to an axiomatic or a merely psychological intuition, These were problems outside his field of interest, but to say as much is not to criticize. It means simply that it is rash if not dangerous to attribute to Galileo some particular philosophical conception just because it may constitute, for us, the most appropriate basis on which to establish his distinction between the objective and subjective qualities of bodies.

Of the two philosophical questions raised by the *Assayer*, however, this is the simpler. The other is subtler and concerns the "language" of nature. It was set forth by Galileo in one of his most celebrated passages: "Philosophy is written in this grand book—I mean the universe—which stands continually open to our gaze, but it cannot be understood unless one first learns to comprehend the language and interpret the characters in which it is written. It is written in the language of mathematics, and its characters are triangles, circles, and other geometrical figures, without which it is humanly impossible to understand a single

word of it; without these, one is wandering about in a dark laby-
rinth." [28]

The Platonic flavor of this assertion seems evident, and it is
quite natural that this passage should be given special emphasis
by those Galilean scholars who tend to interpret his thought as
a form (however attenuated) of mathematicizing Platonism. For
example, Banfi wrote: "The critique of secondary qualities and
the accentuation of the importance of primary qualities by Galileo
is not a declaration of a metaphysical mechanics. Democritus introduces us to Plato, so to speak. . . . The new science illuminates
among rough causal relationships a constancy of proportional
relations, reads it, and thereby transports the latter relations to
the level of quantitative and geometrical consideration. The universe—this universe filled with infinite overtones and appearances
—is then revealed as a harmonic whole in which one part corresponds to another, and is expounded as 'a grand book which
stands continually open to our gaze. . . .' " [29]

I do not mean to deny the presence of Platonic along with
other influences; yet I doubt the possibility of attributing to
Galileo any exact philosophical position, still less a position that
assumes a Platonic dichotomy between the world of phenomena
"filled with infinite overtones and appearances" and the "real"
world, perfectly harmonic, lying behind it and consisting of pure
mathematical entities. Speaking only of the *Assayer* (since the
problem is somewhat different with Galileo's other works), it
seems to me that to rest one's case on this as a support for a
Platonic interpretation of the kind just mentioned is, to say the
least, very daring. One of the methodological rules on which the
whole work turns is the raising of experience to the rank of a
secure source of knowledge. Moreover, there are many things
which lead us to believe that the passage in question here does
not have the decisive Platonic orientation commonly attributed
to it.

First, that passage is not placed in a context of philosophical
arguments. It occurs on a page intended solely to polemicize
against Sarsi's (Grassi's) dangerous habit of introducing appeals
to authority into scientific debates: "It seems to me that I discern
in Sarsi a firm belief that in philosophizing it is essential to sup-   107

port oneself upon the opinon of some celebrated author . . . and possibly he thinks that philosophy is a book of fiction created by some man, like the *Iliad* or *Orlando Furioso*—books in which the least important thing is whether what is written in them is true." [30] No! exclaims Galileo. "Signor Sarsi, that is not the way matters stand. Philosophy is written in this grand book. . . ." and so on. Thus the metaphor of nature as a book does not hide some abstruse metaphysical significance, but is clearly introduced for a specific polemic purpose: that of contrasting one book with another. The book of nature, in which the principle of authority means nothing, because one is not dealing with the work of any man, is contrasted with the books of poets, which may be more or less excellent, and thus more or less authoritative, according to the talent of their authors.

But Galileo says something more. He tells us that the books of poets are dominated by imagination, wherefore he is not interested in whether "what is written in them is true," while the book of nature is dominated by the rigor of mathematics, so that his chief aim there is to grasp truth. This counterbalancing of mathematics and imagination, rather than of mathematics and phenomena, is precisely what must, in my opinion, make us somewhat suspicious of a Platonic interpretation of the passage. May we not believe that Galileo appeals to mathematics for no other reason than that by its rigor it can tie us to the search for truth alone, and prevent us from getting lost in imagination? Why not suppose that he regards mathematics more in its technical aspect, as an aid to logic, than metaphysically, as the expression of a more stable and harmonious reality underlying the fluctuations of phenomena?

In answering these questions, it will be good to reflect briefly on the general character of the *Assayer*. The single red thread running through the work is its hammering polemic against the false dialectic of the Jesuits. But of what does this polemic consist? Galileo's aim is not solely to destroy Sarsi's deceptive logic, but also seriously to counterpoise another against it: "Here Sarsi gets up in arms and in a series of long attacks does his best to show me to be a very poor logician . . . to all of which I answer briefly and simply that it appears to me that Sarsi openly reveals himself to be just what he tries to prove me to be; that is, little cognizant of logic." [31] "If Sarsi thinks he can win acclaim by impugning this way of talking . . . let him beware lest he appear, in trying to show himself off as a great logician, an even greater sophist." [32] "As to the present syllogism, so far as it concerns the matter in hand, let our evidence of its vapidity be that I shall proceed in his very footsteps and conclusively prove the exact opposite." [33] "Whoever possesses the flower of natural logic will, by uniting Sarsi's premises to the conclusion to which they lead, form this syllogism. . . ." [34] It is precisely by this "flower of natural logic" that Galileo wants to oppose the sophistry of his adversary; being tied tightly to experience, true logic will succeed in supplying us with a sure criterion of truth, and in this way will help us arrive at a philosophy different from the imaginings of the poets.

At this point a question spontaneously arises that is directly related to the interpretation of the passage concerning the "book of nature." What, according to Galileo, are the characteristics of the true logic which he so insistently invokes against the false logic of the Jesuit? He has no doubts on this score: true logic must be permeated by mathematics. Proofs, when really conclusive —that is, when they are "pure, geometrical, perfect and necessary"—have the enormous value of laying bare immediately and completely the truth or falsity of any subject. As he explains it: "For just as there is no middle ground between truth and falsity in physical things, so in rigorous proofs one must either establish his point beyond any doubt or else beg the question inexcusable, and there is no chance of keeping on one's feet by invoking limitations, distinctions, verbal distortions, or other fireworks; one must with but few words and at the first assault become Caesar or nobody." [35]

This idea is often reiterated, still more clearly, in other works. Yet there is no doubt that, in the *Assayer* at least, the true logic opposed to the false dialectic of Sarsi is the logic that is uttered in mathematical demonstrations. This, and this alone, is for Galileo the instrument that permits us to start from sensible experiences and construct reasoning free of deceptions.

Now if matters stand thus, then the famous passage in question 109 acquires at once a very clear and precise significance. It expresses in the most suggestive form an appeal to that which was to be the principal conclusion of this polemic; that is, an appeal to the scientist's duty to reason in mathematical terms, in order not to be deceived by imagination and fall into sophistries and equivocations.

Even if we, with our more mature philosophical understanding, maintain that this duty cannot be established outside of a Platonic metaphysics (and I have many reservations on that point), that does not justify us in attributing any such conviction to Galileo. He does indeed declare decidedly that only mathematics can guarantee correct logical form in our reasoning, but he does not appear to be concerned in any way with the metaphysical hypothesis here assumed. In the end, his appeal to mathematics rests upon a methodological rule; the philosophical defense of this rule does not interest him, but is left in the distant depths of the debate. The desire to read more than this into the *Assayer* —to see there a retrogression to mathematical Platonism—may hide from us the living heart of the work.

Chapter 7

The Copernican Manifesto

1. For Galileo, the premature death of his protector Cosimo II in 1621 was a very unfortunate event. Cosimo's young son Ferdinand II succeeded to the throne under the joint regency of his mother, Maria Madeleine of Austria; his paternal grandmother, Christina of Lorraine; and a board of regency appointed by Cosimo. Some twelve years later, the weakness of the new prince was to have great repercussions upon the development of the controversy between Galileo and the Inquisition.

In 1623, however, another event raised high hopes in the minds of Galileo and all the more progressive Catholics; this was the election to the papacy of the cardinal Maffeo Barberini, who took the name Urban VIII. Barberini was a Florentine by birth, had a very acute mind, and was unquestionably concerned with the cultural needs of his time. Thus he appeared to have been sent by providence to put the Church on a new path which would be open wide to the arts and sciences. His candidacy had been supported by the cardinals who favored the French, and this constituted a guarantee that Urban VIII did not share deeply the combative attitude of the Counter-Reformation. (It is to be remembered that Henry IV of France had issued the Edict of Nantes only a few decades earlier, inaugurating an era of religious tolerance.)

Immediately after the election of the new pope, letters were sent to Galileo by friends of his connected with the Lincean Academy at Rome which showed clearly their regard for Barberini. Thus, for example, on August twelfth [1623] Francesco Stelluti wrote: "The creation of the new Pope brought joy to everyone, for your Excellency well knows his ability and goodness, and his special patronage of literary men, so that we are to have a supreme patron. . . . As you will have heard, he immediately appointed our Signore Don Virginio Cesarini as his Lord Chamberlain, and Monsignor Ciampoli will not only remain as Secretary of Princely Affairs, but will also be confidential secretary (*Cameriero secreto*); another of our Linceans, the Cavalier del Pozzo, will serve the Pope's nephew,[1] who will be made a cardinal. Thus we have three Academicians at the palace, in addition to many other friends. Meanwhile we pray that the Lord God may long preserve this Pope, because we expect from him the best of government." [2]

Galileo wrote a letter of congratulation, not to the Pope himself (which would have been lacking in respect), but to his nephew, Francesco Barberini: "To convince you of my inexpressible gratification on hearing of the ascent of His Holiness to the sublime throne, it should be conclusive for me to tell you how sweet it has made the remainder of my life to me, and how much less grave than usual is the prospect of death, whenever I think of it. I shall live most happily, again with the hope (formerly quite dead) of being able to see some most wonderful writings recalled from their long exile, and I shall die content with having lived through the glorious success of the most loved and revered patron I have in this world, and I can neither expect nor desire any other joy so great." [3]

The election of Urban VIII was not without effect upon the printing of the *Assayer*. This work had been composed as a letter to Virginio Cesarini, Lincean academician and the new Pope's Lord Chamberlain. The manuscript was sent to him in October 1622; in January, Cesarini wrote to Galileo on behalf of his Lincean colleagues that the work was to be published at Rome under the auspices of the Academy "despite the power of its adversaries." All resistance to this plan naturally disappeared after the election of Urban VIII, and the Lincean academicians decided to dedicate Galileo's book to the new pope. The letter of dedication, written by Cesarini, said in part:

"As evidence of our devotion and as a tribute from our true fealty, we bring you *The Assayer* of our Galileo, the Florentine discoverer not of new lands but of hitherto unseen portions of the heavens. . . . This we dedicate and present to Your Holiness as to one who has filled his soul with true ornaments and splendors and has turned his heroic mind to the highest undertakings.

The Copernican Manifesto

. . . Meanwhile, humbly inclining ourselves at your feet, we supplicate you to continue favoring our studies with the gracious rays and vigorous warmth of your most benign protection." [4]

The course of events over the next ten years was to show what kind of "most benign protection" Urban VIII reserved for the "wonderful writings" of Galileo. Yet it is probable that at first he was sincerely desirous of granting the support which had been requested of him with such faithful regard. Urban certainly showed himself most grateful for the dedication of the *Assayer*. More than one witness tells us that he had it read to him at table, and took much delight in it. Evidently Galileo's pungent attacks against the Jesuit author did not displease him, though he knew well enough that those fathers, despite their apparent interest in modern culture, were the most unbending defenders of Counter-Reformist intransigence, and hence that a reversal of that intransigence would necessarily be reflected in a progressive reduction of the power they had acquired during the last half-century throughout the entire Catholic world.

Having received confirmation from his Roman friends of the Pope's favorable inclination, Galileo decided to go to Rome again to sound out his position and to seek some concrete pledge, however guarded, of a change in the Church's position on Copernicanism. He arrived at Rome on the twenty-third of April 1624, and was so joyfully received that during his brief stay there (about a month and a half) he had six audiences with Urban VIII, who went so far as to promise him a pension for his son Vincenzio.[5] But with regard to the delicate subject of Copernican theory, which lay closest to his heart, Galileo failed to obtain any positive assurance. To his plea that the decree of 1616 be revoked, the Pope gave an evasive reply; he entrenched himself behind a captious argument that has passed into history bearing his name ("the argument of Urban VIII") to the effect that if many things seemed to prove that the earth turned about the sun, it was still theoretically possible that God, in his infinite power, had obtained those effects by making the sun turn round the earth precisely as was said in the Holy Scripture. Yet there were many indications that Urban VIII would not be wholly opposed to a cautious revival of the debate over the heliocentric theory. 113

Galileo Galilei

Characteristic of these were his words to Cardinal Zollern, which were promptly relayed to Galileo, "that the Holy Church had never, and would never, condemn it as heretical, but only as rash, though there was no danger that anyone would ever demonstrate it to be necessarily true." [6]

Matters standing thus, it was important not to give up, but to test courageously the sticking point of the Pope's tolerance. This was certainly a perilous undertaking, but Galileo knew very well that only by confronting this danger could he again take up the ambitious program for which he had battled so tenaciously some years before. If he dared not take advantage immediately of this change of atmosphere in the Vatican hierarchy, when would he ever again have so favorable an opportunity?

Nevertheless, he decided to proceed gradually. First he drafted a reply to Francesco Ingoli's arguments against the Copernican system, which he began soon after his return to Florence. He sent the finished statement to his friends at Rome to distribute widely, though without actual publication and without putting it into the hands of Ingoli himself. It is certain that many persons read it, and that the Pope took notice of it, though only partially. Its reception was not so hostile as might have been feared. Thus Galileo became convinced that the path he had chosen was a good one, and that he should press on. Many years were to pass before events demonstrated to him that his deduction was merely a tragic illusion.[7]

2. Ingoli's letter had set forth various arguments in refutation of the Copernican hypothesis, divided into three separate categories: astronomical, philosophical, and theological. In his reply, Galileo confined himself to an examination of the astronomical and philosophical arguments, declaring in the most emphatic terms (and here is the difference between his new attitude and that which he had taken in 1616) that he wished in no way to touch on the theological problem, with respect to which he submitted completely to the decisions of the Church. This clear and complete abdication with regard to the theological arguments seems to have been dictated not only by a wish to appear disciplined and submissive to the decrees of 1616, but also by the equal

desire to make concessions to Urban's own particular mode of thought. His manner of presenting those concessions, however, gave them more an ironic than a serious tone. The opening pages of the *Rispota* (*Reply*) are significant in this regard.

"Note, Signor Ingoli," wrote Galileo, "that I do not undertake this task with any intention or design to rescue and to maintain as true that position which has already been declared to be suspect and repugnant to doctrines which, through their majesty and authority, are superior to physical and astronomical studies. . . . I write my reply merely to demonstrate to you that your arguments in the first and second categories are vain, so that the decree of the Holy Office must be accepted only because of religious discipline, and for no other reasons. . . . And I may add, to the confusion of all heretics (among whom I hear those of the best repute are of the Copernican opinion) that it is my thought to deal with this subject at length, and to show them that it is not through any defect of physical reasoning, nor from our having failed to see all the reasons, experiences, observations, and demonstrations which they have seen, that we Catholics remain in the ancient faith taught us by the sacred writers, and that we do this through reverence for the writings of the Church Fathers and through zeal for religion and our faith. Thus, when they have seen that all their astronomical and physical arguments are well understood by us, and even that we have others of greater force than those they have produced so far, they can at most blame us for constancy in our opinion, not for blindness or for ignorance of mundane studies—and this really cannot carry any weight with a Catholic Christian. I mean that such a man will not mind if a heretic laughs at him for placing reverence and faith in the holy authors above the numerous reasons and experiences of all astronomers and physicists put together. And to this may be added another benefit to us, which is that of knowing how little one should trust in human reasoning and human wisdom, and how greatly we are therefore indebted to the superior sciences which alone can enlighten the blindness of our minds and can teach us things at which we should never arrive by our experiences and reasoning." [8]

Galileo's concessions here to the scientific skepticism of Urban VIII are particularly evident. He seemed disposed to assume   115 without discussion that to liberate us from the innate blindness of our minds, human sciences alone are insufficient; the superior sciences of divine inspiration are necessary. But one need only look a little more deeply into the complex content of the work in order to see that Galileo himself was so convinced of the contrary as never to have the slightest doubt about the possibility of conclusively refuting the first two categories of Ingoli's objections, the astronomical and philosophical. This is clear evidence that in the province of the human sciences, the "blindness" shown by the adversary can easily be conquered without an appeal to anything superior to man. All that is required to achieve this victory is the possibility of discussion.

Galileo's chief object in this work was to rekindle among Catholic scholars the debate over Copernicanism. His stratagem of attempting to show to heretics the scope of Catholic culture is obviously a fiction; what interests him is that this stratagem may reopen the discussion, and make known to Catholics the new arguments recently discovered in favor of Copernicanism.

But this stratagem also involved a second objective, which was to remind the Church of the grave cultural responsibilities it would assume by "putting faith before all the reasons and experiences of the astronomers and philosophers." Would the Church be able to persist in that ridiculous attitude after Galileo had respectfully called attention to its absurdity? Would an enlightened Pope like Urban VIII feel himself in a position to keep alive the antithesis between religion and science? To do so might please ignorant friars like Lorini and Caccini, but could only appear foolish to anyone who really understood the value of the respective disciplines. So, at least, Galileo believed, precisely because of his esteem for Urban. Hence the Pope must be convinced that even if Catholics were forbidden scientific research, it would continue inexorably on its path despite every obstacle. If the antithesis between science and religion were maintained, it would in the end turn back to injure the Church. In this situation, the only task of importance was to find means of resuming the debate that had been interrupted in 1616. Galileo was convinced that once he could expound his own arguments, truth would surely emerge victorious over error.

The Copernican Manifesto

Having explained the relation between his investigations and the Church decrees, Galileo went on to develop in an orderly and accurate way his replies to Ingoli's various astronomical and philosophical arguments. Out of this came a limpidly clear work, brief (about fifty pages in the National Edition), vivacious, and yet serene. The debate with his adversary had nothing of the sharp polemic character of the *Assayer*, but appeared to be sincerely devoted to persuasion, to the elimination one by one of all the doubts raised by the opponent, and to the exploration with him of every difficulty. His peroration confirmed this serenity: "It remains for me to beg you to receive in good spirit these replies of mine, as I hope you will do, both through your innate courtesy, and because it is thus that all lovers of truth should act. For if I shall have fundamentally resolved your objections, you will have gained not a little by exchanging false things for true; but if on the other hand I have erred, so much the brighter will shine the teaching of your discourses." [9]

The *Reply* was not sent to Ingoli; hence we must conclude that these lines were in fact written for the eyes of some other person, more highly esteemed, whom Galileo wanted at all costs to win over. The person addressed was no enemy, much less ignorant; he was a "lover of truth" who, though he disagreed with Galileo, shared his desire to arrive at a clear and convincing solution of the problems, whether that solution was Ptolemaic or Copernican. Who could this ideal interlocutor be but Urban VIII, so desirous of presenting himself as the great protector of culture and as a man open-minded to every profound argument of artistic or scientific interest?

Many interesting arguments that were later repeated and amplified in the *Dialogue* were developed here in their essentials; often their form was more rigorous than that employed in the greater work. The two which are most significant to our general interpretation of Galilean thought were: first, an argument which removed one of the chief physical difficulties then usually raised against Copernicanism and, second, an argument concerned with a fundamental mechanical difficulty.

The physical argument bears on the preliminary question whether the earth is truly at the center of the universe. The opponents of Copernicus, clearly inspired by Aristotle, declared: "Among simple bodies, we see that the grosser and heavier occupy the lower places, as earth below water, and water below air; but the earth is a grosser body than the sun, and the lowest place in the universe is the center; therefore the earth, and not the sun, occupies the center." Galileo's refutation of this pseudo-argument turns on three fundamental points:

1. A critique of the concepts of "inferior" (lower) and "superior" (higher), which were assumed by the Aristotelians to have some absolute sense, whereas their sense is only relative and changes from one place to another; on earth these words mean "that which is under our feet, toward the center of the terrestrial globe, and that which is over our heads, toward the sky"; whereas on the moon, the sun, and the stars, the lower place is the center [of each body named] and the higher is the place toward the surface, and beyond that, toward the surrounding sky." [10] As a consequence, he recognized the existence of a multiplicity of centers: "We shall have throughout the universe as may centers and as many lower and higher places as there are world-bodies and orbs that turn round different points."

2. A denunciation of the confusion perpetrated by the Aristotelians between the center of the earth and the center of the universe, assuming that there is such a thing: "But if, in your conclusion, you wish to mean by the lower place not the center of the earth (as in your premises, but the center of the universe, you are either making a syllogism of four terms, equivocating [the meaning of] 'center' from that of the earth to that of the universe, or you are assuming as known that which is in question; that is, that the earth, as a most heavy body, occupies the center of the universe." [11]

3. A denunciation of the inherent dogmatic character of the assumption, set forth as obvious by the Aristotelians, that the earth is a grosser body than the sun: "Something which neither you nor I know, nor can we know for certain." [12] Galileo suggests, on the contrary, that if we wish to grant to Aristotle that the sun is unalterable and incorruptible, we must believe it to be of material more gross than that of the earth, more similar to gold or diamonds than to water or air.

The Copernican Manifesto

Galileo's refutation of the "proofs" from mechanics against the motion of the earth belongs among the most valid and interesting parts of his entire accomplishment. One such "proof" (accepted even by Tycho) was based on the fact that heavy bodies fall perpendicularly to the surface of the earth, and not obliquely, as (according to these men) they must fall if the earth moved. In confirmation of this, they invoked experience, "saying that this is to be seen clearly on board ship. If, when the ship is at rest, a stone is let fall freely from the top of the mast, it descends perpendicularly and strikes at the foot of the mast, precisely at the point plumb to the place from which it is let fall. But, they say, this effect does not occur when the ship is moving rapidly along, for in the time during which the stone, let free, descends perpendicularly, the ship runs on ahead; and the stone will lag far toward the stern from the foot of the mast; and this effect would happen to a stone falling from the top of a tower if the earth revolved swiftly." [13]

Against this anti-Copernican argument and similar "proofs," Galileo put forth what is now usually called the "Galilean principle of relativity." This states that on the basis of mechanical experiments performed within a system, it is impossible to decide whether the system is at rest or in uniform rectilinear motion. "Shut yourself and a friend below deck in the largest room of a great ship, and have there some flies, butterflies, and similar small flying animals; take along also a large vessel of water with little fish inside it; fit up also a tall vase that shall drip water into another narrow-necked receptable below. Now, with the ship at rest, observe diligently how those little flying animals go in all directions; you will see the fish wandering indifferently to every part of the vessel, and the falling drops will enter into the receptacle placed below. . . . When you have observed these things, set the ship moving with any speed you like (so long as the motion is uniform and not variable) ; you will perceive not the slightest change in any of the things named, nor will you be able to determine whether the ship moves or stands still by events pertaining to your person. . . . And if you should ask me the reason for all these effects, I shall tell you now: 'Because the general motion of the ship is communicated to the air and everything else contained in it, and is not contrary to their natural tendencies, but is indelibly conserved in them.' And at another time you shall hear the specific replies and a full explanation." [14]

The great scientific interest of Galileo's answer is evident. But no less fascinating is the method by which he arrived at this dis-covery, based on the one hand on correct and rigorous reasoning, and on the other on actual experiments. The kernel of this method consists in the definitive abandonment of the risky habit, initiated by the Aristotelians, of assuming as obvious that which is in fact debatable, and in particular of appealing generally to untried experiments which were believed to give one result but in reality gave another. Galileo's polemic against the false experimentalism of the Aristotelians assumes here a tone of such gravity as to leave no shadow of doubt concerning the importance which he attributed to the subject: ". . . the other error is your adducing of experiments as actual and as corresponding to your desires, with-out your even having performed them or observed them. . . . If you and Tycho would really confess the truth, you would say you had never tested by experiment . . . whether or not any variation was to be found from that which it seemed to you ought to happen." [15] As in the *Assayer*, Galileo proposed to set up a true logic against the false appeal to experience: "Let us add, more-over, that we have tested this more than a hundred times, making the ship move and having it stand still . . . and never have we been able to recognize, from things inside it, which it was doing." [16]

It is interesting to note that Galileo had also another reproach for his opponents: on the basis of exact reasoning in mechanics, he had been able to foresee that things would take place as they actually do. The failure of his opponents to do so, however, is a minor fault, because it may have been committed in good faith; the inexcusable guilt is that they lied: "And one such experiment is precisely that of the stone falling from the top of a ship's mast . . . in which I have been doubly a better philosopher than they have. For, in asserting that which is the contrary of the effect, they have also added the lie that they had seen it by experiment, whereas I have made the experiment, before which time physical

reasoning had firmly persuaded me that the effect must take

place precisely as it does." [17] Thus Galileo, no less than the Aristotelians, had appealed to reason to foresee how things should take
place; but not content with that, he felt also the need of actually
checking by experiment whether or not they did so. And when
he was unable to carry out an experiment on account of technical
difficulties, he freely confessed it. His adversaries, on the other
hand, knowingly falsified, and once they had been caught in the
wrong, there could be no grounds for faith in their other asser-
tions: "And first, I do not know how far I ought to believe that
you or Tycho ever made diligent observations. . . ." [18]

But the ideal interlocutor to whom Galileo was addressing his
Reply was not a stubborn Aristotelian nor a headstrong follower
of Tycho; he was a "lover of truth," and therefore a man who
could not remain unmoved by these arguments. Hence Galileo
did not turn directly against him the full harshness of his
critique, as he had done against Sarsi. Rather, he played upon
his love for truth, and seemed to hope that he might soon count
him among his allies.

3. Whether or not Galileo's faith in Urban VIII and the more
enlightened part of the high clergy was justified at that moment,
it certainly was the chief force that drove the great scientist to
take up again in 1624 the vast politico-cultural program that
had been arrested in 1616 by his serious discomfiture at the hands
of the Holy Office. No longer did he attempt to demonstrate the
possibility of bringing into substantial agreement Copernicanism
and the Scriptures by recourse to the two different types of lan-
gauge (ordinary and scientific). Now he had to leave any reconciliation entirely to theologians. Galileo's problem was reduced
to one of more modest proportions: that of keeping the Church
from intervening prejudicially in the discussion of Copernicanism
in Catholic countries, and from closing its eyes to the ever-
increasing body of knowledge that made Copernicanism the starting point of the nascent development of science. Catholic culture,
even if disinclined to give its full support to the new science,
must at least stop lending its mighty strength to the most dedicated
adversaries of science.

This plan, less ambitious than that which had gone before, 121 was based on Galileo's conviction that science, if unhindered by blind dogmatic hatred, would eventually impose its own reasons by itself and would victoriously open the road to the modern world. Its advance would be seriously delayed without the collaboration of the scientists of the Catholic countries, and these countries (Italy above all), would soon find themselves behind in civil progress if they were isolated from the scientific debate, rather than in the vanguard as Galileo wished. Hence, for the good of those countries and of science, it was necessary to remove as rapidly as possible the obstacles raised in 1616 by the ignorance of the friars Caccini and Lorini. It was essential to find means of publishing, this time with the full authorization of the clergy, a great objective work on Copernicanism. Read by Catholics, it should serve to convince them of the fundamentals of that theory; spread at the same time among Protestants, it would offer proof that Catholicism was no longer foolishly frozen in its position of 1616.

Galileo had long since promised in the *Starry Messenger* that he would publish a work on the "System of the World" which would unite in a single grand conception the latest discoveries of astronomy and the other branches of science, laying a basis for all new research into nature. That promise, reaffirmed in the *Discourse on Bodies in Water* and in various letters, had still not been carried out, nor is there evidence that Galileo had ever buckled down seriously to the task of drafting his great treatise. He had preferred to devote all his energies to the broadcasting of scientific culture on the widest possible scale among his contemporaries, meanwhile seeking a common ground for the new (Copernican) science and the Catholic Church.

Now his former project began to blossom speedily in his mind, with some new characteristics. It was no longer enough to write a "System of the World" directed to specialists in astronomy; he must compose the great and daring work on Copernicanism required by his cultural plan, containing in clear and developed form all the themes that would ever have been included in the oft-promised work. Once he saw this solution, Galileo undertook the work immediately (1624) and decided to give to his new book the form of a dialogue. This would permit him on the one hand to introduce easily into the conversation the widest variety of subjects most apt to interest the cultured public in the problems of the new science, and on the other hand to present proofs in favor of Copernicanism without becoming personally responsible for them.

Yet even now there were many delays, largely for reasons of health. Galileo was over sixty; his strength had begun gradually to decline, and he suffered a particularly serious illness in 1628. The fortunes of his family also often distracted him from his work. His brother Michelangelo returned to Italy in 1627 and brought his numerous family to live with Galileo, returning to Munich in 1628, leaving his wife and seven children under Galileo's care. Suddenly he sent for them again and reproached Galileo for not having adequately provided for them—a most unmerited accusation which deeply wounded Galileo. Michelangelo died in January 1631, after having asked pardon of his brother and having once again sent to him his wife and children.

During the same period there were other events which had a definite effect on Galileo's life. In 1628, his son Vincenzio took his degree in law at Pisa, and the following year he married Sestilia Bocchineri,[19] the sister of both Geri Bocchineri (attached to the secretariat of the Grand Duke Ferdinand II) and Alessandra Bocchineri, who was very dear to Galileo in the last years of his life. The son's marriage caused a certain amount of anguish to his two sisters; the elder, Sister Maria Celeste, for a time feared the possible loss of part of her father's affection to the sister-in-law and her new family. Fortunately for everyone, this misunderstanding was soon cleared up, and Galileo once more found in his daughter the deep understanding that had always been a comfort to him, and that was to be even more needed some years later, during the storm of the final trial. In order to gratify her wishes, Galileo leased in 1631 a small villa called *Il Gioiello* (The Little Jewel) in Arcetri, next to the convent of San Matteo; here, close to his daughters, he was ultimately confined in December 1633.

Despite frequent interruptions, the composition of the *Dialogue* was finally brought to a close in January 1630, having taken six years. The work was intended to bear the title *Dialogue on the Ebb and Flow of the Tides.* It now remained only to have the work transcribed by a copyist, to obtain the imprimatur of the Church, and to get it printed.

In March, while the work of copying was still in progress, good news arrived from Rome. A letter from Benedetto Castelli assured Galileo of the benevolent attitude of Nicolò Riccardi, Master of the Sacred Palace, sometimes called the Father Monster.[20] Castelli also mentioned that Urban VIII, discussing the condemnation of Copernicanism with Thomas Campanella, had declared "that was never our intention, and if it had been left to us, the decree would never had been issued." Strong support for Galileo came also from Federico Cesi, who intended to have the book printed (as had been done previously with the *Assayer*) under the auspices of the Lincean Academy which he had founded and financed.

Toward the end of March, Galileo journeyed to Rome to take the manuscript to the Church authorities and personally to solicit their approval. He was able to speak at length with Father Riccardi and with Father Rafael Visconti, who had been charged with the editing of the work. He had been recommended to Father Riccardi both by Benedetto Castelli and by the Tuscan ambassador at Rome, the Marquis Francesco Nicolini, whose wife was closely related to Riccardi. From Riccardi and Visconti, Galileo received assurances that the work could receive a license with only a few inconsequential modifications. Fortified by these promises, he left Rome again on the twenty-sixth of June, full of hope and faith. And in fact the book was soon returned "subscribed and licensed" by Father Riccardi, but this was not at all a definitive license, and had mainly the object of authorizing Galileo to enter into negotiations with a printer.

Before long, however, things began to deteriorate. At Rome, Prince Cesi died unexpectedly early in August. Without his moral and financial support, the Lincean Academy had to give up direct responsibility for publication of the work. Castelli next wrote to Galileo advising him to have the *Dialogue* printed at Florence, where the influence of the Grand Duke would facilitate acquisition of the imprimatur, both ecclesiastical and civil. Galileo agreed, and in fact these authorizations were not long in coming, but the definitive opinion from Rome was still lacking.

Father Riccardi, evidently subjected to powerful pressure on the part of Galileo's enemies, began to temporize. To gain time, he wrote to Florence requesting that the text be sent back to him for another revision. Growing suspicious, Galileo produced various reasons for avoiding that request; he proposed instead that the book be re-examined at Florence by some mutually acceptable theologian. This proposal was only partially accepted. It was conceded that the text of the *Dialogue* could be reviewed by the Dominican Father Giacinto Stefani at Florence, but the preface and the end of the book had to be returned to Rome for reworking before publication.

All this was done. Father Stefani soon completed his work, but Rome preferred to move as slowly as possible. Only after innumerable urgings by the ambassador did Father Riccardi consent to carry out his promises. In July 1631 he sent to the Inquisitor at Florence his last directives concerning the granting of the requested authorization, and at the same time he sent "the opening or preface, to be placed on the first sheet, though with the author free to change or polish it as to wording, duly observing the sense of the content." Wording of similar sense to that of the preface was to be put at the end of the book. It was forbidden to make any reference in the title of the book to the tides; that is, to the argument which Galileo considered to afford definitive proof of the truth of Copernicanism.

Concerned only to speed publication, Galileo accepted all these instructions without question. The book finally emerged on the twenty-first of February 1632, from the Florentine press of Landini with its printer's device depicting three fishes.[21] Two years had thus elapsed since the day on which Galileo had brought his composition to an end. In place of his original title appeared this more neutral wording: *Dialogue of Galileo Galilei, Lincean . . . wherein, in the meetings of four days, are discussed the two chief systems of the world, Ptolemaic and Copernican.*[22]

There are three interlocutors in the *Dialogue:* The Florentine nobleman Filippo Salviati (1583–1614), to whom Galileo had dedicated his *Letters on Sunspots;* the Venetian patrician Giovanfrancesco Sagredo (1571–1620); and the Aristotelian Simplicio, an imaginary character. Though he bears the name of a celebrated commentator on Aristotle who flourished in the sixth century, this by no means contradicts the idea that Galileo, in assigning the name Simplicio, meant to discredit the Aristotelian in the *Dialogue* as a scientific simpleton. The protagonists are presented as having gathered in Sagredo's palace at Venice for four days at some unspecified time in order to discuss amicably the heliocentric system and to clarify for themselves the arguments for and against it. Salviati is an admitted Copernican; Simplicio is the avowed defender of geocentrism; Sagredo is open-minded toward Copernicanism but is neutral at the outset, and this induces both the others to clarify and develop their respective arguments.

4. The preface to the *Dialogue*, developed along lines suggested by Father Riccardi, contains a theme which had appeared in Galileo's reply to Ingoli: "Therefore I propose in the present work to show to foreign nations that as much is understood of this matter in Italy, and particularly in Rome, as transalpine diligence can ever have imagined." [23] The so-called argument of Urban VIII is closely linked to this so as to make it look like a natural premise: "I hope that from these considerations the world will come to know that if other nations have navigated more, we have not theorized less. It is not from failing to take count of what others have thought that we have yielded to the assertion that the earth is motionless, and hold the contrary to be a mere mathematical caprice, but (if for nothing else) for those reasons that are supplied by piety, religion, the knowledge of Divine Omnipotence and a consciousness of the limitations of the human mind." [24]

Juxtaposition of these four reasons (piety, religion, divine omnipotence, and the weakness of man's intellect) clearly demonstrates Galileo's intended acceptance of the Pope's way of thinking. This acceptance becomes even more explicit in the final pages of the Fourth Day, where Galileo puts into Simplicio's mouth the following words: "As to the discourses we have held, and especially this last one concerning the reasons for the ebbing and flowing of the ocean, I am really not entirely convinced;

but from such feeble ideas of the matter as I have formed, I admit that your thoughts seem to me more ingenious than many others I have heard. I do not therefore consider them true and conclusive; indeed, keeping always before my mind's eye a most solid doctrine that I once heard from a most eminent and learned person, and before which we must fall silent, I know that if asked whether God in his infinite power and wisdom could have conferred upon the watery element its observed reciprocating motion using some other means . . . both of you would reply that He could have, and that He would have known how to do this in many ways which are unthinkable to our minds. From this I forthwith conclude that, this being so, it would be excessive boldness for anyone to limit and restrict the Divine power and wisdom to some particular fancy of his own." [25]

Having concluded the *Dialogue* in these words, Galileo could maintain that he had scrupulously obeyed the orders of the Church authorities and had given prominence to Urban's argument. Yet the reality was very different, and his judges could not ignore it. The words in question were spoken by Simplicio, which fact alone sufficed to place them in an unfavorable light. It is true that Salviati, the Copernican in the *Dialogue*, assents immediately to Simplicio's argument, but the wording of his acceptance seems to have an ironic and overly explicit sense: "An admirable and angelic doctrine. . . ." What could be the meaning of this unhesitating acquiescence without examination or debate?

Galileo's adversaries sought, with some success, to make the Pope believe that Galileo had intended the figure of Simplicio to represent him and had thus made sport of him. The charge was quite unfounded; Simplicio appears always and unmistakably as a dogmatic Aristotelian rather than a cultured advocate of skepticism. Though at the end it is Simplicio who brings in the argument of God's omnipotence and the weakness of human intelligence, he does so only in desperation, perceiving that there is no other way to refute the Copernican proofs. But impossible as it is to identify Simplicio with Urban VIII, there is little evidence that Galileo ever took the Pope's argument seriously.

One might even say that he took it less seriously than the arguments of Aristotle and Ptolemy, for many pages of the *Dialogue* 127

Galileo Galilei

are devoted to an examination and analysis of the latter, whereas Urban's argument comes in merely as a *deus ex machina* to settle everything without convincing anyone. Indeed, the argument profoundly offended the mind of Galileo; it stood in opposition not only to every proof of the Copernican theory but also to the rationalist philosophy of enlightenment that he embraced. He did not discuss it (and, admittedly, he had no way of refuting it), but this silence merely shows that he did not take it seriously. When all his energies (and those of the best of his contemporaries) were engaged in bringing forth the new science, he would not waste time and effort on quibbles of this kind. It was not that he lacked the requisite critique, considering the acuteness of his methodological reflections, but that he preferred to devote himself to more useful matters. His task was to combat innumerable errors of the old presumptuous, dogmatic, metaphysical science; not to throw doubt on the basis of all science, or cast a shadow on the power of human reason.

An exposition of the contents of the *Dialogue*, as developed throughout the four "days" of the discussion, is virtually impossible. Too many subjects are treated, despite their harmonious integration; there are too many separate observations and apparent digressions. Though these give the whole book life and fascination, they defeat any summary. Only a few suggestions of the arguments can be given here, followed by an over-all appraisal designed to throw light on the general significance and great value of the *Dialogue*.

The First Day begins with a lively critique of the perfection attributed by the Aristotelians (and still more by the Pythagoreans) to certain numbers, such as the number three, and the consequent claim that the world is complete and perfect because it has three dimensions. The discussion gradually broadens into a general critique of Aristotelian physics, of his false reasoning designed to prove the earth to be the center of the universe, and above all of Aristotle's distinction between the celestial and the sublunary worlds. To the logical arguments are then added those drawn from experiment, involving telescopic observations of the stars; Aristotle cannot be blamed because he lacked them, but in this regard modern men are his superiors. There follows a discussion of the vain attempts to reconcile these astronomical discoveries with the old Aritstotelian physics. Simplicio remarks that he finds it extremely repugnant to identify the nature of the earth with that of the stars, and the discussion is then extended to include the capacity of man's mind. This debate offers Salviati the opportunity to outline a celebrated distinction between "intensive" and "extensive" comprehension. Although from the point of view of extension, the human understanding is far below that of God, from the viewpoint of intension it may attain to and equal God's, especially in pure mathematics: "that is, geometry and arithmetic, in which the Divine intellect indeed knows infinitely more propositions, since it knows all; but with regard to those few which the human intellect understands, I believe that its knowledge equals the Divine in objective certainty, for here it succeeds in understanding necessity, beyond which there can be no greater sureness." [26] Concerning the interpretation of this distinction there is much debate among Galilean scholars. To me, it appears to represent a clear attempt by Galileo to stress his detachment from neo-Platonism. For while the neo-Platonists held that the only path to identification with God was that of ascending to a transcendent, mystical knowledge of the whole, Galileo held that the path lay rather in the rational understanding of some limited areas of knowledge, such as arithmetic and geometry.

The First Day ends with a striking eulogy of language, which Galileo considered "the seal of all the admirable inventions of mankind": "But surpassing all stupendous inventions, what sublimity of mind was his who dreamed of finding means to communicate his deepest thoughts to any other person, though distant by mighty intervals of place and time! Of talking with those who are in India; of speaking to those who are not yet born and will not be born for a thousand or ten thousand years; and with what facility, by the different arrangements of twenty characters upon a page!" [27]

The Second and Third Days are devoted to the analysis and resolution of traditional objections (due primarily to Aristotle, Ptolemy, and Tycho) against the two motions of the earth: the daily and the annual. Arguments against the daily motion and the famous experiments Galileo used against the false reasoning of his adversaries reappear here in almost the same words he had addressed to Ingoli. The principal objections to the annual motion of the earth were based on the invariability of the magnitudes and positions of the fixed stars throughout the four seasons of the year. To refute these objections, Galileo appeals to the order of magnitude of the distance of the fixed stars from the earth—a distance enormously greater than that of the space traversed by the earth around the ecliptic. In developing this argument he also advances the daring conception of an infinite universe, though only hypothetically.

Having eliminated the arguments against the earth's motion, Galileo goes on finally to show how the hypothesis of the double rotation (diurnal and annual) advanced by Copernicus offers the simplest explanation of all celestial phenomena, including the new telescopic discoveries, which discoveries can accordingly be considered as almost a direct confirmation of the theory in question. On this subject the *Dialogue* reflects with great clarity the author's scientific sentiments.

Sagredo:
O Nicholas Copernicus, what a pleasure it would have been for you to see this part of your system confirmed by so clear an experiment!

Salviati:
Yes, but how much less would his sublime intellect be celebrated among the learned! For as I said before, we may see that with reason as his guide he resolutely continued to affirm what sensible experience seemed to contradict. I cannot get over my amazement that he was constantly willing to persist in saying that Venus might go around the sun and be more than six times as far from us at one time as another, and still look always equal, when it should have appeared forty times larger.

Salviati:
It remains for us to remove what would seem to be a great objection to the motion of the earth. This is that though all

the planets turn about the sun, the earth alone is not solitary
like the others, but goes together in the company of the
moon and the whole elemental sphere around the sun in
one year, while at the same time the moon moves around
the earth every month. Here one must once more exclaim
over and exalt the admirable perspicacity of Copernicus,
and simultaneously regret his misfortune at not being alive
in our day. For now Jupiter removes this apparent anomaly
of the earth and moon moving conjointly. We see Jupiter,
like another earth, going around the sun in twelve years
accompanied not by one but by four moons, together with
everything that may be contained within the orbits of its
four satellites.[28]

The Fourth Day restates the argument outlined in the *Discourse
on the ebb and flow of the seas* which Galileo composed in 1616
at the invitation of Cardinal Orsini. This was an explanation of
the tides as a result of the compound effects of the earth's rotation on its axis and its revolution about the sun. According to
Galileo, the explanation had two outstanding merits: (a) it
linked the tides to purely mechanical laws without appealing to
any force such as the attraction of the moon for the waters, which
he considered as little short of an occult property, though it is
closer to the explanation we adopt today and had been suggested
by the other astronomers of his time; [29] and (b) it indicated one
phenomenon which was terrestrial rather than celestial and yet
might constitute a direct confirmation of the Copernican hypothesis.

Despite the fact that Salviati qualified this argument as a pure
fantasy "which may very easily turn out to be a most foolish
hallucination and a majestic paradox," [30] we know that Galileo
himself held it to be not merely valid, but perhaps his most decisive
argument in favor of Copernicanism. Actually it was entirely
wrong, and Galileo should have been the first to see this if he
had correctly applied to the earth the laws of composition of
motion that he himself had discovered. But even the greatest
scientists fall sometimes into gross errors.[31]

It may be noted that elsewhere in the *Dialogue* (in the Second

Day) Galileo had mentioned with true scientific insight a very important mechanical phenomenon that might have led to a correct experimental proof of terrestrial rotation. This is the fact that because of the earth's rotation, a ball falling freely from a sufficient height must strike somewhat forward of the vertical point, rather than behind it as the adversaries of Copernicus assumed: "And far from failing to follow the motion of the earth and necessarily falling behind, it would even go ahead of it, seeing that in its approach toward the earth the rotational motion would have to be made in ever smaller circles, so that if the same speed were conserved in it which it had within the orbit, it ought to run ahead of the whirling of the earth, as I said." [32] But Galileo did not perceive the full importance of this observation, and did not understand that on this basis alone it would have been possible to conceive of an actual proof of terrestrial motion, the kind of proof he so much desired, and sought erroneously in the tides. Be that as it may, the simple fact of his having glimpsed such an apparently paradoxical consequence of the earth's motion constituted a scientific achievement of the highest order.

5. The plan of the *Dialogue* seems to me to show that it is not a true astronomical treatise. Neither is it a treatise on physics, or in short a purely scientific work of any kind. As Koyré has well said: "Actually, the *Dialogue* is neither a book of astronomy nor a book of physics. It is above all a work of criticism, a polemic work, a battlefield; and at the same time it is a pedagogical work, a philosophical work; finally, it is a work of history—the history of Galileo's mind.

"A polemic work, a battlefield: it is this which at least partly determines the literary structure of the *Dialogue*. It is against traditional science and philosophy that Galileo aims his guns. But if the *Dialogue* is directed against the Aristotelian tradition, it is not addressed (or is hardly addressed) to the defenders of that tradition, to the philosophers of Padua or Pisa. . . . It is addressed to the cultured layman, and is written not in Latin, the language of the universities and the philosophers, but in colloquial language, in Italian, the language of the courts and of the middle class. . . . It is the cultured layman whom Galileo wants to win to his cause. Now the cultured layman must be persuaded and convinced, not wearied and oppressed. To this we owe, in part, the dialogue form of the work, its light conversational tone, its continual digressions and repetitions, the apparent disorder of the debate; for thus did men converse and discuss things in the salons of Venice or the courts of the Medici. To this we owe the variety of weapons employed by Galileo—the serene discussions leading to search for proof and attempts at demonstration, the eloquent discourse designed to persuade, and finally the most potent weapon of the polemicist, incisive criticism, penetrating and cutting: irony that sports with the adversary and makes him ridiculous, stripping bare and exposing the authority that still remains to him.

"A pedagogical work: it is not just a matter of convincing, persuading, and demonstrating, but also, and more so, of leading the cultured lay reader little by little and letting him persuade and convince himself, so that he may understand the demonstration and grasp the proof. And for this purpose a twofold work of destruction and of education is necessary—destruction of prejudices and traditional mental habits and of common sense; creation in their place of new habits, of a new attitude toward reasoning. To this we owe the longwindedness insupportable to the modern reader (the reader who has benefited from the Galilean revolution); to this we owe the repetitiousness, the returns to things already said, the repeated criticism of the same arguments, the multiplicity of examples. . . . It is necessary in fact [for Galileo] to educate the reader, to teach him to have faith no longer in authority, in tradition, in common sense. It is necessary to teach him to think.

"A philosophical work: it is not only traditional physics and cosmology which Galileo attacks and combats, it is the whole philosophy and *Weltanschauung* of his adversaries. At that time physics and cosmology were consolidated with philosophy—or, if you like, were a part of it. Now if Galileo combats the philosophy of Aristotle, he does so to the advantage of another philosophy, under the banner of which he marches—the philosophy of Plato. Of a certain philosophy of Plato." [33]

133

Galileo Galilei

Although we cannot concede to Koyré that Galileo really intended to oppose a precise form of Platonism to the Aristotelian tradition, we are nevertheless in complete accord with him in interpreting the *Dialogue* as a work more pedagogical and philosophical than strictly scientific; we might even say, more as a manifesto directed toward a cultural renovation than as a scientific treatise operating within an already renovated culture.

This is the interpretation that is more or less generally accepted by modern Galilean scholars. Olschki, for example, states that Galileo wrote his *Dialogue* not for the future but for his time and his surroundings; to point out to his cultural world that which belonged to the way of the new science; to teach them that adherence to Copernicanism had not only an astronomical significance, but also ethical and philosophical consequences.[34] And Banfi remarks that the *Dialogue* is "the coordination and synthesis of the new knowledge," designed "to disperse the theoretical assumptions of the traditional solution and to open the way, through conquest of physical certainties, to a remodeled conception of the universe." [35]

Yet this is not to say that the *Dialogue* is without value in a strictly scientific sense (as some opponents of Galileo suggest even today). Though Galileo sought to write a work of scientific and philosophical propaganda rather than one of pure astronomy, and though he did not succeed in finding a rigorous demonstration of the earth's motion, he nevertheless made an enormous contribution to the victory of the Copernican theory. He managed to eliminate the most serious obstacles raised against it by common sense, and he did so with precise scientific reasoning to the extent that he was able to demonstrate logically the intimate connection between Copernicanism and the principles of the new mechanics. His battle against prejudices that arose out of apparent common sense was the more difficult in that they had very deep roots in the minds of all scholars of the seventeenth century —in Galileo himself no less than in his contemporaries. This battle was decisive for the history of science because it alone opened the road to more specific researches which were to furnish definitive proof of the Copernican theory after Galileo's time.

It is in similar terms that so eminent a scholar as Federigo

The Copernican Manifesto

Enriques with incomparable clarity resolved the much debated question of the scientific value of the *Dialogue*:

"In the battle which . . . Galileo undertook against the Peripatetics, it is necessary to recognize not so much a polemic against external adversaries as a battle that had first to be carried on within the mind of the philosopher himself against the paradox of the new ideas which were striking against inveterate habits of thought. The Peripatetic arguments invoked against the Copernican hypothesis those sensible phenomena which suggested that the earth, if it moved, must leave every object behind, and that a freely falling body . . . must hit the ground somewhat behind the vertical point. The Copernican system entails the necessity of destroying these arguments, and from that necessity spring the laws of dynamics and with them that which seems most remote from the experience of everyday life, the principle of inertia and the principle of relativity, which indeed form a single discovery. . . .

". . . Therefore the principles of dynamics and the justifications of the Copernican system are joined inseparably in Galileo's thought, and woe betide that critique which breaks the connection. Yet some may observe that in this there is not so much a true demonstration of the theory as a removal of obtacles that prevented its acceptance. But the main difficulty in grasping Copernicus' viewpoint was precisely the paradox of those mechanical consequences which seemed to result from it. . . .

"*For the philosopher, there is never any absolute certainty in a scientific theory, nor even a precise point at which it becomes demonstrated for the first time in history.* But the relative value of the demonstration is increased whenever it affords a basis for ever new convalidation. . . . Galileo accomplished the task . . . of the philosopher who must overcome common sense and carry the problem into new territory where its solution becomes possible." [36]

Chapter 8

The Collapse of the Galilean Program

1. In his *Dialogue Concerning the Two Chief World Systems* Galileo had two aims: first, to arouse general interest in the problem of Copenicanism among cultured persons, even though they were not versed in astronomy, and to persuade them of the foolishness of the old Peripatetic science; and second, to educate the highest Vatican authorities to the dangers that the Catholic Church would encounter if it insisted arbitrarily in maintaining its attitude of 1616.

The first aim was quickly and overwhelmingly achieved; a unanimous chorus of praise from the widest circle of readers greeted this limpid and delightful book. Galileo received many letters in the early months from his friends and admirers:

"The title of the work, its dedication and preface to the reader, so excited my curiosity that before settng myself to the task of reading it . . . I could not resist skimming eagerly through . . . a part of the text, where there appear new theories and noble observations which you have reduced to such simplicity that even I, of a different occupation, am certain I shall be able to understand at least some parts of it." [1]

"The clearness with which points are explained that seemed incomprehensible must be admired by everyone." [2]

"You have succeeded with the public to a point at which no one else has arrived. . . . Frankly, who in Italy cared about the Copernican system? But you have given it life, and, what really counts, have laid bare the breast of Nature." [3]

"Everything about it pleases me, and I see how much stronger your argument is than that of Copernicus, though his is fundamental. . . . These novelties about old truths, new worlds, new stars, new systems, new nations, and so on, are the commencement of a new age." [4]

The Collapse of the Galilean Program

But things were to go very differently for Galileo's second aim. In fact, only a few months later there was very discouraging news about the reception of the *Dialogue* in the most influential spheres of the Church. In a letter of June nineteenth, Benedetto Castelli wrote Galileo that he had heard that "Father Scheiner, being in a bookstore with an Olivetan father . . . and hearing that father give to the *Dialogue* the praise it deserves . . . became very agitated; his face changed color and his voice and hands shook so violently as to astonish the bookseller, who told me the story." [5] Two months later Campanella wrote of having heard "with great displeasure . . . that a Congregation of angry theologians is being assembled to probe your *Dialogue*." [6]

A more serious incident, and one which was to determine the entire course of the affair, was the unexpected switch of Urban VIII from the ranks of Galileo's friends to those of his most inflamed adversaries. On the fifth of September, ambassador Niccolini wrote Cioli that he had found the Pope extremely angry about the *Dialogue*, and so acrimonious that he could not "be in a worse frame of mind toward our poor Signor Galileo." [7]

How explain this sudden change of heart on the part of Urban VIII? In the first place, one must take into account a strictly personal factor: the Pope had allowed himself to be convinced by insinuations of astute opponents of Galileo that the scientist had intended to make sport of Urban himself by impersonating him in the ingenuous and ignorant figure of Simplicio. Although there was little enough basis for this, it was a suspicion that badly wounded Urban's pride. It was enough to make him suddenly forget his old benevolence toward Galileo and replace it with no less pervasive hatred and a desire for revenge.

Yet it would be unfair to attribute this surge of anger solely to the impulsive character of the Pope. At another time he might perhaps have been able to think things out with greater objectivity. But in the summer of 1632 he was under such tension that for him every suspicion at once became an indisputable reality. The reasons for his susceptibility are to be found in the extremely delicate political situation that came to a head in those very months.

Galileo Galilei

Urban had been elected by the support of the Francophile cardinals. Immediately upon his accession to the Chair of St. Peter, he had sought to impress a new line on the politics of the Church, a line particularly favorable to the group to which he owed his appointment. "Against the pact between Spain and the Holy Roman Empire, which threatened to put all Europe under Habsburg hegemony, he supported the French policy by pressing for neutrality on the part of the Duke of Bavaria, by opposing the Emperor's application of the edict of restitution, by requiring the dismissal of Wallenstein and supporting the French intervention in Italy in the war for Mantua and Monferrato, and even by favoring early in 1631 the entente between the King of France, the Duke of Bavaria (neutral German representative of the Catholic League) and the victorious Protestant armies of Gustavus Adolphus of Sweden. When Spain and the Empire asked him to head a league of Catholic states, he replied that this involved a political rather than a religious struggle, and that he would not link the fate of the Church with dynastic interests." [8] With the passage of time, this line aroused a gradually strengthening reaction among the Habsburg partisans. In 1632 this reaction plunged the Pope into a political crisis, which in turn was the indirect cause of his sudden change of heart toward Galileo. The crisis came during the Consistory held in March of that year, when the Spanish Ambassador, Gaspar Cardinal Borgia, had the courage to launch an open and violent attack on the Pope, accusing him of protecting heretics and daring him to demonstrate once and for all that he was motivated by the "apostolic zeal" of which so many proofs had been given by his "more pious and more glorious" predecessors.

This attack became the more dangerous when reinforced by widespread murmurs among the Roman populace accusing the Pope of unrestrained nepotism and of decidedly mundane ambitions that were hard to reconcile with the responsibilities of the head of Christianity. Confronted by these threatening accusations, Urban VIII clearly perceived the precariousness of his apparent power and commenced to seek ways to bolster it. These were truly dramatic months; wherever he looked, he saw enemies, supporters of the hostile party, even traitors trying to poison him.

The Collapse of the Galilean Program

In this situation it is no wonder that he quickly gave ear to Galileo's enemies, and fancied that the main purpose of the author of the *Dialogue* was to undermine him with the cultured public. Hence his decision to be avenged, to punish Galileo, to regain his own prestige through the humiliation of the faithless friend.

The punishment of Galileo would also have two other indisputable advantages. On the one hand, it would prove that the Pope was strong enough to put down, through Galileo, his pro-Spanish protector, the Grand Duke of Tuscany; on the other hand, it would show the Catholic world that its leader could defend the true spirit of the Counter-Reformation even by sacrificing, in the supreme interests of dogma, the well-known personal links that had previously bound him to the author of the incriminating work. The condemnation of Galileo would thus in the end assume a new character, a more than personal significance, which made it a genuine political necessity: it "involved not only the personal resentment of the Pope, but the defense of his dignity and authority, and due respect for Catholic discipline and Church decrees; the zeal of mankind and that of the institutions of the Counter-Reformation; and Urban's unyielding will to power over culture and knowledge." [9]

2. The first official document showing a change in the Church's attitude toward Galileo was a letter sent by Father Riccardi to the Inquisitor of Florence, Father Clement Egidi:

"Signor Galilei's book has arrived in these parts, and there are many unsatisfactory things in it which the superiors wish adjusted at all costs. Therefore His Holiness orders (though only my name is to be used) that the book be withheld, and not leave that city without the necessary corrections being sent from here; nor shall the book be issued. Your Reverence may discuss this with the illustrious [papal] nuncio [to Florence], and proceeding gently, make sure that everything is done effectively." This letter ends with a curious postscript inquiring whether "the device of the three fishes is that of the printer or whether it is Signor Galilei's." [10] The Pope suspected that the typographer's mark concealed some irreverence, perhaps a reference to three nephews whom he had audaciously promoted.

On the seventh of August, Father Riccardi sent another letter to the Inquisitor of Florence, insisting on the need to proceed gently with respect to Galileo, and meanwhile asked him to find out quietly the number of copies sent out by the printer and the places to which they had been delivered "in order that they may diligently be got back." [11]

Though the Grand Duke was anything but combative, he could do no less than protest this prohibition of sale of the volume, written by his Chief Mathematician and Philosopher and published with all the prescribed ecclesiastical authorization: ". . . a book presented by the author himself in Rome to the hands of the supreme authority, and there attentively read and reread, and, not only with the author's consent but at his request, amended, altered, amplified, and edited in every way that pleased the superiors, and furthermore examined here according to the order and command of Rome, and finally licensed both here and there." [12] It was when Niccolini sought to present this remonstrance of the Duke that he had faced the Pope's extreme rage with regard to Galileo. Everything now indicated that events would be precipitated rapidly, and that it was absurd to hope to check them short of a test of strength with the Pope. But that was far from the Grand Duke's intention, and perhaps beyond his power.

During the first phase, the *Dialogue* was sent for examination to a commission of experts charged with the duty of judging whether (as Galileo's enemies asserted) it really had an unequivocally Copernican character despite the tone of the preface and conclusion. The second phase, which followed immediately, placed the matter before the Congregation of the Holy Office, and it was then that the trial which was to be concluded in 1633 began to take official form.

On the twenty-fifth of September 1632, Antonio Cardinal Barberini, a younger brother of the Pope, wrote the Inquisitor of Florence to instruct Galileo, in some place where a notary and witnesses would be present without their purpose being known to Galileo, that he must come to Rome during the month of October and report to the Commissary General of the Holy Office. This instruction was given on the first day of October, and Galileo made the following statement: "I, Galileo Galilei, affirm that on this day it has been intimated to me by the Reverent Father Inquisitor of this city, by order of the Holy Congregation of the Holy Office of Rome, that I must journey to Rome for all the present month and present myself to the Father Commissary of the Holy Office, by whom I shall be told what I must do; and I voluntarily accept the commandment for all the present month of October." [13]

How "voluntarily" Galileo accepted this order is revealed by his many attempts to secure exemption from it. He wrote to all the powerful friends he thought he could count on (from the Grand Duke to Francesco Cardinal Barberini), giving to each of them the reasons that made his departure inadvisable: the poor state of his health, his advanced age, the epidemic of plague that was going through the country, and so on. But everything failed; the statements of doctors, his support at Rome, the objections of ambassador Niccolini, who proposed that the interrogation of Galileo be carried out at Florence by the Inquisitor there rather than at Rome—all proved useless. The most Galileo obtained was a delay of some months before the journey.

On the first of January 1633, Antonio Cardinal Barberini, who had sent the first order for Galileo to come to Rome, wrote to the Florentine Inquisitor a letter that brooked no reply: "This Congregation of the Holy Office has taken it very ill that Galileo Galilei has not promptly obeyed the precept made to him that he come to Rome, and his disobedience is not to be excused on account of the season, because it is his own fault that he is reduced to coming at this time; and he does very badly to try to soften matters by pretending to be ill, for neither His Holiness nor their Eminences, my patrons, are willing for a moment to listen to these fictions, or to excuse his arrival here. Therefore your Reverence must tell him that if he does not obey immediately, a Commissary and physicians will be sent from here to take him and to conduct him to the prisons of this supreme tribunal in chains, as up to this time he has abused the benevolence of this Congregation; and moreover, he will have to pay all the expenses thus incurred. You are to carry out these instructions and advise us here." [14]

Galileo Galilei

The harshness of the order speaks for itself. Galileo tried one last time to get support from the Grand Duke, who politely excused himself. On the eleventh of January, Cioli wrote to Galileo:

"I am very sorry that you have had a new and rigorous intimation to leave immediately for Rome because of the peril to your life at the present winter season, considering your grave illness and your great age; and His Highness, to whom I have read your letter, also sympathizes. But since in the end it is necessary to obey the highest courts, His Highness regrets that he is unable to arrange that you may not go. Perhaps your prompt obedience and the rectitude of your mind, however, in your actual presence, may reconcile the minds of those who seem to be stirred up against you. His Highness wishes that it may be so because of the love and esteem he bears you. And in order that you may travel comfortably, His Highness is pleased to give you one of his litters and an understanding driver, and has so ordered the major domo; he is also willing to have you accommodated in the house of ambassador Niccolini, assuming that within a month you will have received your freedom. So, *bon voyage* to you, in accordance with His Highness' wishes and my prayers; you may write and command, wherever you are." [15]

Thus miserably deprived of his chief support, Galileo had no recourse but to resign himself to the journey. He left on the twentieth of January, at the worst of the winter season. He was detained several days at Ponte and at Centina by the quarantine imposed on all travelers as a measure of precaution against the spread of the plague. It was a delay made bitter by the discomforts of cold and hunger and by premonitions of what was to happen at Rome.

After twenty-five days of travel, the tired Galileo arrived on the thirteenth of February, dismounting from the litter in front of the palace of the ambassador. To his great consolation, Niccolini and his wife gave him a genuinely friendly reception, much more friendly than required by their official duties. When the time for which the Grand Duke had authorized payment of the expenses of Galileo's residence at Rome had expired, they decided to keep him in their home as an honored guest.

The Collapse of the Galilean Program

3. We can easily imagine how great must have been Galileo's disillusionment when the rapid sequence of events unmistakably demonstrated to him how useless were all the forces he had counted on to induce the Church to recede from the intransigent anti-Copernican attitude it had assumed in 1616. Yet not even the harshness of his summons had sufficed to deprive him entirely of the hope that he might still manage to rescue something. It was only in April that he yielded to the evidence, and this was to produce a crisis of mental prostration that was among the most serious events of his entire life.

The months from October 1632 to April 1633 were characterized by alternating moments of despair and that energetic revival that illustrate Galileo's rich human qualities. Most dramatically, at moments of despair his bitterness aroused in him harsh doubts as to the utility not only of the forces he had reckoned on to move the Church from its erroneous position, but even of the energies he had consumed in pure scientific research and of the enlightened attitude that had induced him not to keep his discoveries to himself. One of the most disturbing documents is a letter that the great scientist sent on the thirteenth of October 1632, in a moment of particular sadness, to his friend (or presumed friend) Francesco Cardinal Barberini, nephew of the Pope:

"Both my friends and I foresaw that my recently published *Dialogue* would find contradictors. Of this we were assured by the fate of other works of mine previously printed, and because it seems that this generally happens with doctrines which distinctly depart from common and inveterate opinions. But that the hatred of some men against me and my writings . . . should have had the power to convince the most holy minds of the superiors that this book of mine is unworthy of publication was truly unexpected. Hence the order sent a couple of months ago to the printer and to me not to issue this book of mine was heavy news. Yet it is very comforting to me that my own conscience is clear, which persuades me that it should not be hard for me to show my innocence. . . .

"Yet I cannot deny that the intimation finally made to me of the order of the Holy Congregation of the Holy Office that I must present myself his month before that high tribunal is a   143 great affliction. Whenever I think of it, the fruits of all my studies and labors over so many years, which had in the past brought my name to the ears of men of letters with no little fame, are now converted into grave blemishes on my reputation, giving a foothold to my enemies that they may rise up against my friends . . . and say that finally I have deserved to be ordered before the tribunal of the Holy Office, a thing that happens only because of the most serious delinquencies. This afflicts me in such a way that *it makes me detest all the time I have consumed* in those studies, by means of which I hoped and aspired to separate myself somewhat from the trite and popular thinking of scholars; and by making me regret that I have exposed to the world a part of my compositions, *it causes me to wish to suppress and condemn to the flames those which remain in my hands,* entirely satiating the hunger of my enemies, to whom my thoughts are so troublesome." [16]

After this moment of abandon, however, Galileo succeeded in recapturing his faith and tried once more to make clear to the Church authorities the good faith that underlay his program:

"I shall be glad to set down on paper most minutely and sincerely the whole course of the things I have said, written, and done, from the first day when questions were raised about the book of Nicholas Copernicus and his revived theory. . . .[17] For no one devoid of passion and inflamed spirit would deny that I have behaved so piously and so like a good Catholic that not even those fathers who are distinguished by the title of 'holy' could have shown more piety. . . . Everyone will understand that I have been moved to become involved in this task only by zeal for the Holy Church, and to give to its ministers that information which my long studies have brought to me, some of which might perhaps be required by them, being obscure matters and remote from the accustomed doctrines." [18]

This is the same thought that Cioli had expressed in a letter to Niccolini; Cioli energetically maintained that Galileo had written "as His Highness sincerely knows" only "for the benefit of the Holy Church, in order that, with regard to matters naturally difficult to comprehend, those who deliberate may understand with little effort and expenditure of time the side toward which truth inclines, and with which the sense of the Holy Scriptures accords." [19] But the Church did not want to be enlightened, and preferred to maintain its decrees unchanged, without worrying about the side toward which scientific truth might incline.

Fortunately for science, when Galileo found himself coldly confronted with the immovability of the Church he did not allow himself to be overcome by the despair which prevaded the opening of his letter to Barberini, but had the fortitude to separate the two themes, on which he had centered his activities up to that time. That is, he dropped (this time definitively) the program he had so long pursued, and sought a *modus vivendi* between the Church and science. Nor did he in fact put to the flames the notes of his old labors; rather, he elaborated them and systematized them in a new work (the *Two New Sciences*), which from a strictly scientific point of view constitutes his masterpiece.

After 1633, Galileo kept his past illusions to himself, and merely emphasized occasionally, when opportunity presented, his contempt for the ignorance of those who had judged him guilty. His spiritual heirs went far beyond this position; they have interpreted the deafness of the Church to Galileo's efforts at conciliation as an irrefutable proof of the incompatibility of dogma and science, and they have drawn the conclusion that Galileo's spirit of enlightment must be integrated with something else, unknown to Galileo: an open and uncompromising attack against every form of religious prejudice.

4. Although Galileo was taken at once to the prisons of the Holy Office, authorization for him to reside with ambassador Niccolini was soon conceded, though not without difficulty, on condition that he should not leave the house or receive friends. There he remained about two months without incident; he was visited from time to time only by Monsignor Ludovico Serristori, who, under the pretext of comforting the old scientist, had the delicate assignment of discovering the line of defense he would adopt, in order most effectively to facilitate the Holy Office in its formulation of the charges.

Meanwhile Niccolini ardently prosecuted his own inquiries, to get some hint of the secret proceeding that had been opened by the authorities against Galileo. In this way he discovered, among other things, that the central point of the accusation was based on the famous conversation with Bellarmine that went far back to 1616.[20] He notified Galileo of this about the end of February, but Galileo was not alarmed, and even showed himself perfectly assured of his safety on this point.[21] Not only that, but he again took heart; he hoped no less than that he might reopen a friendly discussion on the scientific foundations of Copernicanism with the inquisitorial authorities, and that he might succeed, if only *in extremis,* in drawing them away from the irreparable error of rigidly opposing the new orientation of science.

About the beginning of April, Niccolini at last received word that Galileo was about to be brought before the Holy Office and held there for an indefinite number of days, and decided to speak frankly with Galileo in order to overcome his hitherto unyielding faith in his own judgment. The letter of April ninth, in which the ambassador informed the minister Cioli of his conversation with Galileo, is a document of the highest historical value:

"He nevertheless claims that he can well defend his own opinions, but I have exhorted him, in order to bring the affair to a close as soon as possible, not to trouble to maintain them, and to submit himself to whatever he can see they want him to believe or hold about that matter of the earth's motion." [22]

Favorably disposed though he was, the ambassador did not understand why Galileo attributed such importance to "that matter of the earth's motion," or why he would not resign himself without further resistance to the pretense of believing "what he can see they want him to believe." Niccolini's sincere devotion, shown by his regard for his guest-prisoner, was not enough to enable him to penetrate the meaning of the battle that was clearly going on in Galileo's mind. But that it was a serious battle is again testified by Niccolini in the lines that follow the above extract:

"He is much afflicted about it, and I myself have seen him from yesterday to the present time so dejected that I have feared for his very life."

146

The Collapse of the Galilean Program

Though historians have stressed the importance of the crisis Galileo went through as a result of this conversation with Niccolini, I have the impression that no one has yet sufficiently emphasized the truly decisive significance it had not only for the personal fortunes of Galileo, but also for the history of his philosophical and scientific conceptions.

I do not think that Galileo's almost mortal affliction can be explained simply by his apprehension over the woes that confronted him. Indeed, he had long foreseen them, and Niccolini's words gave him no news on that score. They even gave him hope that if he submitted to the wishes of the inquisitors, he would soon be through with them. Nor could this affliction depend, in my opinion, on Galileo's repugnance toward feigning sudden acceptance of anti-Copernicanism. Something of the sort had already been included in the final speeches of the *Dialogue* in the words Simplicio used to summarize the argument of Urban VIII, which Salviati pretended to recognize as completely irrefutable, and Galileo had accepted Father Riccardi's request that the *Dialogue* close in this way without any particular complaint.

I believe that the cause of Galileo's extreme affliction is to be sought in something more profound: the clear notification given to him by Niccolini in sincere friendship that the time for discussion was now over; that there was to be no more analysis of the arguments for and against Copernicus. Galileo had made no difficulty over all the emendations suggested to him by Riccardi two years previously, because he knew that this was an indispensable condition of his bringing to the attention of the Church the latest and most noteworthy results of the Copernican debates. Beneath his submissiveness lay the firm conviction that once these results were understood, the Church authorities would proceed more cautiously than in 1616. What Niccolini was now requesting him to do was a very different matter: it was to renounce not only the expression of his own faith in Copernicanism, but also the expounding of the scientific reasons supporting that theory; he was to renounce the task of enlightening the Church, and the Catholic world in general, concerning a matter of prime importance. In a word, he was to abandon forever the politico-cultural program for which he had fought so long.

Hence Galileo's desperate affliction; hence his bitterness when faced with the collapse of his true mission. ("I should not have been moved to become involved in this task, except through zeal for the Holy Church.") It now mattered little whether he decided to abjure or to face the extreme penalty for refusing. The heavy, the irreparable loss was something else; it was that his dialogue with the inquisitors, the dialogue between science and the Church, was irrevocably cut off. The phase of rational debate had given way to that of pure and simple force.

5. Having received the order to present himself to the Holy Office, Galileo appeared there on the morning of April twelfth without knowing that he would be detained until the end of the month. From that moment, the vicissitudes of the trial lose a great part of the broad philosophical significance that inheres in the events up to this point. It became nothing more than a dark succession of maneuvers by means of which his prosecutor, the Dominican Vincenzio Maculano [of Firenzuola], sought to trap Galileo in a net ably woven beforehand, and of the much less able countermaneuvers by which Galileo tried to escape from his adversary.

The main difficulty with the accusation lay in the fact that the *Dialogue* had been published with full ecclesiastical authorization. We have already seen the importance of this authorization to Galileo; to his mind, it must have meant that the Church of Rome had decided not to prevent Catholic scientists from occupying themselves with the Copernican question—precisely the opposite of what the Holy Office now desired. It was therefore necessary to find some means of charging Galileo with having fraudulently obtained the ecclesiastical license, thus transferring to him the blame that properly should have fallen on the Master of the Sacred Palace, Father Riccardi (if on anyone). The means were offered by the supposed minute of the conversation between Galileo and Bellarmine on the twenty-sixth of February 1616. By assuming this to be authentic, the prosecutor could charge Galileo with the grave fault of having ignored the precept given him at

The Collapse of the Galilean Program

that historic session, and in particular of having failed to acquaint Father Riccardi with the existence of that precept.

This unquestionably clever solution nevertheless ran into a serious obstacle: the irregular character of the document itself, which lacked the signatures necessary to a minute of such importance. This explains the extreme caution of Maculano's questions, and their evident intent to induce Galileo himself to admit the existence of *some* precept received by him on that occasion. Once this confession was obtained, it should be simple enough to conclude that the precept admitted by the accused was precisely that which was specified in the minute; that is, the precept not to hold, defend, or teach in any manner (*quovis modo*) the Copernican doctrine.

The first interrogatory took place on the twelfth of April. It began with a request for precise clarification concerning the manner in which the audience of the twenty-sixth of February 1616 had taken place, and the persons present at it. Galileo described the notification Cardinal Bellarmine had given him of the decree issued by the Holy Office, and in support of his statement referred to the document given him by Bellarmine himself the following May. As to the persons present, he admitted that some Dominican friars were in the room, but denied that any of them had spoken to him. The minute affirmed, on the contrary, that it was the Father Commissary who had given him the notorious precept. At this point, Father Maculano read to the accused the text of the supposed wording. Galileo protested energetically that he did not recall it; meanwhile, however, even he let slip the word *precept*, and the Inquisitor took this as a half-confession. He then went on to ask him why not a word had been said of this to Father Riccardi, Master of the Sacred Palace, when he was later asked for the license to publish the *Dialogue*. Galileo, irresolute, said he had not seen any necessity for this, and went on to advance the thesis (clearly untenable) that the *Dialogue* was not contrary to the precept given him, but was even designed to show that the arguments for Copernicus were "invalid and inconclusive." [23]

This absurd pretense was in fact the downfall of Galileo's position; it impaired the value of all his subsequent replies.

Galileo Galilei

During the interval between the first and second interrogations—until the thirtieth of April—Galileo remained imprisoned by the Holy Office, though in the comfortable suite of one of its officers. There he allowed himself to be convinced that he should modify the position he had taken. Finally, on April 30, he confessed that at various points the *Dialogue* had an obviously Copernican character, and he gave as his excuse for having fallen into an error so foreign to his intentions "the natural pleasure that every man feels in his own cleverness, and in showing himself smarter than ordinary people by finding, even in false propositions, ingenious and plausible arguments of probability." [24] This confession completed, he was again released to the custody of ambassador Niccolini on condition that he be kept in a place of confinement.

On the tenth of May, Galileo was again called to the Holy Office where he was given ten days to write out his defense. But he had brought with him a memorial designed for this purpose, so he had nothing more to do than to present it, adding: "For the rest, I submit myself wholly to the usual piety and clemency of this tribunal." The memorial offered nothing new; it was limited to an explanation that Galileo, being in possession of the document given to him by Bellarmine in May 1616, had made no "other application of my mind or memory" to the words spoken at the audience of the twenty-sixth of February, and therefore claimed to have completely forgotten it: "so that," he concluded, "the two phrases . . . *quovis modo* and *docere*, which I hear are contained in the command given to me and recorded, came to me as entirely new and [previously] unheard," for which reason "it seems to me I am excused for not having notified the Master of the Sacred Palace of the precept made privately to me." [25]

The inquisitor now needed nothing more. He believed that Galileo's own words justified his assumption that the version of the session of the twenty-sixth of February 1616, set forth in the unsigned minute, was correct. This ably prepared maneuver succeeded perfectly; Galileo could not escape condemnation. Yet he had to wait a month before the sentence was given out, and meanwhile there was one more interrogation to face "concerning intention." [26]

The Collapse of the Galilean Program

6. This brief summary of Galileo's first interrogations is sufficient to show that after his painful crisis at the beginning of April, he had in the end adopted, though most regretfully, the counsel of his friend Niccolini. Entirely abandoned was any attempt to discuss before his inquisitors the scientific basis of the Copernican theory. From that moment, his actions were directed to a single end: freeing himself as soon as possible from the sad business, and returning to other, noncontroversial, studies. The politico-cultural scheme for which he had battled so long was forever set aside.[27] He did not foresee how long his path was yet to be, or how many griefs were still in store for him before the end of the trial.

Later Galileo sought reasons for the Church's rage against him in the hatred of the Jesuits. On the twenty-fifth of July 1634, he wrote to Elia Diodati:

"From this and from other events, which would take too long to write to you, you may see that the rage of my potent persecutors continues to increase. And they have finally decided to make themselves known, inasmuch as a dear friend of mine, finding himself about two months ago in Rome in conversation with Father Christopher Grienberger, a Jesuit and the mathematician of their College, got round to my case, and the Jesuit uttered these words to my friend: 'If Galileo had been able to keep the affection of the Fathers of this college, he would be living gloriously in the world, he would have suffered none of his misfortunes, and he could have written at will on any subject, even about the motions of the earth, and so on.' So you may see that it is not any opinion of mine that started the war, but my being in the bad graces of the Jesuits." [28]

Although there is no direct proof, everything indicates that Jesuit hatred for Galileo did have a notable influence in causing the Church to assume the attitude it took. Letters of various persons, both near to and far from Galileo's circles, give explicit hints of that pernicious influence.[29] Sad though it may be, almost all of them give the name of Father Scheiner as one of the Jesuits most persistent in underground intrigues against Galileo. It is truly regrettable that scientific rivalry should have led a man of Scheiner's ability to such baseness, the more so when it is

151

recalled (as Descartes observed in a letter to Marin Mersenne) that in all probability Scheiner himself secretly subscribed to the Copernican view.[30]

Nor can we exclude the possibility that the actions of the Jesuits were in part determined by their antagonism toward the Dominicans. There is no doubt that the trial of 1633 cast a heavy shadow of blame on the latter order. If on the one hand the Dominican Father Vincenzio Maculano displayed the very great abilities of his order in leading Galileo to confession and abjuration, on the other hand Father Riccardi cannot escape the charge of negligence for having given the original license to publish the condemned work. Indeed, he was later punished for this grave delinquency.

Granting all this, it must yet be recognized that beneath the personal hatreds, there were deeper causes which determined the behavior of the Church, causes which Galileo never took fully in account; at least he preferred never even to hint at them, perhaps because in so doing he would have publicly recognized the failure of his original program. It is clear that once the Church had refused Galileo's offer to open the way to the new science, the logic of the action would constrain it to sustain its closed position ever more intransigently. From that position, the program for which Galileo had fought for so many years could only appear as something diabolical, more execrable and more pernicious for the Holy Church than the teachings of Luther and Calvin themselves.[31]

No less sad were the consequences to Galileo resulting from the abandonment of his program. The first of these was sketchily touched upon in the explanation of his line of defense; it was his presposterous claim that the *Dialogue* was not designed to present the Copernican theory favorably. Once this position was taken, the logic of events carried him on to another: the solemn declaration that he had never adhered to Copernicanism after its condemnation in 1616; that is, to the renunciation of his whole work, to public abjuration, to that "depth of abasement," as Banfi rightly called it, in which Galileo finally lost all energy for

rebellion.

The Collapse of the Galilean Program

7. On the twentieth of June, Galileo was once more called by the Holy Office for interrogation as to his "intention." He appeared on the twenty-first, and was immediately subjected to rigorous examination" concerning his convictions with regard to the Copernican theory. "Rigorous examination" could go as far as torture to oblige the accused to confess the whole truth; however, there is no proof that the "rigor" applied against the famous old man was carried to any such point.[32]

The minutes, signed by Galileo, show that his answers were decidedly negative: "I do not hold nor have I held to this opinion of Copernicus since the precept was given to me that I must abandon it; for the rest, I am in your hands, and you may do as you please." [33]

Since it was impossible to go further, the interrogation was ended. Galileo was not returned to Niccolini's house, however, but was detained by the Holy Office. Thence, on the twenty-second, he was taken to the great hall of the Dominican convent of Santa Maria Sopra Minerva, and his sentence was read to him in front of the Congregation of the Holy Office. It included the prohibiting of the *Dialogue* and the condemnation of its author to formal imprisonment at the pleasure of the Holy Office, in addition to some "salutary penances" consisting of the recitation once a week for three years of the penitential Psalms. The Holy Office reserved the power to moderate, alter, or remove in whole or in part the pains and penalties inflicted.[34]

Upon hearing the sentence, Galileo was obliged to recite, on his knees, the following public abjuration: "I, Galileo, son of the late Vincenzio Galilei of Florence, my age being seventy years, having been called personally to judgment and kneeling before your Eminences, Most Reverend Cardinals, general Inquisitors against heretical depravity in the entire Christian dominion, and having before my eyes the sacred Gospels, which I touch with my own hands, do swear that I have always believed, do now believe, and with God's aid shall believe hereafter all that is taught and preached by the Holy Catholic and Apostolic Church. But because, after I had received a precept which was lawfully given to me that I must wholly forsake the false opinion that the sun is the center of the world and moves not, and that the

153

earth is not the center of the world and moves, and that I might not hold, defend, or teach the said false doctrine in any manner, either orally or in writing, and after I had been notified that the said teaching is contrary to the Holy Scripture, I wrote and published a book in which the said condemned doctrine was treated, and gave very effective reasons in favor of it without suggesting any solution, I am by this Holy Office judged vehemently suspect of heresy; that is, of having held and believed that the sun is the center of the world and immovable, and that the earth is not its center and moves;

"Therefore, wishing to remove from the minds of your Eminences and of every true Christian this vehement suspicion justly cast upon me, with sincere heart and unfeigned faith I do abjure, damn, and detest the said errors and heresies, and generally each and every other error, heresy, and sect contrary to the Holy Church; and I do swear for the future that I shall never again speak or assert, orally or in writing, such things as might bring me under similar suspicion; but if I shall know any heretic or person suspected of heresy I shall denounce him to this Holy Office or to the Inquisitor or governor of the place where I shall find him.

"I swear and promise also to comply with and observe fully the penitences that have been or that may be imposed upon me by this Holy Office, and should I contravene any of my said promises and oaths—which God forbid—I shall submit myself to all the pains and punishments promulgated by the sacred canons and other general and special constitutions, and particularly imposed against such delinquents. So help me God and these his Holy Testaments which I touch with my own hand.

"I, Galileo Galilei aforesaid, have abjured, sworn, promised and am obliged as above; and in testimony of the truth I have signed the present document of my abjuration with my own hand and have recited it word for word in the Convento Sopra Minerva in Rome, this twenty-second day of June, 1633." [35]

A significant popular tradition, unsupported by any contemporary document, has it that upon rising from his knees afterward, Galileo struck the earth with his foot and muttered, *"Eppur si muove!"* (And yet it does move!) [36]

The Collapse of the Galilean Program

A letter from Niccolini to the minister Cioli dated the twenty-sixth of June and informing him of the final developments provides an appropriate conclusion to the solemn drama:

"On Monday afternoon, Signor Galileo was called to the Holy Office, to which he went on Tuesday morning, as ordered, to learn what might be desired of him; and being detained, he was taken on Wednesday to the Minerva before the cardinals and prelates of the Congregation, where not only was the sentence read to him, but he was made to abjure his opinion. The sentence contains the prohibiting of his book, as well as his condemnation to the prisons of the Holy Office at the pleasure of His Holiness, it being claimed that he transgressed the precept given to him on this subject sixteen years ago. This condemnation was at once changed for him by His Holiness to that of relegation or confinement at the Gardens of the Trinità dei Monti [the ambassadorial palace], to which I took him on Friday evening, and where he now awaits the effects of the clemency of His Holiness. And because he would like to go there [to Florence] for various reasons, I entered into negotiations (since neither Cardinal Barberini nor His Holiness appears to favor freeing him entirely) [with the object] that they be content at least to change his confinement to Siena, to the house of his friend Monsignor the Archbishop [Ascanio Piccolomini], or in some convent of that city. . . . It appears to me that Signor Galileo is much afflicted by the punishment imposed, which came as a shock to him, though as to the book itself he indicated that he did not care if it was prohibited; so much he had foreseen." [37]

We may safely assume that the prohibiting of his book caused Galileo little worry, for he knew well enough that nothing now could prevent its diffusion throughout the vast world of culture where the deliberations of any tribunal other than that of free-thinking men are without power.

The change of confinement requested by Niccolini was granted on the thirtieth of June: "His Holiness granted the prayer for Siena, he [Galileo] not to leave that city without license of the Holy Congregation, and [only] if he dwell with the Archbishop of that said city." [38] Thus on July 6, 1633, Galileo was able to leave forever the city which had been the scene of his ignominious abasement. Three days later he arrived at Siena.

Chapter 9

The Return to Pure Science

1. The ten months which followed Galileo's condemnation in June 1633 represent one of the most important periods for the study of his personality, so rich in human qualities and so great even in its weaknesses. It was a period in which he applied the most heroic forces to lift himself out of the dejection into which he had fallen, and give a new direction to his life. Yet at the very moment when he seemed to have overcome his most serious obstacles, we see him again plunged for a time into a state of near-desperation by the death of his dearly beloved daughter Virginia [Sister Maria Celeste].

For some time Galileo had been maturing the project of a return to pure science, in which he might forget the detestable affront he had received. Amazingly enough, a few weeks now sufficed for him to regain his old serenity and submerge himself in work with renewed energy. Ascanio Piccolomini, Archbishop of Siena, to whom he had come as a virtual prisoner, gave him the most able support in this phase of his rapid recovery.

Piccolomini was linked to Galileo by bonds of sincere and profound friendship, and he felt intuitively that his first duty was to make the old scientist feel that the palace of the Archbishop was no prison, but rather a place capable of restoring his faith in himself and stimulating him to scientific research. Accordingly he organized continual visits from the chief personages of the city who, either by showing their unaltered admiration for Galileo or by raising interesting questions before him day after day, made him directly aware that his work was still useful to the progress of culture. Thus the discomfited old man was able in a short time to marshal his forces once more, and the "prison" was transformed into a veritable school of free scientific debate.

156

The Return to Pure Science

The most reliable testimony as to this happy state of affairs comes to us from adversaries of Galileo. Annoyed to see him not dispirited and penitent but bit by bit more sure of himself, they sent energetic protests to the Holy Office. These culminated in an anonymous letter which denounced not only Galileo's action, but also that of his too-generous host the Archbishop. "Galileo," it said, "has sown in this city opinions which are not Catholic, encouraged by his host the Archbishop, who has suggested to many here that Galileo was unjustly treated by the Holy Congregation, which could not and should not reprove the philosophical opinions he sustained with true and invincible mathematical arguments, and that he is the foremost man of all the world, and that he will live forever in his writings even if they are prohibited, and that his followers will include all the better modern men." [1]

Though the Holy Office could not officially act on these rumors, doubtless they served to convince that body that the vanquished Galileo was still a very dangerous man. The best thing to do in the circumstances was to get him out of Siena as soon as possible and oblige him to live in some locality really isolated from every contact with the world.

The problem was quickly and effectively resolved by granting the request made by Galileo himself at the end of June "to commute the place of imprisonment from Rome to a similar place at Florence." This action was taken on the first of December 1633; Galileo was authorized to move to his villa at Arcetri, where he could attend to his own interests and could live in daily contact with his daughters. The order stated clearly, however, that he must "live in complete solitude without receiving any visitors, and for a period to be determined by His Holiness." [2]

The elderly man greeted the arrangement with infinite joy, and it enabled him to end the fateful year 1633 in an atmosphere of recovered health. Yet the early months of 1634 held for him new and more touching troubles.

2. Among Galileo's family, only his elder daughter, Sister Maria Celeste, had taken any active and profound interest in the calamities that had recently befallen him. Galileo had attempted to conceal from her the terms of the sentence pronounced

against him by the Holy Office, fearing that it would cause her too much suffering because of her delicate religious sensitivity. But Sister Maria Celeste had quickly found out about the penalty and was greatly disturbed by it. She had felt intuitively the meaning of the conflict, and though she never spoke out against the Church's action, she had no doubt of her father's fundamental rectitude.

Extracts from letters she sent to Galileo during his absence suffice to show the comfort she was able to give him despite the distance at which they were obliged to live:

(April 30, 1633) "Dearest Father, I wished to write to you at once, that you may know I am with you in your troubles, which should be of some comfort to you. I have not said anything to anyone else, desiring that all this unpleasantness should be mine alone. . . . And who knows but that at this very moment, while I am writing, you may be out of all misfortunes and every worry?" [3]

(July 2) "Dearest Father, now is the time above all to use that prudence that the Lord God gave you, sustaining these blows with that strength of mind conferred by religion, your profession, and your years. And since through long experience you are fully aware of the fallacy and instability of all things of this world, you must not pay much heed to these storms, but rather hope that they will soon be stilled and changed again to your satisfaction." [4]

(July 16) "While you were in Rome, I said in my thought: If it is my good fortune that he leaves there and goes to Siena; it is enough, and I may almost say that he is in his own home. But now I am not content, and hope to see you still closer." [5]

It is no wonder that the aged Galileo anticipated with tender joy the moment when he could return to Arcetri and again embrace her who had comforted him from afar with the warmth of her affection. But this consolation was to be only too brief, and was soon to change into inconsolable anguish. For in the early months of 1634 Sister Maria Celeste fell seriously ill, and it was soon apparent to the doctors and to her father that nothing could save her.

In those weeks the letters to Galileo from his most intimate friends show at least indirectly what he had to go through, though he had barely recovered from a period filled with similar bitterness. Thus, for instance, Niccolò Aggiunti wrote to him on the fifth of March: "I have read with heavy heart of the troubles you presently suffer, and am deeply disturbed. . . . I know the paternal and filial affection that exists between you; I know the elevation of intellect, the gentleness, the prudence and goodness with which your daughter is endowed, and I most earnestly hope that she who has been your unique consolation in trouble may not now go, leaving you matter for inconsolable lament." [6]

Sister Maria Celeste died on the second of April 1634. She was not yet thirty-four years of age, and for Galileo her loss was truly a "matter for inconsolable lament."

On the twenty-seventh of April he wrote a letter to Geri Bocchineri which seems to me particularly expressive precisely because it was not directly concerned with his daughter's death; yet this in a way constitutes its undercurrent, an undercurrent of desperate sorrow, the more urgent because it is deliberately hidden under a description of his purely physical ailments: "My hernia is back, larger than ever; my pulse is interrupted by palpitations of the heart: [I have] an immense sadness and melancholy, complete lack of appetite, am hateful to myself, and above all I hear myself continually called by my beloved daughter." [7]

Yet even in this distracted situation Galileo once again demonstrated his strength of character. Even with a heart burdened by comfortless sadness, he was able little by little to resume the work of concluding the great book which constitutes the most brilliant proof of his ability as a scientist.

3. The unhappy spring of 1634 was followed by years of solitude, interrupted only occasionally by the visits of foreigners, which always required formal authorization. Neither his younger daughter, Sister Arcangela, nor his son Vincenzio could afford the old scientist any great consolation; they were remote from him in moral sensibility and cultural interests, and could never fill the void left in his heart by the loss of Sister Maria Celeste. [8] Galileo found greater understanding among the family of his daughter-   159

in-law, especially her brother, Geri Bocchineri, who constituted the natural bridge between Galileo and the offices of the Grand Duke's government, in which Bocchineri was employed. Still greater was his interest in her sister Alessandra, of whom we shall speak in the final chapter.

The injunction against visitors to the "prisoner of Arcetri" was applied with particular strictness to his pupils; above all, the authorities wished to prevent the survival of a Galilean school. These harsh restrictions were relaxed only in the last years of Galileo's life. The case of Benedetto Castelli is illustrative. Castelli filed a formal request to visit his old teacher, then seriously ill, to "prepare him for a Christian death" (Castelli was a Benedictine friar) and to get from him clarification of some important scientific questions, particularly with regard to the application of Jupiter's satellites to the calculation of longitudes. He succeeded in getting permission, but only on condition that a friar of the Inquisition be present at the conversations: "His Holiness thus desires that you [Castelli] be given a companion suitable to the Abbot, to be present at such conferences, so that when the Abbot cannot come, this companion may be there; for all this is conceded in view of your known piety, and your Reverence will do as you have promised." [9]

During the years from 1634 to 1638, Galileo's only comfort besides scientific research was his correspondence with friends and admirers, who often made use of faithful acquaintances at Florence to get compromising letters to him secretly. Galileo's surviving correspondence is far from complete, but the letters of this period form precious documents for the reconstruction of his psychological history. They show his laborious but sure reconquest of complete dignity after the humiliations he had undergone. They also show that Galileo retained his inclination toward a philosophy of enlightenment, that he considered ignorance the root of all the ills of society and the true enemy to be combated in the interests of a life of freedom worthy of mankind.

"Thus having suffered no loss in the two things which alone are to be esteemed by us above all, that is, life and reputation," he wrote, ". . . the wrongs and injustices which envy and malice have engineered against me did not and do not trouble me.

160

The Return to Pure Science

Rather . . . the magnitude of their injuries has tended to console me . . . and the infamy rebounds upon those who are deceitful and those with the highest degree of ignorance—mother of malice, envy, rage, and all other wicked and stupid vices and sins." [10]

"Yet these restrictions have not shattered or dwarfed the spirit, which always deals with free and worthy thoughts." [11]

"Unhappy is our land, in which reigns a fixed resolve to exterminate anything new, especially in the sciences—as if everything worth knowing were already known." [12]

After 1633 the credit for securing publication or republication of Galileo's works goes to his foreign admirers, though frequently some Italian friend such as Fra Fulgenzio Micanzio acted as intermediary. Thus despite ecclesiastical prohibition, the diffusion of his thought was assured. In 1634 Father Marin Mersenne published a French translation of the *Mechanics* (written by Galileo during his Paduan period, but not published in its original language until several years after its author's death). In the same year, Mathias Bernegger translated the *Dialogue* into Latin; this was published in 1635 by the Elzevirs in Holland.[13] Shortly thereafter, the same publishers also brought out Galileo's famed *Letter to Madam Christina* with a Latin version by Elia Diodati. [14]

Vincenzio Viviani, Galileo's last pupil (of whom we shall speak in the next chapter) took note of these translations in his official biography of Galileo, written at the order of Prince Leopold de' Medici: "It was impossible that his work on the System of the World should remain unknown beyond the Alps, and hence it was soon translated in Germany by Mathias Bernegger and published. . . . When Galileo learned of these translations and new publications of his writings, he was greatly mortified; he foresaw that it would be impossible ever again to suppress them or the many other works on the same subject already spread through Italy and abroad in manuscript. These he had written on various occasions during the time when he was of the opinion . . . of Copernicus, which eventually, through the authority of the Roman court, he abandoned as a good Catholic." [15] The truth is that Galileo was far from mortified by these translations, and sent his personal expressions of gratitude to Bernegger and Diodati, together with valuable gifts.

Galileo Galilei

At this time he had in mind something more important than the mere diffusion of those works already either published in Italy, or (like the *Letter to Madam Christina*) privately circulated among hosts of his friends. He was looking toward the completion and publication of that new dialogue "concerning local motions, natural and violent" that had been announced at the end of the *Dialogue*. In this way he expected not only to gain further glory, but also to offer to the world a splendid proof of the efficacy of the new mechanics, and the marvelous results man might achieve once he understood how to follow the path of coherent reasoning.

The urge to complete and publish this work is a theme that recurs with growing insistence in all the Galilean correspondence of these years: "I should like to show to the world, before I leave it, the remainder of my labors, which I am now polishing and transcribing." [16] The publication of this new work lay so close to his heart that even before he had finished it he entered into negotiations to have it printed at Venice, in Austria, in Germany, or in France—or for that matter anywhere else. The difficulty in these negotiations was the rigorous prohibition (effective only in Catholic countries) issued at Rome against printing any work of Galileo's, old or new. Finally he came to an agreement with the Elzevirs, who had already published translations of the *Dialogue* and the *Letter to Madam Christina,* and his famous *Two New Sciences* emerged from their press at Leyden in 1638.

Nor were Galileo's fears much exaggerated when he thought he might not live to see his masterpiece printed. His health was rapidly declining, and his forebodings were justified. Toward the end of 1637 a new and particularly distressing misfortune became evident; a progressive and incurable malady commenced to deprive Galileo of the sight of his right eye, and went on to destroy his sight completely. Just then he was attempting to conclude his long and glorious activities as an astronomer with two works: one, with the title *Astronomical Operations,* was theoretical; the other, more practical, was directed to the perfection of his method of calculating longitudes. Blindness cut short this dream, adding another cause of bitterness to the many he had accumulated in the final years of his life.

The Return to Pure Science

The irreparable loss was recorded in a letter to Elia Diodati of January 2, 1638: "In reply to your last welcome letter . . . I must tell you in answer to your first question, concerning the state of my health, that as to my body I have returned to a very mediocre degree of strength; but, alas! good sir, your dear friend and servant Galileo has for a month been hopelessly blind. You may imagine the affliction this causes me when you stop to consider that that sky, that world, and that universe which, by my remarkable observations and clear demonstrations, I had opened a hundred or a thousand times wider than anything seen by the learned of all the past centuries, is now diminished and restricted for me to a space no greater than that occupied by my own body. The recency of the event has not yet given me sufficient time to accustom myself with patience and tolerance to this misfortune, to which the passage of time must still train me." [17]

4. The *Two New Sciences* cannot be considered an entirely new work, but rather a reworking and expansion of results which for the most part Galileo had obtained during his Paduan period. These findings had been communicated only by letter to friends and pupils, and it was now appropriate that he should put them together in a great dialogue to be left as his scientific testament to future generations of scholars.

The actual drafting of the work began only after the condemnation of 1633, during his months at Siena "where I composed a treatise on a new subject, full of curious and useful speculations."

In 1634 it was practically finished, at least as to its principal lines, but Galileo continued to retouch it, perfect it, and add to it bit by bit: "The treatise on motion, entirely new, is ready; but my restless mind cannot desist from mulling it over, and with great expenditure of time, because each thought that brings to mind some new thing makes me throw away all past discoveries." [18] Even in 1637, when Louis Elzevir had begun the printing of the volume, Galileo continued to revise the final sections.

The work came out in 1638 under a title chosen by the editor. Galileo did not like it, and even wanted to change it. It was, in fact, rather long and complicated: *Discourses and mathematical demonstrations concerning two new sciences pertaining to mechan-*

ics and local motions. It was written in the form of a dialogue among the same three interlocutors (Salviati, Sagredo, and Simplicio) who had been the protagonists of the *Dialogue*. The style of the various parts is, however, quite different. In the first two "days" an authentic dialogue takes place, with all the characteristics that we find in this type of Galilean composition: fragmentary investigations, unbroken successions of debates on widely different subjects, daring digressions, acute personal observations, and so on. In the last two "days," however, the author adopts a new literary device: he has Salviati read aloud a Latin treatise on motion composed by his "Academician friend"—that is, Galileo. The reading is only occasionally interrupted by the other two interlocutors, who request and obtain clarifications.[19]

Important fragments outlining proposed continuations of the work have also been found. Of these, one part was published in 1674 by Viviani as the *Beginning of the Fifth Day.*[20] Another part was published in 1718 as the *Sixth Day*, though from the thread of the conversations there is no definite chronological order, and there is some reason to believe that in Galileo's projected continuation the so-called Sixth Day would have preceded the Fifth.[21] Other fragments were first published by Favaro in the eighth volume of the National Edition.

5. The two first "days" have as their theme the first new science described in the title of the work; that is, the mechanical resistance (or strength) of materials. The subject was suggested, Galileo says, by consideration of a fact well known to those who fabricate mechanical objects. When machines or frameworks of various sizes are constructed, "the larger machine, made of the same materials and in the same proportions as the smaller, will correspond to it with perfect symmetry in all respects except that of strength and resistance to breakage; the larger it is, the weaker it will be." [22] This fact seems to reveal an odd discrepancy between matter and geometry; from a geometrical point of view the two machines should be perfectly similar, because their proportions are similar, but from the material viewpoint the larger machine strangely displays quite different strength from the smaller. Thus, at least at first sight, the phenomenon of "resistance

to breakage" introduces something different in kind from the factors taken into account in pure geometry. Of what does this factor consist? How is it to be explained scientifically?

Confronted with these questions, Galileo's attitude reveals a certain perplexity. In the First Day, he opens bold debates in quest of the hidden cause of coherence among the parts of solid bodies. In the Second Day he restricts himself to the assertion that "a resistance to being separated" is undoubtedly to be found in solid bodies. He completely ignores any consideration of its causes, and bends his efforts to a determination of the mathematical relations between that resistance and the length and breadth of the bodies involved. The marked divergence of the two treatments is evident from a difference not only in content, but also in style, and we are left with the impression that the Second Day ignores many significant hints contained in the first.

The First Day begins with a clear recognition that the solution of the problem in question requires first a precise and systematic investigation of the structure of matter. This investigation, however, brings into the discussion so many other subtle and interesting questions that the interlocuors become obliged to defer to the Second Day an examination of the problem with which they started.

Galileo saw quite clearly that an investigation of the structure of matter involves the study of some very complicated questions concerning the concepts of continuity, the void, and atoms, in order to give precision to the similarities and differences between mathematical and physical divisibility. The pages devoted to this debate, despite their shortcomings, are among the most fascinating in the book. The atomism of Democritus, which in antiquity was conceived purely as a metaphysical hypothesis, becomes here a scientific theory with great practical significance, capable of leading us to an approximate explanation of well-defined physical phenomena.

The discussion of the void (or vacuum) as a physical notion is particularly important. It leads Galileo to a comprehensive polemic against Aristotelian mechanics, especially against its absurd claim that movement would be impossible in a vacuum. The laws which Aristotle mistakenly believed he had discovered in the falling of bodies are analyzed and criticized, in particular that which asserts a proportionality between the weight of bodies and their speed of fall. With clever theoretical and experimental arguments, Galileo explains how he arrived at the view that "if the resistance of the medium were entirely removed, all bodies would fall with equal speed." [23] These pages obviously constitute a kind of introduction to the treatise on motion which is the subject of the Third and Fourth Days.

The debate proceeds next to a precise examination of the vibrations of a pendulum and their laws: isochronism for equal lengths, and the proportionality of periods to the square roots of the lengths for different pendulums.[24] The results obtained are in turn applied to the study of acoustic phenomena, with which Galileo had been concerned at various times. Special interest attaches to his explanation of resonance and of musical intervals.

The course of the discussion in the much shorter Second Day is of a completely different character. Here the presentation of the investigation is surprisingly classical and Archimedean: Galileo seeks to arrange the various phenomena of resistance of materials and to reduce them to more or less complex combinations of levers. The rigorous study of the proportions of these levers and their conditions of equilibrium is presented as the nucleus of the new science of mechanics, giving it the aspect of a mere application of statics, a science known in antiquity. Galileo attached great importance to this process of reduction, since it enabled him to point out the exceptional efficicacy of geometry in the analysis of scientific problems; that is, in the determination of elementary principles that come into play in apparently more complex phenomena.

Sagredo:
What shall we say, Simplicio? Must we not confess that geometry is the most powerful of all instruments for sharpening the wit and training the mind to think correctly? Was not Plato perfectly right when he wished that his pupils should be first of all well-grounded in mathematics? As for myself, I quite understood the property of the lever and how, by increasing or diminishing its length, one can increase

or diminish the moment[25] of force and of resistance; and yet in the solution of the present problem I was not slightly, but greatly, deceived.

Simplicio:
Indeed, I begin to understand that while logic is an excellent guide in reasoning, yet as regards stimulation to discovery it cannot compare with the power of sharp distinction which belongs to geometry.[26]

Strict geometric development of his arguments, however, does not prevent Galileo from introducing a wide variety of interesting digressions. Of particular importance are his excursions into the biological field, which afford him an opportunity to examine the nature and function of hollow bones, the proportions of the limbs of giants, and so on. These digressions lay the basis for biological mechanics, which after Galileo's time was to reach very interesting results.

The Third and Fourth Days are devoted to the second new science announced on the title page of the book; that is [in modern terms] to dynamics. They constitute the most perfect part of the work; that which, according to Galileo, shows in the clearest manner the enormous advance of modern over classical science. In the Second Day, the study of the resistance of materials had been brought within the scope of a discipline as ancient as statics. In contrast, the study of motion is presented as an entirely new science—not, indeed, the subject itself, which had been examined by Aristotle, but the results arrived at and the method applied in reaching them.

In the Third Day the classic laws of uniform motion, of naturally accelerated motion, and of uniformly accelerated or retarded motion are demonstrated. The treatment is deductive in character, starting with an abstract and general definition of each of the above motions, in order to deduce with mathematical rigor their respective properties. It is only later that empirical verification of the results thus obtained is given by experiments carried out on inclined planes expressly constructed for the purpose. Because of the importance of the methodological problem

167

faced by Galileo (a problem involving complicated relationships of deduction and experience), we shall reserve that matter for the two final sections of this chapter.

One of the chief merits of the work is the clarity with which Galileo points out and even emphasizes the most delicate part of his own theory, which is also the most difficult point to accept. The difficulty is that his theory involves the obscure concepts of infinity and the infinitesimal. Today, the significance of this fact is well known, for these concepts, and the mathematical concept of limit, are seen as essential to the novel ideas of instantaneous velocity and acceleration on which all Galilean dynamics hinges. But infinity and the infinitesimal are no longer troublesome because the infinitesimal calculus provides a trusty instrument for handling them. Now, Galileo did not have the calculus, and for just that reason he deserves special admiration. His courage in introducing a definition of motion that implied "infinite degrees of slowness" and his ability to deal correctly with such motions are merits that place him among the greatest scientists of his time.

The Fourth Day is devoted to a detailed study of the trajectory of projectiles, based upon his celebrated principle of composition of movements. Again, the treatment is deductive in form; it starts with general propositions assumed as hypotheses (*ex suppositione*), not drawn from experience. To the latter is reserved only the role of testing the consequences previously demonstrated theoretically. Noteworthy also is the methodological courage shown by Galileo in compounding two motions of seemingly antithetical types—the "natural" [downward] motion of a heavy body [such as a cannon ball] and the "violent" motion imparted by the explosion of gunpowder. Aristotelian physics forbade the uniting of these supposedly incompatible concepts in any scientific treatment.

The most important result of this "day" is the demonstration that the trajectory thus compounded has a parabolic form. This result permits Galileo to solve many practical problems; it was, for example, possible to calculate that a cannon tilt of 45 degrees should produce the longest shot. Sagredo's comment on this result reflects Galileo's excitement at finding once again that theoretical prediction agreed with experimental verification.

The Return to Pure Science

"The force of rigid demonstrations such as occur only in mathematics fills me with wonder and delight. From accounts given by gunners, I was already aware of the fact that in the use of cannons and mortars, the maximum range, that is the one in which the shot goes farthest, is obtained when the elevation is 45 degrees or, as they say, at the sixth point of the quadrant; but to understand why this happens far outweighs the mere data obtained from the testimony of others, or even from repeated experiments." [27]

The so-called Fifth and Sixth Days of the discussions were left incomplete. The Fifth Day is concerned with the celebrated Euclidean theory of proportion, which Galileo seeks to render clearer and more comprehensible. The investigation is connected with the various demonstrations of proportionality developed in the discussion of motion. The subject is purely mathematical, and does not lend itself to the introduction of new and original ideas. The Sixth Day deals with the difficult physical problem of the force of percussion. Aproino, who replaces Simplicio here, expounds the tests carried out by the Academician (that is, by Galileo) in "seeking in the effect and operation of percussion the part played by the weight of the hammer and by the greater or smaller speed with which it is moved." The conclusion reached is that "the force of percussion has an infinite moment; for there is no resistance, however large, that is not overcome by the force of the smallest percussion." [28]

6. When he first turned with much enthusiasm to "mathematics," Galileo understood it to be a discipline inextricably linked with technology, design, the study of natural phenomena—a quantitative study derived from the most accurate measurement practicable. With the passage of years, he attributed greater importance to the purely rational aspect of this science, to the *necessary* progress of its arguments. But not even then did he abstract the *ideal* content of mathematics, the complex of abstract concepts upon which are constructed the theories of what we call "pure" geometry and arithmetic. For him, mathematics continued to have its value not as an end in itself but as a means; it was the great adjunct of logic, the unique effective guarantee of our hav-

ing proceeded correctly in our reasoning. This was the function attributed to mathematics in the *Assayer*. Galileo's tendency to interpret mathematics in terms of its instrumental function remained substantially unchanged even in the last stages of his life, although then he was also interested in the relations of mathematics and logic.

To confirm Galileo's slight interest in mathematics as a science in itself, there is, first of all, the singular but undeniable fact that he never seriously read Kepler's works, either those which are strictly mathematical or those on astronomy and optics which are thoroughly imbued with the mathematical spirit. It is hard to explain this attitude unless we assume some real personal antipathy on the part of Galileo toward the treatment Kepler employed. Nor did this antipathy diminish with time. Even in 1634, some years after Kepler's death, Galileo felt that he should stress the profound difference between his own philosophizing and Kepler's. Specifically, in a letter to Fulgenzio Micanzio, he said that perhaps in "writing of the same matters, and especially about the celestial motions, we have sometimes (though not often) hit on the same ideas, whereupon we have assigned to some actual effect the same true cause; but this will not be found to have happened in one per cent of my thoughts." [29]

With regard to Galileo's attitude toward mathematics, much is revealed by letters written to Galileo by his pupil Bonaventura Cavalieri, the distinguished author of *Geometria indivisibilibus continuorum quadam ratione promota* (*Geometry advanced in a certain way by indivisibles of the continuum*).[30] Cavalieri was profoundly interested in pure mathematical research, particularly in the problem of indivisibles—which had been suggested to him by Galileo. Because he knew of Galileo's ideas on the subject, it is understandable that he wished to see them collected and published as soon as possible, both so that he might learn Galileo's most recent conclusions, and because he might then feel free to publish his own results without danger of unintentionally crediting himself with things belonging to his teacher.[31] The futile insistence with which the pupil wrote over a period of many years to the teacher, begging him to write out his mathematical works, is rather distressing; thus: "And remember the work on indivisibles which you previously decided to compose; it will be most welcome"; [32] "As to the work on indivisibles, I should be obliged if you would apply yourself to it as soon as possible, so that I might hasten my own, which meanwhile I continue to polish." [33] But his prayers were in vain; Galileo always had other studies in progress which were more to his interest.

Nor is that all. Cavalieri sent some results of his own mathematical investigations in order to get Galileo's authoritative opinion on them. When even this failed to stir Galileo out of his indifference, Cavalieri wrote: "I shall have to declare myself the sworn enemy of your infinite occupations since they are the reason I receive not a word in reply to my letters. . . ." [34] "Then I wrote you again after Easter, sending you a copy of my *Logarithms*,[35] but I doubt if you received it, since a reply was desired . . . [and] you have said nothing of it in your letters." [36]

On the tenth of January 1634, when he heard that Galileo was preparing a new scientific work, Cavalieri hastened to renew his earlier plea: "I pray that if opportunity presents itself, you will be pleased for the sake of my *Geometry* to touch somewhat also on the doctrine of indivisibles, as you considered doing several years ago; I shall be much obliged to you for it. I think that the dialogue form may give rise to such an occasion, and therefore I hope to be favored." [37]

Galileo was usually punctilious about replying to questions concerning things of interest to him. Furthermore, he had the greatest admiration for Cavalieri, who had obtained the chair of mathematics at the University of Bologna with Galileo's support. I think we may conclude that mathematics as a science in itself, as it was cultivated by Cavalieri, had little appeal to Galileo. Not that he lacked ingenious ideas in this discipline, but he could not find time to occupy himself seriously with them.

When Galileo finally did decide to take up the problem of indivisibles in the *Two New Sciences,* giving heed to the last letter of Cavalieri, he still made it clear enough that he wanted to treat this not in a purely geometrical and abstract way, but with specific reference to the physical problem of divisibility, and thus to the question of atoms and the void. One of Galileo's great merits with respect to this problem was that he felt intuitively 171 the sharp difference in significance between the operation of division in the physical field on the one hand and in the mathematical field on the other. In physics we think of a thing as divisible only into particles of finite magnitude (called by Galileo *parti quante*—roughly, parts having measure); in mathematics we think of a thing as capable of being divided infinitely; that is, until we reach *parti non quante*, or geometric indivisibles. It was the methodological need to resolve the paradoxes that arise from confusion of these two types of divisibility that tempted Galileo into a subject which is now considered part of pure mathematics: the study of *parti non quante*, or infinitesimals.

Although we consider this study part of pure mathematics, Galileo did not so consider it. He was firmly convinced that even the *parti non quante* must correspond to something in nature. He thought that although it is impossible to carry the division of a solid body all the way to *parti non quante*, such division actually occurred in fluids:

Sagredo:
Are we then to believe that substances become fluid in virtue of their being resolved into their infinitely small indivisible components?

Salviati:
I cannot find any better means of accounting for certain phenomena. . . . From this it seems to me that we may reasonably conclude that the smallest particles into which water can be resolved (seeing that water has less firmness than even the finest powder, or no firmness at all) are quite different from the smallest divisible particles; nor can I find any other difference here than that they are indivisible." [38]

Furthermore, Galileo was convinced that the introduction of *parti non quante* had an important physical significance inasmuch as it offered an explanation for the mysterious phenomena of condensation and rarefaction "simultaneously avoiding the void and the interpenetration of bodies." Thus in Galileo's eyes the theory of infinite and infinitesimal quantities was a part of ap-

172

plied mathematics. Yet in his treatment of this subject he reached intuitively some highly important results which today we are accustomed to consider as belonging to pure mathematics.

One of the most noteworthy was his accurate perception of the structural difference between the division of a line into a finite number of *parti quante* and its resolution into an infinite number of *parti non quante*. The relevant passage from the *Two New Sciences* has indisputable currency even today: "Here I wish you to note that after dividing and resolving a line into a finite number of parts, that is into a number which can be counted, it is not possible to arrange them again into a greater length than that which they occupied when they were continuous and joined, without the interposition of an equal number of [finite] empty spaces. But if we consider the line as resolved into *parti non quante*, that is into an infinite number of indivisibles, we shall be able to conceive it to be immensely extended without the interposition of any finite empty spaces, by interposing an infinite number of indivisible empty spaces." [39]

In another passage of great genius, he compares various kinds of infinity.[40] It is true that he concludes, with a trifle too much caution, that "the attributes of greater, less, and equal are lacking not only among infinite quantities, but also even between the infinite and the finite." First, however, he had pointed the way by which mathematicians were to arrive, some centuries later, at the extension of these attributes even to collections of infinites.

Since he was dealing with so delicate and difficult a matter, we need not be surprised to find his new and fruitful ideas intermingled with ancient and ambiguous notions inherited from the confused speculations of the neo-Platonists. Such, for example, is the statement that "if there is any number which may be called infinite, it is the number one." [41] But the opening of a new road across the old permitted the outlines of a distant undiscovered continent to be discerned, a continent in which mathematicians of the nineteenth century were to unearth incalculable treasures.

It took courage to face these topics, beset with paradoxes, and attempt to render them amenable to intellectual conquest by throwing some light on them. Nor was Galileo unaware of the difficulties of divisibility; on the contrary, he demonstrated with   173 extraordinary sharpness that division into *parti quante* gives rise to most subtle problems. But his conclusion is still positive, and leads him to recognize that "the resolution of a line into its infinite points . . . is not impossible," and even that "it contains no difficulty inherently greater than that of distinguishing its *parti quante*." His conclusions induce us to continue the investigation, unfrightened by paradoxes; for even that which is repugnant to our intuition must somehow be subjected to reason.

7. The role which Galileo attributed to mathematics in dealing with problems of mechanics brings us to the delicate problem of the relations between deduction and experience. First, however, it is necessary to discuss the general principles on which he based this important science.

As Sebastian Timpanaro correctly remarks: "The *Two New Sciences* is a book no less Copernican than the *Dialogue Concerning the Two Chief World Systems*. Theologians did not condemn it because they did not understand it." [42] If Galileo's chief contribution to the victory of Copernicanism was the elimination of objections based on mechanics that were customarily raised against it (for example, the vertical fall of bodies), it follows that his last book, which was expressly directed to the consolidation of the laws of mechanics that had been applied in the previous book to refute those objections, brought added proofs in support of that refutation. Thus it was a Copernican work insofar as it perfected the arguments already used in the *Dialogue* to establish the truth of Copernicanism. To understand the degree to which this was done, it is necessary to analyze the contribution of his final book to the clarification of the principle of inertia, the cornerstone of his Copernican reasoning in the *Dialogue*.

The principle of inertia is developed in both books by almost the same considerations. Both base it on a thought experiment, an experiment which could not be carried out but was conceived by an imaginative stroke of scientific genius. In the *Dialogue*, Salviati proposes that his fellow interlocutors consider the motion of a perfectly round ball on an exquisitely polished surface, and he has them note first that if the motion is downward, the ball accelerates, while if it is upward, it slows down: "Now tell me," he says, "what would happen to the same movable body placed upon a surface with no slope, either upward or downward?" [43] He receives the reply that its motion would be perpetual and uniform. In the *Two New Sciences,* the demonstration is similar: "Furthermore we may remark that any velocity once imparted to a moving body will be rigidly maintained as long as external causes of acceleration and retardation are removed, a condition which is found only on horizontal planes; for in the case of planes which slope downward there is already present a cause of acceleration, while on planes sloping upward there is a [cause of] retardation. From this it follows that motion along a horizontal plane is perpetual; for if the velocity is uniform, it will not be diminished or slackened, much less destroyed." [44]

The parallel between these two discussions is evident. In the second work, however, there is more clearly an elaboration of the problem as we pass from the demonstration of the principle of inertia to the conclusions drawn from it. While the *Dialogue* erroneously deduces the inertial character of uniform circular motion concentric with the earth,[45] the *Two New Sciences* asserts in general terms the inertial character of motion in a plane where there is no cause for acceleration or retardation. How important is Galileo's correction of this error? [46]

Koyré, at the outset of an analysis which is quite rigorous but perhaps rather limited and a bit severe, remarks that the heavy bodies of the universe studied in the *Two New Sciences* "do not fall toward the center of the earth. And yet they fall." The illustrious French critic goes on to say that Galileo "definitely affirms the downward character of the movement," and that he "is incapable of abstracting [mass from] weight." [47] The movement of Galileo's famous ball does not remain [uniform and] rectilinear except when it rolls on a plane perpendicular to the downward lines of force. As soon as this plane ends, the ball, attracted downward (but no longer specifically toward the center of the earth as in the *Dialogue*), must necessarily fall along the lines of force of its weight: "Its movement continues in a straight line only while the heavy body rests on the horizontal plane; beyond that, this movement is prolonged of its own accord, but the heavy body no longer moves in a straight line." [48] In other words, Galileo conceived of gravity not as a force which acts on bodies but as some property which belongs to the bodies themselves. Even in the *Two New Sciences,* he did not succeed in abstracting weight from bodies, and hence could never pursue his extension of the principle of inertia far enough to give it a truly general formulation. Koyré concludes from this that Galileo did indeed reach the threshold of the inertial principle, but did not enter with full scientific understanding.

This critique illustrates the depth of modern researches into the history of the principle of inertia. Koyré seeks also to prove that it is Descartes who deserves credit for having first given a completely general formulation of the principle of inertia. For our present purposes, however, it will be enough to consider the reasons for which I believe Koyré's analysis too restricted and severe. As Federigo Enriques remarks, it is vain to seek in Galileo's works a treatment of the principle of inertia as a separate law. It exists only as part of the general reasoning in which Galileo includes mechanics; indeed, Galileo defends and analyzes inertia only as a prelude to his discussions of relative motion. "It is clear that the principle, thus enunciated, is not taken as a purely abstract law, but exists in relation to the momentary composition between inertial motion and an acceleration impressed by force." These words, which appear to agree with Koyré's, are actually intended to support a thesis almost antithetical to his. They say, in fact, that it is historically senseless to criticize Galileo for not having felt the need to announce a general principle of inertia. Galileo was able to apply the principle correctly to the cases that interested him, and recognized it as the point of departure for his principle of relativity, to say nothing of its application to the mechanical objections against Copernicanism. Then what right have we to deny that he gave the principle of inertia full generality? To him, its full value was a fruitful practical knowledge, and not something purely theoretical. Nor is it to be forgotten (as Koyré himself recognizes) that Galileo's pupils felt no need to open a scientific debate on the principle of inertia: they all agreed in considering it as a result already definitively achieved in the new mechanics.

176   The decisive importance which Galileo attributed thus to the

connection between the principles of inertia and relativity suggests to Enriques that it is in this link that we should look for the chief advance over the *Dialogue* made by the *Two New Sciences*. This was a truly notable advance, connected with the new clarity given to the principle of *composition of motions* in the later work. Almost all the Fourth Day is devoted to that principle. The parallelogram of movements [49] is applied generally to the composition of a straight uniform (inertial) movement and a straight naturally accelerated (gravitational) movement, and the parabolic form of the resultant motion is demonstrated. Sagredo, who has followed the demonstration of the new theorem, expresses his admiration and stresses the essential concepts of this important result: "One cannot deny that the argument is new, subtle and conclusive, resting as it does upon this hypothesis; namely, that the horizontal motion remains uniform, that the vertical motion continues to be accelerated downwards in proportion to the square of the time, and that such motions and velocities can combine without altering, disturbing, or hindering each other, so that as the motion proceeds, the [parabolic] path of the projectile does not change into another kind [of curve]." [50]

As usual, Galileo does not stop with a general enunciation of the theorem, but goes on at once to draw from it various interesting applications. With this demonstration of its remarkable fecundity, the principle assumes a new authoritativeness, and Galileo claims that its consequences are accepted by every serious scholar. We know from the *Dialogue* that among these consequences were Galileo's replies to the mechanical objections against Copernicanism, so that those replies, too, indirectly came to assume a new scientific importance.

Thus the *Two New Sciences* was in reality a Copernican work. But unlike the *Dialogue*, it was not a Copernican manifesto; rather, it was a work developed entirely in accordance with the new Copernican direction of modern science, deepening its principles and broadening its development.

8. The more interesting results of the Third and Fourth Days of the *Two New Sciences* have become part of the general heritage

of modern scientific culture. The method by which those results were obtained is ordinarily considered one of the most solid foundations for the Platonic interpretation of Galileo's thought.

The Third and Fourth Days are built around a Latin treatise *De motu* (*On motion*), read by Salviati to the other two interlocutors. Discussions in Italian are interpolated among the various theorems read. The form of the treatise itself is rigorously deductive. It begins with precise definitions of particular motions and intuitively evident general axioms. Assuming these to be accepted by the reader, Galileo deduces from them a long series of theorems and corollaries. All this is done in mathematical form, permitting the author of the treatise to achieve an exemplary rigor. Observation is invoked only in the discussions which serve as commentaries on the theorems and is intended to test the correspondence between the results demonstrated in the treatise *On motion* and the facts of experience. These empirical tests, however, seem to be relegated bit by bit to a secondary place, and toward the end they lose almost all importance.

It is significant that in the Third Day, the task of defending the empirical requirement is left to the Aristotelian Simplicio, who says, for example: "But whether this acceleration is that which one meets in nature in the case of falling bodies, I am still doubtful; and it seems to me, not only for my own sake but also for others who think as I do, that this would be the place to introduce one of the experiments, of which I understand there are many, which agree in various cases with the conclusions reached." [51] The request is reasonable, and Salviati describes in reply the famous experiments in which Galileo watched a "very hard bronze ball, well rounded and polished," running along a groove cut in an inclined plane. [52] These experiments were not inserted directly in the Latin treatise, and occur only in the accompanying Italian discussion. This seems to suggest that Galileo considered the experiments little more than accessories. Koyré remarks: "Aristotelian empiricism insists on 'experiences' that may serve as base and foundation to the theory. Galilean epistemology, aprioristic and experimental at the same time, offers in reply some experiments constructed according to a theory, experiments of which the specific task is to confirm or invalidate

The Return to Pure Science

the application to reality of laws deduced from principles having their foundation elsewhere." [53]

This attitude toward experiment becomes even more evident in the Fourth Day, and is still more favorable to the Platonic interpretation. Sagredo affirms that to understand mathematically the cause of an event "far outweighs the mere data obtained from the testimony of others, or even from repeated experiments." Sagredo's affirmation acquires a more specific meaning when it is read together with the words of Salviati which follow immediately: "You speak very truly; knowledge of a single effect acquired by understanding its causes opens the mind to a sure understanding of further effects without need of recourse to experience."

Does it follow from this that experience plays a completely subsidiary role in the Galilean method? Koyré has no doubt in the matter. He holds that after analyzing the last two "days" of the *Two New Sciences*, one cannot deny that Galileo's purpose is to know the essences that underlie facts rather than the sequence of facts themselves. He even adds, for greater clarity, that these essences necessarily can be only approximately confirmed by facts; hence it would make no sense to start from facts to ascertain them; it is up to mathematics alone to arrive at them directly.

Another authoritative interpreter of Galilean thought, Ernst Cassirer,[54] states that Galileo's method, though it starts and ends in experience, has as its primary aim the resolution of observational data into general relations of a conceptual rather than an empirical nature. In other words, in Galileo's research processes only an occasional function is performed by sensible experience; the more important task falls to reason. By determining the mathematical relations between one experience and another, reason teaches us to "transform the empirical accident into a necessity governed by laws," and thus leads us to discover the intelligible, systematic, unitary order in which the true, ultimate and fundamental reality resides. "The essential laws of nature according to Galileo," wrote Cassirer, "are not laws of the immediately given, but refer only to ideal cases which can never be completely realized in nature. But this in no way prejudices their 'objectivity.'" [55]

Galileo Galilei

Galileo's position as to the role of sensible experience cannot be resolved unless reading of the *Two New Sciences* is integrated with that of Galileo's other writings. Thus the letter of 1604 in which Galileo communicated to Fra Paolo Sarpi his discovery of the law of naturally accelerated motion, if compared with later writings, reveals that the deductive procedure expounded in the *Two New Sciences* was not the one which Galileo originally followed in arriving at the law. In fact, Galileo already knew the law, but he still lacked an accurate definition of naturally accelerated motion. In the letter to Sarpi he affirmed that he had arrived at "a natural and evident principle" from which the law could be deduced, but he later saw that this principle was erroneous, and subjected it to sharp criticism. Now, what was it that first assured him of the truth of the law? He did not originally have a correct principle from which to deduce it, and was still looking in the wrong direction for one. Platonist interpreters of Galilean thought find it hard to answer this question.

The fact remains that to judge by the treatise *On motion* contained in the last two "days" of the *Two New Sciences*, Galileo felt such enthusiasm for the hypothetical-deductive method as to give it absolute pre-eminence over the method he presumably followed thirty years earlier in the discovery of this law. Yet despite this enthusiasm, he never confused the hypothetical demonstration of such laws with actual proof of their validity. Indeed he often stressed the sharp difference between these two problems, and went so far as to say that they were completely independent of each other, so that the hypothetical demonstration would preserve its value (but as purely theoretical, which Platonist interpreters seem always to forget) even when it led to results which had no counterpart in nature. For instance, Galileo wrote to Giovanni Battista Baliani, on the seventh of January 1639: "But returning to my treatise on motion, I argue hypothetically about motion defined in this way, so that even if the consequences did not correspond to the events of natural motion, it would matter little to me; just as it in no way detracts from the proofs of Archimedes [concerning spirals] that no moving body is to be found in nature that moves in spiral lines." [56]

This statement seems at first sight to contain a rejection of experiment, but in reality it merely expresses Galileo's complete understanding of the necessity not to confuse mathematical deduction with physical demonstration. This is an important insight, as every student of rational mechanics knows today, for we feel perfectly free to define and study in theory the most singular motions without worrying about whether anything that exists in nature corresponds to them. For the modern scientist, the essential thing is not to confuse such theoretical study with the real description of phenomena; and Galileo was far from doing so. Of course a theoretical motion may correspond to some actual motion, but this is no more than a happy coincidence. Galileo continued in the letter to Baliani, "In this I have been lucky, if I may say so, because the actual motion of heavy bodies corresponds exactly with the events demonstrated by me for the motion I defined." This example is indisputably against the advocates of a Galilean Platonism. Here Galileo makes a sharp break between the logically necessary deduction of a law from a hypothetical definition and its actual occurrence in the real world—an occurrence which is not "necessary" because in the unlucky cases it may turn out to be completely lacking.

I believe that the distinction between hypothetical truth and factual truth was already present in Galileo's other works, and that this example supplies us with the true key to an understanding of the profound significance of the whole work we are examining. It has been said that in excluding experimental proofs of his celebrated laws from his Latin treatise, Galileo wanted to demonstrate to his readers the minor scientific importance of such proofs. Yet what evidence is there that Galileo attributed greater weight to his Latin pages than to the Italian sections of the book? Perhaps the truth is otherwise, and refutes the Platonic interpretation of the Galilean method. Perhaps Galileo wanted to use two languages primarily to emphasize the irreducibility of the two treatments. Perhaps he wanted only to prove to everyobdy that mathematical demonstration, even though it absorbs into itself the experimental, is something independent of experiment, and that the two are developed on entirely separate planes.

Now if that is how matters really stand, why did Galileo devote such a large part of his research to the mathematical treatment of motion? How can one explain his great care to show deductively something which he might have restricted to experimental verification?

Such questions can be answered only if one is aware that to maintain the distinction between mathematical demonstration of an "event of motion" and its superficial experimental verification does not imply a denial that the latter may be of some use to the former. Mathematical demonstration cannot indeed guarantee its own physical validity, but it may still throw light on the logical connections between one event and another. Above all, it may help us to grasp the general principles implicit in the conclusions suggested by experience. If any of these implied principles is openly contradictory to experience, we must painstakingly re-examine the problem and apply greater rigor to the evaluation of answers given by nature.

Nothing is more instructive in this respect than a penetrating methodological observation contained in the Sixth Day. Aproino has outlined an apparently convincing explanation of the effects of percussion, but Salviati has demonstrated to him by simple reasoning that it cannot be correct. Since Aproino is embarrassed by the error he has committed, his friend comforts him with words which clearly refer to Galileo: "Do not be dismayed, Signor Aproino, for I assure you that you have plenty of company in your entanglement in knots that someone else can easily untie. Every fallacy would naturally be easy to discover if people proceeded in an orderly fashion to develop and resolve it into its principles, for one of them will quickly be found that is patently false. Our Academician had a special genius for reducing with few words to absurdity and inconsistency various false conclusions that had always been believed true. I have made a collection of conclusions in physics which had always passed for true until he showed them to be false by means of simple and brief reasoning." [57]

Here the importance of methodological concern over the orderly development and resolution of every scientific proposition into its principles is revealed. Such resolution, as Galileo points out, is the most appropriate way to discover a fallacy in physical conclusions. Only when a conclusion suggested by experience demonstrably entails no false principles, and contradicts no other physical conclusions, can it be accepted as scientifically secure. Otherwise, it must be re-examined by means of a new and more careful interrogation of experience.

Geometry, for Galileo, is "the most potent instrument to sharpen the mind and dispose it to reason perfectly." It is likewise the most suitable instrument for developing and resolving natural conclusions into their principles. Though it always remains in the field of pure hypothesis, it nevertheless accomplishes a primary function in the investigation of nature. This is because it guides us to the discovery of intricate linkages between various physical propositions and thereby aids us to establish the exact value of each observed fact without undertaking either to deduce them a priori or to resolve them into abstract conceptual relationships.

9. This explanation of Galileo's recourse to mathematics in its logical and operationalist aspects, so basic in the two last "days" of the *Two New Sciences,* does not pretend to eliminate every trace of Platonism in the work. Its very modest aim is only to illustrate the true complexity of Galileo's thought. It may also serve to narrow the gap that exists between the *Two New Sciences* and Galileo's earlier works, where his tendency was clearly to attribute to mathematics a merely auxiliary role in comparison with that of empirical knowledge and of logic.[58]

It is worthwhile, therefore, to integrate this with the function attributed to empirical data in the *Two New Sciences.* In the Third Day, the Aristotelian Simplicio has the task of defending such data, and this is often interpreted as a denigration of them by Galileo. Is such an interpretation correct? Perhaps Galileo merely wished in this way to recognize the existence of a profound linkage between the new science and the best parts of Aristotelian thought. Indeed, when in 1640 he again discussed the relations between his own methodology and that of Aristotle, Galileo admitted the existence of a real link between them. He even went so far as to assert that he, rather than his adversaries, was the true heir of Aristotle. Similar declarations, though less explicit, had also appeared in his previous works.

Galileo Galilei

In the *Dialogue*, for example, he had maintained energetically and beyond question that he was perfectly in accord with Aristotle in the statement that "what sensible experience shows ought to be preferred over any argument, even one that seems to be extremely well-founded." [59] Interpreters who find Platonic tendencies in Galileo may object that the citation is out of context and not truly representative of the *Dialogue*, because in the same book Galileo gave special credit to Copernicus for having "resolutely continued to affirm what sensible experience seemed to contradict." [60] As to Copernicus, I believe, the apparent contradiction may be resolved in this way: Galileo was perfectly aware that the great Polish astronomer could not prove the physical truth of his hypothesis (something achieved by science only in later times and on the basis of very precise astronomical and terrestrial observations); yet he felt the greatest admiration for him because he succeeded in divining that those proofs would be found sooner or later. Above all, Copernicus understood that crude sense experiences adduced against heliocentrism by the defenders of Aristotelian and Ptolemaic astronomy had no real value.

I should say that Galileo definitely agreed with Aristotle in placing before reason "that which is demonstrated by experience and our senses," but denied that our senses offered us, along with the data, the correct interpretation. Instead, in many cases (for example, in Copernicanism) he held that what seems to us a contradiction between certain facts and a theory is really a contradiction between our first crude interpretation of those facts and the said theory. Hence the necessity of removing from the facts (in themselves incontrovertible) the clothing in which we have unwittingly dressed them; hence also the necessity of finding new, more precise facts that may be taken as they are and apart from any traditional dress.

To know how to find new, exact data derived from unequivocal experiences and subject to precise description was for Galileo to know how to interrogate nature. For this purpose it is necessary to go beyond the first qualitative appearances, since they are charged with perilous traditional interpretations; one must imagine or create techniques or models such that nature's reply will emerge from them clearly and beyond any possible misunderstanding.

In the *Two New Sciences*, Galileo gave one splendid example of the interrogation of nature which has become a scientific classic. This was the verification of the laws of naturally accelerated motion by his celebrated experiments on inclined planes, "experiments repeated a hundred times" always with the same result, as Salviati tells his interlocutors, "and at all slopes of the plane." [61] The observations thus carried out constituted a truly effective interrogation of nature because they led to reliable measurements of the spaces traversed by the ball and the velocities successively reached. Faced with this type of interrogation, nature replied without equivocation, and her reply was that the ideas of the old Aristotelian and Ockhamist mechanics were untenable, because they were in open contradiction with "that which experience and sense demonstrate to us."

In all probability before 1604, and hence long before Galileo had the correct definition of naturally accelerated motion, he had imagined various possible relations between the space and the time of fall of heavy bodies. The results of his interrogation of nature by means of the inclined plane served to prove the truth of *one* of these relations and the falsity of the others. From that moment on, he sought a rigorous general definition of the concept of naturally accelerated motion, a definition that would permit him to deduce the correct relation and no other. He took the experimentally verified result as a standard of truth in the theory of motion. In the face of so characteristically experimental a process, it is hard to believe that experiment had for Galileo only an occasional and secondary role, as Cassirer maintains.

Galvano Della Volpe, an able Italian scholar of Marxist tendencies, has recently portrayed Galileo as the energetic supporter of a "materialist logic." He appeals to the decisive role which Galileo attributed to experimental verification, and leaves aside the problem of interpreting the role he attributed to mathematics.[62] Without fully sharing this opinion, I find myself in accord with Della Volpe when he polemicizes actively against the interpretation of Galilean thought given by Cassirer on the basis of the value of experiment for testing or invalidating a theory.

Galileo Galilei

Did Galileo in fact ever reach full understanding of the nature of experimental method? Did he satisfactorily explain the relation that exists between reason and experience? I believe that a careful and unbiased reading of all his works obliges us to answer decidedly "no." He oscillated between recourse to the purest deductive method and appeal no less energetically to empirical observation. No wonder, then, that interpreters find in Galileo's writings abundant reasons for attributing to him ideas as widely antithetical as the Platonist and the materialist.

It may seem odd that despite these uncertainties, despite these oscillations, Galileo was able to make an enormous contribution to the development of the methodological understanding of science. Historians of every persuasion have been forced to recognize this. His works are an inexhaustible mine of vivid methodological observations. The explanation of this seeming oddity lies in the enormous complexity of the problem of method, which even modern epistemology has not completely resolved. Galileo intuitively felt this complexity more strongly than any of his contemporaries, and hence could refrain from putting himself in a dogmatic position, either rationalist or empiricist; thus he succeeded in pointing out, though with some uncertainty, the path by which modern science might progress. If in the complexity of his interests he may sometimes seem philosophically inconsistent, from the methodological viewpoint the same behavior nevertheless appears as an expression of informed maturity. It is conclusive proof that Galileo's interest in scientific research reflected a new spirit outside that of any previously constituted scheme, whether Platonic or Aristotelian.

Chapter 10

The Serene Conclusion
of an Embattled Life

1. His prolonged confinement at Arcetri, his distressing loss of vision, and the many troublesome misfortunes of old age did not prevent Galileo from finishing his life in an atmosphere of serene and composed dignity. He knew how to teach his friends, his pupils, and even his adversaries a final lesson in humanity which was by no means the least of his many valuable services.

First of all, one may observe that the obvious deterioration of his physical condition had at least one good result for the aged scientist: it reduced the severity of the orders issued against him by the Church authorities. In 1639 he was allowed to have at his house in Arcetri a very young and extremely intelligent scholar, Vincenzio Viviani, who remained with him to the end, and who later wrote a biographical sketch of Galileo. This work was composed at the express request of Prince Leopold de' Medici, and its tiresome obsequiousness to the persecutors of Galileo is largely due to its official character. Still, its author's deep affection for his teacher cannot fail to move us.

Among the things that Viviani could offer which were especially welcome to Galileo were not only the devotion of an admiring pupil, but also his youthful and insatiable interest in scientific problems, his desire always to secure new explanations, and his ability to keep alive in Galileo the taste for research. There is no better evidence of this than Galileo's words in a letter to Benedetto Castelli dated December 3, 1639: "It is obvious . . . that in philosophy, doubt is the father of invention, opening the way to the discovery of truth. The objections raised for many months now by this youth, my present guest and pupil, against the principle [1] that I assumed in my treatise on accelerated motion, which he has been studying with great attention, forced me to think it over with a view to persuading him that he should accept it as an acceptable and true principle; and I have finally emerged, to his and my great delight, with the conclusive proof, which I have already discussed with several persons. This he next wrote out for me; for I am deprived of my eyes and would perhaps be confused about the diagrams and figures required." [2] The stimulating company of this young student was doubtless one of the chief sources of the serenity achieved by the teacher. Gradually it enabled him to put aside bitter memories of the past and it gave him a keener sense of that invincible power by which human knowledge could progress from generation to generation without allowing itself ever to be checked by its adversaries, however strong, or by the death of any single contributor, however able.

In October 1641, another young scientist appeared at Arcetri to receive the last teachings of the master. This was Evangelista Torricelli, who was unquestionably the greatest genius among the direct heirs of the Galilean spirit. But by that time Galileo's voice was fading out, and he was no longer able to add anything new to what he had already written.

One of the most characteristic episodes of the final period in Galileo's life was his dispute with Fortunio Liceti, an Aristotelian scholar, professor of philosophy and medicine first at Pisa, then at Padua, and finally at Bologna. Conspicuous in this debate was its change of feeling. Beginning with a sharpness not unlike that of his old polemics, Galileo after a short time adopted an unusually moderate tone; his deep serenity of mind is clearly evident together with a more mature awareness of his thought.

Fortunio Liceti had published a treatise with the title *Litheosphorus sive de lapide bononiensi* (*Litheosphorus, or Of the Bolognese Stone*), on the so-called light-bearing ore of Bologna, a species of barite discovered in 1604 on Mount Paderno near Bologna by an alchemist named Vincenzio Casciarolo. This stone had the singular property of becoming phosphorescent by exposure to sunlight—or, as was said then, of absorbing light and then giving it up again little by little. The fiftieth chapter of Liceti's book dealt with the ashen light discernable in the shadowed part of the moon, especially when it is near conjunction with the sun. After attempting to refute Galileo's theory (set forth in the *Starry Messenger*) that this phenomenon was no more than the effect of sunlight reflected from the earth to the moon, Liceti tried to explain it as a brilliance originating in an atmosphere surrounding the moon (*ab aethere contermino ad Lunae globum*), which (like the Bolognese light-bearing stone) had the property of conserving for a certain time the light that had previously come to it from the sun (*ut, absente Sole, ac in umbra . . . in parte lumine solari tacta, conservet aliquandium lucem, quam prius a Sole susceperat*).

Liceti sent a copy of his book to Galileo with a request that he communicate his judgment of it. Meanwhile, Prince Leopold de' Medici had urgently asked Galileo to reply to the fiftieth chapter. In March 1640 Galileo decided to set forth his views on this interesting question. He dictated the reply to young Viviani in the form of a letter to Prince Leopold.[3] This letter did not conceal his small respect for this adversary, whom he subjected to pungent criticisms. The attack was further sharpened by the fact that the letter was sent not only to Prince Leopold (as was proper) but also circulated among various friends before it came to Liceti's attention. Liceti accordingly wrote to the famous scientist, respectfully but without hiding his resentment, and asked permission to publish the letter with a reply.

At this point the debate might either have suffered a brusque interruption or assumed a progressively more acid character. Instead (on August 25, 1640) Galileo replied to his opponent with sincere cordiality (a cordiality that increased in the ensuing months) and promised to compose a new version of his letter as soon as possible. (This second version was couched in more courteous words than the original, though it still had a certain ironic tone.) In offering to write it, Galileo said:

"The modesty and delicacy in which you clothe your ideas are truly admirable. Though the ideas in themselves may contain some little bitterness, yet they are presented so sweetly that they have been kindly received, with delight and pleasure. . . . I had no thought of publishing that letter of mine [to Leopold] . . . but if you are resolved to print my replies, I will recast it without changing the content of what I wrote in any way, addressing my arguments, if you like, directly to you. . . . As to abstaining from goads: if (as I hope from your courtesy and generosity) this is to be done, I assure you that should it be neccesary for me to reply further, even if I am defeated by your doctrines, I shall not allow myself to overstep the bounds of the reverence that I owe your high merits." [4]

Galileo was evidently not disposed, from mere courtesy to his opponent, to change his opinions in the least, nor would any such pretense make sense on the part of a serious thinker who was in full possession of his mental faculties despite his great age. What he did change was his approach. This was important, for the abandonment of his former asperity in favor of greater serenity placed him in a position to examine the significance of his own scientific position with increasing objectivity. Galileo's correspondence with Liceti not only continued after the first clash, but even broadened and became more serious. Eventually Galileo reconsidered in all its generality the problem of the spirit of the new science in relation to the true core of Aristotelian philosophy. Galileo's clarifications for Liceti—clarifications which represented not so much a summary as a deepening of his previous positions —offer us perhaps the best key to a rounded interpretation of his thought.

Yet his scientific position was unchanged. Even with respect to the touchy problem of Copernicanism, he remained faithful (despite the abjuration) to his old convictions, at least so far as prudence permitted. Proof is afforded by his letter to Francesco Rinuccini on the twenty-ninth of March 1641, in which the sense of his words is so clear as to require no comment: "The falsity of the Copernican system should not be doubted on any account, especially by us Catholics. . . . And just as I consider the Copernican observations and conjectures insufficient, so I regard as even more fallacious and erroneous those of Ptolemy, Aristotle, and their followers, for (remaining always within the bounds of human reason) their inconclusiveness can be quite clearly shown." [5]

The richness of Galileo's personality is further revealed by an entirely different kind of episode—his relations with Alessandra Bocchineri. This woman had the merit, in Banfi's words, of touching with "ultimate grace the spirit of Galileo," drawing from him "with the fervor of her limpid, rich, vibrant vitality . . . an almost pure rage of this spirit at the forgotten exhaustion of his body [coupled with] a harmony of moving affection and tender courtesy, the sweetness of a serene enchantement like a dream (alas, only a dream) of spring in the last warmth of autumn." [6]

Alessandra, sister of Geri Bocchineri and of Sestilia, the wife of Vincenzio Galilei, had experienced both pain and joy in her brief life.[7] Widowed by the death of Lorenzo Nati of Bibiena, she had married Francesco Rasi of Aretino and accompanied him to the court of the Grand Duke of Mantova. But Rasi also died after a short time, and Alessandra was once again left alone in a strange city far from her own family. Rather than leave the Gonzagas, she entered into the service of Eleonora, the Duke's sister, whom she followed to Vienna as a lady of the court when Eleonora married the Emperor Ferdinand. At Vienna the Empress presented her to a brilliant Florentine diplomat, Gianfrancesco Buonamici, who became her third husband. In 1630 Alessandra returned suddenly to Italy, and (as her brother wrote to Galileo) "was able to escape by only eighteen days of travel from the evils of war and plague, to the delight of all who knew her." [8]

Naturally, Vincenzio soon introduced his father to this beautiful and intelligent sister-in-law who had managed to arouse so much interest at the most elegant courts of Europe. In the correspondence of Galileo and Alessandra which soon began, there is a lively reciprocal spiritual sympathy which did not diminish with time. Rather, in the last year of Galileo's life it took on a particularly affectionate tone, and brought to him that restorative breath of disturbed tenderness mentioned above. Alessandra wrote from Prato on the twenty-seventh of March 1641: "I often wonder to myself how I shall be able before I die to find a way to be with you and spend a day in conversation without scandalizing or making those people jealous who have made fun of us for this wish. If I thought that you were in good health, and that you would not be fatigued by traveling in a carriage, I should like to send my horses and find a small carriage so that you might favor me by coming to stay a few days with us the next time we have good weather. Therefore I beg you to do me the favor of replying, that I may send for you at once; you may come slowly, and I do not believe you would suffer. . . . I do not wish to write further, in view of my hope that you will write and tell me when to send the carriage; then we shall say what the Arno says when it is at flood and carries off great treasures." [9]

It is hard not to feel the bitterness in Galileo's immediate reply, dated the sixth of April. After having spoken of his "inexpressible pleasure" on receiving the invitation, he has to admit that it cannot be accepted: "I can never tell you sufficiently the pleasure I should take in uninterrupted leisure to enjoy your conversation, elevated above usual feminine talk, so much so that little more significant and perceptive can be expected from the most experienced and practiced men in the world. I am sorry that your invitation cannot be accepted, not only because of the many indispositions that oppress me in my old age, but because I am held in prison for reasons well known to my lord your husband, the distinguished cavalier." [10]

Although he could not see her again, it is certain that he felt her spiritual presence at the serene sunset of his life. It was to Alessandra that his last letter was written, on the twentieth of December 1641: "I have received you welcome letter at a time when it is a great consolation to me, as I have been confined to bed by serious illness for many weeks. My cordial thanks to you for the courteous affection that you show for my person, and for the condolence you send me in my miseries and misfortunes. . . . I beg you to excuse my involuntary brevity, and with most cordial affection I kiss your hands." [11]

2. In the first section of his letter to Prince Leopold, Galileo accurately defended against Liceti's objections his "antiquated" explanation of the secondary light of the moon, set forth thirty years earlier in the *Starry Messenger*. In a second section he subjected to detailed criticism the arguments in defense of Liceti's theory, which adduced the supposed phosphorescence of the lunar atmosphere. In both parts, Galileo confronted the problem of the connections between physical concepts and observational data. He maintained that "the senses, in their initial perceptions, may err" and that therefore it is necessary to correct them with "the

aid of correct reasoning." [12] Liceti had been able to make this correction because he could not take into account all the empirical data, and because he ran into gross logical errors. "That there is an absolute fallacy, I shall prove by taking the threads of his argument, without going a hairsbreadth beyond them, and deducing a false conclusion from them; but the conclusion would have to be true if the form of argument were not fallacious." [13] In this work, as in others before it, Galileo definitely affirmed the utility of mathematics for avoiding such errors. This he reaffirmed with greater insistence when Liceti wrongly claimed to have developed his own "physico-mathematical" investigations. "Your Highness sees, then, how mathematical reasoning serves to avoid reefs upon which the pure physicist is sometimes in danger of running aground and smashing himself." [14]

The last lines of the letter deserve particular mention. Here Galileo explains why he has not turned his critique against Aristotelianism in general, "but against some of those men who wish to extend Aristotelian and philosophy authority beyond its proper limits, and thus to shield themselves against the opposition of anyone else, though he may argue rationally." [15] This remark significantly extends the debate against Liceti to a more general problem: the relation between Galilean thought and Aristotelian philosophy. This theme was amply developed in several of Galileo's letters to Liceti, especially that of the fifteenth of November 1640:

"I am glad to hear that you, together with many others, hold me to be—as you say—against the Peripatetic philosophy. This gives me an opportunity to free myself from this reproach (for so I consider it), and to show that I yield to no man as an admirer of Aristotle. Here I shall content myself to say briefly that which, with more time, I think I could explain and confirm in more detail and more evidently." [16] Although there is reason to believe that he had thought much about it in the last years of his life, Galileo did not actually elaborate on this subject beyond the sketchy contents of this letter.

"I believe (and I think others also believe) that to be a true Peripatetic—that is, an Aristotelian philosopher—consists principally in philosophizing in accordance with the teachings of

Aristotle, proceeding by those methods and with those true assumptions and principles upon which scientific reasoning is founded, and assuming those general axioms from which any deviation would be a serious defect. Among these suppositions are all the teachings of Aristotle in his *Logic*, pertaining to the careful avoidance of fallacies in reasoning, which would be aimed and directed at forming good syllogisms and drawing from the premises the necessary conclusion. These teachings have to do with the form of direct arguments. As to this part I believe I have learned, from innumerable pure mathematical arguments which are never fallacious, such certainty in demonstrations that I rarely if ever fall into equivocations in my arguments. Therefore I am a Peripatetic."

This explicit declaration certainly confirms my view that Galileo was completely convinced of the importance of Aristotelian logic as a precious aid in "escaping fallacies of reasoning"; at the same time, because of the abstractness and generality of its rules, it was not sufficient by itself, and had to be integrated with mathematics. According to Galileo, mathematics alone is practically and theoretically suited to supply us with "such certainty in demonstration" as to guarantee us against nearly every error and mistake, however concealed and inveterate. A few passages previously cited will acquire greater perspective in this new light:

"For just as there is no middle ground between truth and falsity in physical things, so in rigorous proofs one must either establish his point beyond any doubt or else beg the question inexcusably, and there is no chance of keeping on one's feet by invoking limitations, distinctions, verbal distortions, and other fireworks; one must with but few words and at the first assault become Caesar or nobody." [17]

"What shall we say, Simplicio? Must we not confess that geometry is the most powerful of all instruments for sharpening the wit and training the mind to think correctly?" [18]

"Our Academician had a special genius for reducing with few words to absurdity and inconsistency various false conclusions that had always been believed true." [19]

Having explained the nature and limitations of his own acceptance of Aristotelian logic, Galileo continued: "Among the reliable ways of pursuing truth is that of placing experience above any reasoning whatever, for we are sure that any fallacy must be contained in the latter, at least covertly, since it is impossible for any sense experience to be contrary to truth. This is also a precept highly esteemed by Aristotle, and stands far above the credit or power of authority of all the men that ever lived."

I think it particularly important that in this significant passage Galileo returned to the position he had maintained in the *Dialogue* [20] but without granting those concessions to Platonism which he had apparently made in certain parts of the *Two New Sciences*. In this context, therefore, it seems to me unjustifiable to argue only from the *Two New Sciences* and ignore what Galileo wrote in plain words before and after it, both in the *Dialogue* and in this letter to Liceti. His energetic affirmation of the impossibility "that a sense experience be contrary to truth" unequivocally confirms, in my view, Galileo's wish to place experimental verification at the core of the proof or disproof of scientific theories. When reasoning contradicts a "fact," there must be found in it "at least covertly" some fallacy, and the task of the scientist must be precisely *to discover the nature of this fallacy.* This does not mean that at the first apparent contradiction between a theory and an empirical observation, the theory ought in Galileo's opinion to be abandoned; were that the case, he would have had to abandon the Copernican theory immediately when scholars thought they had found in it contradictions to such everyday facts as the vertical fall of heavy bodies. In this instance *a fallacy exists not in the theory,* but in the manner in which certain supposed consequences are drawn from it, which consequences are contradicted by experience. Thus, there is a fallacy in supposing that from the Copernican hypothesis there *follows* the impossibility of the vertical fall of heavy bodies. In order to eliminate this fallacy, it is necessary to *correct false reasoning,* not abandon the hypothesis. But it is precisely in this correction that mathematics can give us the most valuable assistance; for example, just as Galileo taught in the case of Copernicanism, mathematics can show that from the hypothesis of the earth's motion it *does not follow* that heavy bodies, allowed to fall freely, will lag behind with respect to the vertical. If anything, the result will be quite the contrary: heavy bodies should fall somewhat in front of the vertical. But this was not experimentally demonstrated until much later.

Galileo, having explained his qualified assent to the two fundamental methodological canons of Aristotle, next declared with equal energy his disagreement with certain Aristotelians. These, and Liceti in particular, forgot the Stagirite's teaching that one must place experience above "the credit and power of authority of all men that ever lived." They subjected themselves to absolute authority, "for the maintenance of which they are prepared to deny sense experiences and to give strange interpretations to the texts of Aristotle, and in order to explain and delimit these, they would often put in that philosopher's mouth still other extravagant things which were surely remote from his imaginings." Such Aristotelians never consider that Aristotle might be wrong despite the correctness of the methodological canons he had proposed to follow: "It is quite possible that a great artisan might know the surest and best precepts of his art, but sometime make mistakes in some particular point. For example, a musician or a painter having the true precepts of his art might in practice play a discord or commit some error in perspective. Suppose I know that such an artist not only has the true precepts, but even that he himself discovered them; if I then see some defect in one of his works, must I accept it as well done and worthy of being defended and imitated because of his authority? To this I should certainly never assent."

According to Galileo, a similar position should be taken with regard to Aristotle by anyone who wishes to be a faithful follower of his methodological teachings. "Here I merely wish to add that if Aristotle were to return to earth, I am sure he would accept me among his followers in view of my few but conclusive contradictions [of him] much more readily than he would accept many others who attempt to defend his every word by deriving from his text concepts that never entered his head. And if Aristotle were to see the new discoveries in the heavens, which he declared to be inalterable and immutable because no alteration had ever been seen in them, undoubtedly he would change his opinion and would now say the opposite. For remember that although he said that the heavens were inalterable because no alteration in them had been seen, he would now say they are alterable because alterations are perceived in them." —

This part of the letter to Liceti concludes with a final significant appeal to experience. Between the theoretical declaration "the heavens are inalterable and immutable" and the empirical evidence "alterations are perceived in them," there is an open contradiction. In this case, therefore, no special mathematical demonstrations are needed to grasp the incompatibility between the two; it is so evident that no "distortions of words," no "fireworks" of any kind can reconcile it. Hence it is necessary either to accept the theoretical statement and deny the empirical evidence, or to accept the latter and deny the former. In so clear a case there was no doubt for Galileo; to be faithful to Aristotle, he must deny the Aristotelian theory of the heavens; to "place experience above reasoning," he must wage open battle with the Aristotelianism of his contemporaries.

3. Must we conclude, then, that Galileo was an Aristotelian? This engaging question, in my opinion, cannot be answered with a simple "yes" or "no." A more complex answer must be given.

First of all, it seems to me that Galileo's serene examination of the relations between his own position and that of Aristotle is nearly sufficient to show that profound traces of Aristotelianism exist in Galilean thought. Since the most important of these traces is the superiority of experience to reason, it is impossible to accept any purely Platonic interpretation of Galilean science.

Yet Galileo's appeal to experience is quite different from Aristotle's. Galileo knows that experience, in order to have any value as a criterion, must be wisely questioned; in fact, he often declared that "the senses, in their first perception, may err." How can one correct them? In this work of correction Galileo is no longer a pure Aristotelian, for he appeals not to logic but to mathematics as the great elaborator of correct reasoning, as the guide to more precise observation of nature, to quantitative and not merely qualitative observation; as the source of inspiration for decisive techniques or models for the testing of theories. Galileo also holds, rightly or wrongly, that to go beyond Aristotle is not necessarily to go against Aristotle. If he often calls on Plato, it is not a return to some type of subordination of experience to reason; it is rather a means of strengthening his attack against the Aristotelians—that is, the false Aristotelians. By appealing to Plato he could stress the importance he attributed to mathematics in its integration with logic: "truly I begin to comprehend that logic, though it is a most potent instrument for the regulation of our reasoning, does not reach . . . the sharpness of geometry."

I think we may deny that the instrumental importance attributed by Galileo to mathematics may be interpreted as an adherence to metaphysical mathematicism. In the first place, he incorporates mathematics with logic, or to be more precise, with the grand process of linguistic correction which he considers indispensable to the development of scientific research. This correction, according to him, must consist not only in the use of correct reasoning, but also in the elimination from scientific language of misleading and equivocal references to metaphysical (in the sense of nonoperational) concepts.[21]

In the second place, Galileo almost always considers mathematics as a study connected with technology, not as pure mathematics in the modern sense, precisely because he attributes to it the function of getting us closer to the physical world, and not to a world of transcendent ideal entities. It is true that Galileo sometimes indulged in expressions that lend themselves to Platonizing interpretations. One of the most celebrated is his simile of nature as a book written in mathematical characters. Yet in those cases the purely polemic purposes of the phrases adopted is evident. That particular simile is suggested in the *Assayer* to contrast the actual world of the scientists with the imaginary world of the poets. It is interesting to note that the same metaphor reappears in a letter to Liceti of January 1641. This time the book of nature is contrasted not with the fantasies of poets, but with Aristotle's books. Despite the different objects of comparison, the intent in both cases is to combat the principle of authority, not to assert a geometric reality which underlies phenomenological appearances. "I conclude only that Your Excellency's goal being that of supporting the truth of every statement of Aristotle and maintaining that experience shows us nothing that was unknown to Aristotle, you are doing what many other Peripatetics would perhaps be unable to do. And if philosophy were that which is contained in Aristotle's books, you would in my opinion be the greatest philosopher in the world, judging by the extent to which you have at your fingertips every passage in those books. But I really think that the book of philosophy is that which perpetually stands open to our gaze, though since it is written in characters other than those of our alphabet, it cannot be read by everyone; the letters of this book are triangles, squares, circles, spheres, cones, pyramids and other mathematical figures, very appropriate for such reading." [22] The initial words "Your Excellency's goal being that of . . . maintaining that experience shows us nothing. . . ." clearly say that the appeal to experience and the fight against the principle of authority are one and the same for Galileo. This extract also confirms the thesis that Galilean thought cannot be reduced to some more or less overt form of Platonism.

The attack against the principle of authority involves one of the most decisive matters in the evaluation of Galileo's "philosophy." In all his works he had insisted at great length on his arguments against authority. There is no doubt about this. But it is much less certain that he thoroughly understood the complex basis of such disputes. Why did Aristotelians of the sixteenth and seventeenth centuries go to such lengths to tie their science to the name of Aristotle? The question was in all probability never formulated by Galileo; at any rate, he never answered it. But we know that the Aristotelian efforts had a definite philosophical significance; they were designed to weave scientific investigations into a great metaphysical system. According to the Aristotelians, such a network was indispensable in order to give unity and seriousness to scientific researches. Without a fabric woven in this way, these investigations in their continual development ran the risk of splitting into a thousand threads, of being sundered, of being reduced to mere technology, of losing in sum all theoretical value. Beneath this position lay the assumption that science could not govern itself, and could have consistency only if this was guaranteed by some metaphysics.

Galileo Galilei

Only too clear, then, was the peril they saw in the Galilean procedure. Little did it matter to them that he held fast to Aristotle's methodological canons. In their eyes danger arose when the new science pretended to break every relation of subordination to an ancient and solid metaphysics. The Jesuits understood best of all what a profound rupture this would be, and they hoped that by some artifice they could find a compromise between the new science and the ancient metaphysics. But the Aristotelians cherished no illusions on this score. Nor was their prognostication wrong; the birth of the new science really did represent a heavy blow to metaphysics, for it was a revolutionary leap that would brook no compromise. Where would it all lead, this perilous multiplication of special researches carried on outside any system?

About the same time even a thinker of Descartes' stature shared this grave concern of the Aristotelians, though in a different guise. Descartes was convinced that modern science could never be denied, so he did not persist (as did the Aristotelians) in a hopeless battle against it. Instead, he sought a new metaphysics capable of offering the newborn science a philosophical basis as solid as that which Aristotelianism had afforded to pre-Galilean researches.

From this point of view, Galileo was clearly not an Aristotelian. But neither was he a Platonist. Indeed, we may say he was no true philosopher. He did not comprehend the philosophical import of the scientific revolution he was fighting for; he did not want to concern himself with the consequences that would stem from it, then or later.[23] His only real concern was to aid the development of the new science in every way, and courageously to open the road for it, overcoming every obstacle that could be put in its way by either metaphysics or theology. Hence his great methodological interest; hence his tenacious struggle to disencumber scientific debates from everything that might impede the free development of scientific investigations; hence also the lack of any serious research on his part designed to explore the philosophical presuppositions of the new methods necessary to science. Only one thing was important to him: that these new methods be really efficacious, so that in availing itself of them science might make ever more rapid progress.

200   In a valuable communication to the International Congress of

The Serene Conclusion of an Embattled Life

the History of Science held at Florence in 1956,[24] A. C. Crombie showed clearly why Galileo has become a symbol of several different philosophical positions, themselves irreconcilable—Platonism, Kantianism, experimentalism, positivism, and others. Each of these schools has found in Galileo's works some expression that would justify its own interpretation. I think this can be explained by the fact that Galileo really had no consciously elaborated philosophy of his own. But there is no discredit in this. If he was not a philosopher in the technical sense of the word, he nevertheless occupies a place of the first rank in the history of philosophic thought for his bold breakaway, for his victorious battle on behalf of autonomy in scientic research, for the faith in reason which he was able to establish among large groups of his contemporaries. In the very act of recognizing that he should not be made a symbol of any one philosophical system, we must also recognize that he is the man most suited to symbolize the modern era; more than that, to have been its initiator, its tenacious, invinicible, first mover.

4. From the beginning of November 1641, Galileo was confined to bed by a continual low fever, with pains in the kidneys and great palpitations of the heart. His two pupils Evangelista Torricelli and Vincenzio Viviani remained with him constantly; he enjoyed following their scientific discussions with an attentive mind, but he was less and less able to take direct part in them.

On the night of the eighth of January 1642, as Viviani wrote, "with philosophic and Christian firmness he rendered up his soul to its Creator, sending it, as he liked to believe, to enjoy and to watch from a closer vantage point those eternal and immutable marvels which he, by means of a fragile device, had brought closer to our mortal eyes with such eagerness and impatience." [25] It was only a month before his seventy-eighth birthday.

"His body," continued Viviani, "was taken from the villa at Arcetri to Florence, and by commission of our most Serene Grand Duke was separately interred in the temple of Santa Croce, where lies the ancient sepulcher of the noble family of Galilei, with the thought of erecting to him an august and sumptuous monument in the most conspicuous place in that church, that thus, after death no less than in life, might be generously honored the immortal fame of Florence's second Amerigo [Vespucci]—discoverer not of a little land, but of innumerable celestial globes and new lights, under the happy auspices of the most serene House [of Medici]." [26]

The "august and sumptuous monument" could not yet be erected, however. On the twenty-fifth of January 1642, Francesco Cardinal Barberini, nephew of Pope Urban VIII, wrote to Father Giovanni Muzzarelli, the Inquisitor of Florence: "Monsignor the Assessor has read before His Holiness our Lord the letter of your Reverence in which you gave notice of the death of Galileo Galilei and mentioned what it is believed should be done concerning his tomb and obsequies; and His Blessedness, with the opinion of their Eminences [the Cardinals Inquisitors], has decided that you, with your usual skill, should get the ear of the Grand Duke and suggest that it is not good to raise a mausoleum over the corpse of one who has been punished in the Tribunal of the Holy Inquisition and has died while under that punishment, because this might scandalize the good, with prejudice to the piety of His Highness. But if you cannot dissuade him from this idea, you should notify him that in the epitaph or inscription that is to be placed on the tomb, there must be no words which might injure the reputation of this Tribunal. You must give the same notification to him who will make the funeral oration; arrange to see it and consider it well before it is spoken or printed. His Holiness reposes the care of this affair in the wise prudence of your Reverence." [27]

No doubt the "usual skill" of Father Muzzarelli was considerable, and so was the submissiveness of the Most Serene House of Medici. The monument to Galileo was not erected until about a century after his death. It was only in 1734 that the Holy Office, consulted on the matter, decided to authorize its construction: "It is to be written back to the Father Inquisitor that nothing prevents the construction of Galileo's tomb, but solicit his care that the inscription to be made on the said tomb be communicated to him, he to transmit it to the Holy Congregation, so that proper orders may be given concerning it before it is done." [28]

The intransigence of the Church toward Galileo was maintained with equal severity against his pupils at Florence when in 1657 they wanted to found the Academy of the Cimento [29] with the purpose of carrying out physical investigations in the spirit of their teacher. Once again the Most Serene House of Medici could not give sufficient support to resist the pressures of the theologians. In 1667, after scarcely ten years of life, the Academy had to cease its glorious activity.[30]

Not until 1757 did the Holy Congregation of the Index decide to cancel the decree which prohibited *all* works intended to teach the stability of the sun and the mobility of the earth: *"quod . . . omittatur Decretum quo prohibentur libri omnes docentes immobilitatem solis et mobilitatem terrae."* [31] Still another half-century was to pass before the Holy Office reached a similar decision. Its first decree on this subject was issued in 1820, and was limited to the authorization of a book on the *Elements of Astronomy* written by Professor Giacomo Settele. Two years later the eminent members of the Holy Office decreed that from that time on, license should not be refused for publication of works intended to deal with the mobility of the earth and stability of the sun: *decreverunt non esse a presenti et futuris protempore Magistris Sacri Palatii Apostolici recusandam licentiam pro impressione et publicatione operum tratantium de mobilitate terrae et immobilitate solis juxta communen modernorum astronomorum opinionem, dummodo nihil aliud obstet.*[32] Thus in 1822, for the first time since the seventeenth century, the works of Copernicus, Galileo, and Kepler were removed from the Index of Prohibited Books.

Obviously this reversal had no effect on the history of modern culture, coming so late in the development of the Copernican conception. As to Galileo, his thought had long been broadcast through all the nations of Europe. As was said in the French *Encyclopedia* (the most famous publication of the philosophers of the Enlightenment), he was looked upon as "a man above all prejudice"; "he who dissipated the errors of the ancient school." Even if we no longer subscribe to the exact words of these judges, we must yet recognize that it was the Enlightenment which made the most of Galileo's legacy. The Enlightenment drew from his work effective and productive instruction, not only from the genius of his scientific and methodological conceptions, but also from his politico-cultural program. The collapse of that program consti-

Galileo Galilei

tuted a decisive experience for European civilization—an experience that was bitter but nonetheless necessary to dissipate errors and prejudices of which Galileo had been the supporter and the victim, in so far as they determined his illusory program and suggested his attempt at a reconciliation of Copernicanism with the Bible.

Appendix A
The Galileo–Bellarmine Meeting:
A Historical Speculation
by Stillman Drake

Two theories have long prevailed concerning the events of February 26, 1616, when Galileo was called before Cardinal Bellarmine and admonished to abandon the Copernican theory. Either theory has strong points in its favor and equally strong objections. One theory places Galileo in a good light and the Church in a bad one; the other reverses this. Competent scholars for nearly a century—that is, since all the known documents have been opened to examination and publication—have taken one side or the other, or have scrupulously withheld judgment. No real third alternative, to the best of my knowledge, has been put forth.

As Professor Geymonat has indicated, everything seems to hinge upon the reliability of one crucial document, the copy of a supposed minute of the proceedings, bound into the official records used by the Inquisition at Galileo's trial in 1633. Advocates of the theory which places Galileo in a good light, led in recent years by Professor Santillana, regard this document as a fabrication, a spurious account that includes events which never took place. This entails certain difficulties, for the minute has precisely the same authority as most of the documents which must be accepted in order to reconstruct the events. But this apparent disadvantage is not fatal, since the adversaries of this view labor under similar difficulties. In accepting the minute at its face value, they in turn are constrained to give a labored explanation of the existence or meaning of two or three documents of unquestioned authenticity. Moreover, strong psychological and circumstantial objections exist against the explanations they have put forth, objections which are supported by a great wealth of surviving evidence concerning the characters of Galileo and Bellarmine, two popes, some cardinals, and other persons of importance who are significantly involved in the story.

205

The two received theories appear to be poles apart, especially when considered in terms of the fundamental question whether the minute itself is true or false. Any third alternative may seem preposterous. Yet I shall advance the thesis that another theory is tenable; furthermore, that in the light of this theory, neither of the two prevalent interpretations is far from the truth, nor are they so far apart as they have previously seemed to be.

For several years I have debated the wisdom of advancing this alternative view. It is not strictly historical or biographical in character because it contains a large element of conjecture. On the other hand it is not mere fiction, in that I believe nothing will be found in it that is inconsistent with the existing documents or the known characters of the persons mentioned. Its merit lies not in any claim to demonstrability, but rather in its interest as an exercise in the nature of historical research. What I should like to show is that a set of events can be postulated which would account for the existence and contents of all the known documents, construed in their simplest and most probable interpretations. But in attempting this, I do not wish by any means to pretend that my narrative embodies the only possible set of events fulfilling this condition; still less, that each of them is actually supported by a specific document. All I can say is that to the best of my knowledge, nothing contained in my narrative is in flat contradiction with any source material.

The narrative is presented here without documentation. Those who are specialists in the field are already familiar with the evidence, and others will surely find this presentation more interesting, or at least less boring, than a fully documented account.

I.

In the winter of 1615–1616, Galileo debated often and publicly at Rome on the topic of the earth's motion. In these debates he succeeded in demolishing the position of his opponents, even if he did not win many converts to his own views. It was an inevitable consequence of his position that certain statements in the Bible would have to be reinterpreted. Now, freedom to interpret the Bible was a sore point with Catholic authorities at the time; this was one of the particular issues between them and

Appendix A

the founders of various Protestant sects. Hence Galileo's plea that the Church continue to tolerate the teachings of Copernicus was one that could not be readily granted.

Though personally unsympathetic with the intellectuals of his time, Pope Paul V was cautious about alienating this influential group. Accordingly he consulted Cardinal Bellarmine, who was not only the leading theologian at Rome but was also an able administrator. As theologian, Bellarmine remarked that so long as astronomers took the idea of the earth's motion only hypothetically, there was no overt contradiction of the Bible; as administrator, he maintained that it was always a poor idea for the Church to take an official position on any matter where decision could be postponed or avoided. The Pope replied that he was aware of all this, but that Galileo was making an infernal nuisance of himself and had forced matters to a point where some official action had to be taken. In that event, answered Bellarmine, it would be necessary to stop all theological discussions of the earth's motion and to correct or suppress any books containing theological arguments in its favor. The proper procedure would be to submit the question to a duly constituted committee of theologians and to base official acion on their ruling, the nature of which was easily predictable. Galileo, he was certain, would obey such an edict as a good Catholic; and since he alone was the present source of difficulty, the problem would be solved without the actual prohibition of Copernicanism. To make sure of this, however, he would undertake to test Galileo's obedience privately before the edict was published, and if there were any doubt about his cooperation, stronger measures could be applied. In view of the strong support Galileo enjoyed politically, intellectually, and in Church circles, it would be good to avoid the appearance of any personal or vindictive action in the matter.

Satisfied with Bellarmine's advice, the Pope appointed a council which duly reported its findings against the doctrine of the motion of the earth and stability of the sun. On the twenty-fifth of February, 1616, the Pope specifically instructed Bellarmine to call Galileo before him and admonished him to abandon these views as contrary to Scripture. If he refused, then the Commissary General of the Inquisition was to command him in the presence of a notary and witnesses to desist from such teachings, lest he be imprisoned. It is perfectly clear from the wording of this order that two separate actions were contemplated, the second to ensue only if the first failed; and it is equally clear that the presence of a notary and witnesses would be entirely out of place at the first action, which was to be informal and friendly in character.

Seghizzi, the Commissary General, was present when the Pope gave these instructions. He belonged to the Dominican order, which traditionally had charge of the Inquisition. He did not particularly like or trust the Jesuits, who had usurped the role of the Dominicans as leaders in Catholic education, and he was especially distrustful of the relatively liberal views of Bellarmine. Accordingly he decided to be personally present at Bellarmine's interview with Galileo, in order to make sure that if Galileo did object, Bellarmine would not reason with him and win him over rather than subject him to official action by the Inquisition. Thus on the morning of the twenty-sixth, shortly after Bellarmine had dispatched two of his familiars (special officers of arrest attached to the household of each Cardinal Inquisitor) to fetch Galileo, Seghizzi with a notary and some Dominican fathers paid a visit to Bellarmine's residence.

The visit was unusual, and Bellarmine quickly guessed its true purpose, which was personally offensive to him. At his age, and in his high position, he did not need any lesser officials present to see that he carried out his assignment properly. Still, there was no tactful way to get rid of them, and he could scarcely order them out of his house. Before long, the arrival of the officers with Galileo was announced. Bellarmine rose and went to the door of the audience chamber to greet Galileo, hat in hand, as was his custom with every guest of whatever condition. Indignant at Seghizzi's abuse of his hospitality and determined to render it pointless, he said in low tones to Galileo as they turned to enter, "His Holiness expects your precise obedience to what I am about to tell you." They then returned together to the Cardinal's chair, and after seating himself, Bellarmine benignly announced to Galileo the decision of the council and admonished him to obey it.

Appendix A

Meanwhile, Seghizzi was thinking rapidly. He was no fool, and he guessed easily enough that Bellarmine had warned Galileo to voice no objection. Thus he had not only been outwitted, but by the very act of coming uninvited he had cut off any chance, however slight, that Galileo might be recalcitrant and that Bellarmine would turn him over to the Inquisition. Time was running out. There was only one way to save the day. When the Cardinal had finished his admonition, the Commissary was ready. Without allowing Galileo time for any reply, he proceeded to deliver his own stringent precept not to hold, defend, or teach Copernicanism in any way, orally or in writing, lest Galileo suffer imprisonment. The latter, forewarned, simply replied that as a good son of the Holy Church he would obey, perhaps adding that he was relieved to know that the matter had at last been settled by superhuman authority, and thanking the Cardinal for his having given him advance notice of the edict that would soon be published.

The notary, sublimely ignorant of the Pope's instructions, was faithfully recording these events, and had written that the Commissary "immediately and without holding back" had delivered his precept on the heels of the Cardinal's admonition. Bellarmine was astonished and exasperated at this further affront to his dignity and clear disobedience of the Pope's orders by the Commissary. But he knew precisely what to do. Taking Galileo by the arm and ushering him to the door, he said that he was pleased by his submission to the Church, and that at another time he wished to speak further with him, but that he had important business to discuss with the others and could not detain him longer that day. If Seghizzi tried to interrupt, the Cardinal quelled him with a glance. When Galileo was safely out of doors, he returned and asked the Commissary to confer with him privately.

Seghizzi may have begun the conference by angrily remonstrating against Galileo's having been permitted to leave without signing the notary's account of the interview. Bellarmine replied that it would have done little good for Galileo to sign this, since he himself had not the slightest intention of putting his name to a wholly illegal proceeding in direct violation of the Pope's orders. Seghizzi would do well to destroy this minute, he said.

If the Pope were ever told precisely what had happened, he would be much incensed. "I have half a mind to tell him," he went on, "and to see you punished. However, I shall not do so, for the Church can only be the loser, and Galileo the gainer, by such a scandal. I am willing instead to regard your visit this morning as a mere coincidence, and the words you uttered as an inadvertence. The only thing that legally happened here this morning was that I delivered the admonition required by His Holiness, and Galileo received it without objection. Whatever else took place has no legal existence, and therefore no existence at all. I hope you will agree to this before we leave this room, and I shall then advise Galileo that he is to remember only my admonition, and to treat everything else as if it had never happened. Or, if you choose, I shall officially report everything as it took place. You may then have an opportunity to see for yourself how His Holiness will regard your actions. But before you choose, consider this: I myself discussed this whole proceeding with His Holiness before it was ordered, and I am in a better position than you to know all its implications." If Seghizzi did not concede at once that he had acted unwisely and wished his words forgotten, he was given time to reflect. "I shall report that my admonition was given to Galileo and accepted by him. You will be present when I make my report. If you wish to add to it, you will be perfectly free to do so. Think it over. If you say nothing, then I shall understand by your silence that the matter rests, and your action this morning will be regarded henceforth as if it had never occurred."

Bellarmine gave his report to the Pope and the Cardinals of the Inquisition on March third precisely as if his own admonition were all that had been given to Galileo. Seghizzi, who was present, said not a word. The Pope then gave instructions for publication of the edict. Only Foscarini's book was completely prohibited, because it was devoted entirely to the reconciliation of Copernicanism with the Bible. Diego de Zuñiga's *Commentary on Job* and the *De revolutionibus* of Copernicus, which contained but a few passages of theological significance bearing on the matter, were merely suspended until corrected. Galileo's books were not

Appendix A

mentioned because he had published nothing concerning the theological aspects of the theory.

Now it is a remarkable fact that on the sixth of March, the day after the edict was published, Galileo was able to write to Picchena the precise corrections that were to be made in the *De revolutionibus*, though these were not officially divulged until long afterward (and in fact no "corrected" edition was ever printed). Six days later he repeated them in detail, and recounted an interview he had had with the Pope on the preceding day. Paul V had given him every reassurance against any lingering suspicion in his mind or in those of the Cardinals of the Inquisition, adding that so long as he (the Pope) lived, Galileo had no cause for alarm. Galileo's perfect acquaintance with the changes to be made in the work of Copernicus suggests that he had already seen Bellarmine again, and had been told that he must hold firmly in mind the instructions of the Cardinal, but that the Commissary had spoken impulsively and that it was not the Pope's intention that he should be threatened. Perhaps Bellarmine himself had arranged the interview with the Pope (on March eleventh) for Galileo's reassurance. The Pope's remark that during his lifetime Galileo had nothing to fear suggests that Bellarmine had privately informed him of the actual state of affairs.

But there was one thing which the Cardinal was powerless to prevent, and that was the wagging of the tongues of the other Dominican fathers who had been present and had heard the Commissary's threat. Delighting in the defeat of Galileo and unaware of the illegality of the proceeding, they spread rumors that Galileo had been forced to abjure and do penance. In due course, these rumors reached friends of Galileo's at Pisa and Venice, from whom he received condolences. This was a very serious matter to him, for (acting in good faith on Bellarmine's assurances) he had long ago written to the minister of the Grand Duke that he personally had suffered no reproaches. Accordingly, in May, before he left Rome, Galileo went once more to Bellarmine, taking copies of the letters he had received. "Your Eminence has asked me to forget all but your admonition," he said, "but see what is being rumored about me." The Cardinal saw how serious

211

this matter was to Galileo. True to his word, he certified in his own handwriting that Galileo had neither abjured nor done penance before him or anyone else at Rome or elsewhere, declaring further that he had only been advised of the general edict against holding or defending the earth's motion. This certificate Galileo carried back with him to Florence, as a defense against calumny.

But Seghizzi, though he had remained silent as to his actions when Bellarmine reported to the Pope, did not destroy the worthless unsigned minute of the notary. Whether he retained it deliberately or casually, and whether he ordered it copied into the record or whether it was routinely copied by some scribe who remained unaware of its status, it passed in slightly abbreviated form into the official records of the Inquisition.

II.

In 1632, when the *Dialogue* was finally published and sent to Rome, the principal persons involved in the proceedings of 1616 were all dead except Galileo. The cardinals and officers of the Inquisition in 1633 had no reason whatever to doubt the authenticity of the copied minute as a faithful account of the instructions given to Galileo in 1616. Thus the rage of Pope Urban VIII, who had been Galileo's friend, is not hard to understand. It appeared to him that Galileo had persuaded him to permit publication of an "impartial" discussion of the Ptolemaic and Copernican theories, while concealing from him a specific injunction never to teach the latter theory in any way. On the other hand, Galileo was not aware of any misdeed, for he had faithfully followed Bellarmine's instruction to remember only his admonition, treating all else as if it had never happened. Nor did Galileo suspect that the official records belied this instruction, for Bellarmine had been a Cardinal of the Inquisition and presumably had had authority to keep the record consistent with his own affidavit.

Thus was the ground laid for one of the most dramatic trials in history. At its outset, both sides were acting in good faith. When Galileo was interrogated about the events of 1616, he gave precisely the account that Bellarmine had told him to give, and he produced a copy of Bellarmine's certificate in support of this, adding that he could produce the original if required. Considering that none of the inquisitors could possibly have suspected the existence of such a document, it must indeed have created a sensation in the mind of the new Commissary, Maculano. However, he calmly entered it in the record and proceeded with his examination. Galileo frankly admitted that some Dominican fathers were present on the occasion of the interview, but said he did not remember that any of them spoke to him. Pressed to repeat in detail what had happened, he said:

"I recall that the affair came about in this manner. One morning Cardinal Bellarmine sent for me, and he told me a certain thing which I should like to speak in the ear of His Holiness before anyone else; but it then followed that he told me that the opinion of Copernicus could not be held or defended, as contrary to the Holy Scriptures. As to those Dominican fathers, I do not remember whether they were there first or came afterward, nor do I recall whether they were present when the Cardinal told me that the said opinion could not be held; and it may be that some precept was made to me that I might not hold or defend the said opinion, but I have no memory of it, because this was many years ago."

One cannot but sympathize with Galileo at this point in his examination. He earnestly wished an opportunity to tell his old friend, now Pope, the whole truth; but apart from the fact that it would be suicide for him to tell it to the inquisitors, he had every reason to suppose that the official records disclosed only the admonition of Cardinal Bellarmine.

Maculano now pursued the question by asking whether, if he should read to Galileo what had actually been said at the time, Galileo would recall it. Galileo stood his ground resolutely, saying that he had frankly stated his recollection, and that he did not know that such a reading would alter his memory. Maculano then read to him the additional phrase "or teach in any way," and asked him if he remembered who had said this to him. Galileo reiterated that he did not recall anything having been said to him except by Cardinal Bellarmine. But for the first time, he now realized what the records must contain, and it was already too late for him to admit that anyone else had spoken to him.   213

Galileo Galilei

The balance of the first hearing relates to the securing of the license for the *Dialogue,* and does not concern us here. Nearly three weeks passed before the second interrogation, during which time a number of events occurred.

The existence of Bellarmine's affidavit could not have been suspected, for it was a private matter between Galileo and the Cardinal; even Seghizzi, had he been living, would not have known of it. The patent contradiction between the official minute and this affidavit from a respected theologian and cardinal once high in the Inquisition must have seriously disturbed Galileo's judges. Until this time, none of them had given a thought to the absence of the original signed minute. But under the rules of evidence, Galileo's holograph affidavit from Bellarmine would outweigh the copied minute on which his judges had relied. Doubtless a search was made for the original. When it was not found, the inquisitors probably suspected that it had been purloined by someone favorable to Galileo rather than that it had never existed, or lacked authority. Still, the fact remained that he had better evidence than they had, if he could indeed produce the original. This he ultimately did. Meanwhile, the predicament of the inquisitors was a difficult one. It was quite impossible to exonerate Galileo, even if they had wanted to. The Holy Office itself had brought the charges, and a false charge of heresy carried the same penalty as heresy itself. Nor could Galileo's judges admit that he had been accused on the basis of a defective document in their own records.

Nevertheless, these men were judges and jurors of a strict tribunal, and they could not ignore the evidential value of Galileo's document. It is true that on April seventeenth, a committee of experts had found that Galileo had at least defended Copernicanism in the *Dialogue,* so that if the inquisitors were to drop the charge that he had been enjoined not to teach it in any way, he could still be found guilty of defending it. But no one wanted to drop the original charge at the cost of impugning the official records.

Finally, on April twenty-seventh, Maculano broke the deadlock. Because the Pope and the powerful cardinal-nephew Francesco Barberini had gone to Castel Gandolfo ten days before, we

Appendix A

have Maculano's letter to Barberini (dated April 28, 1633) recounting the events:

Most Eminent and Reverend Patron:

Yesterday, in accordance with orders from His Holiness, their Eminences of the Holy Congregation took up the case of Galileo, reviewing its state briefly. And having approved what has been done thus far, they then considered various difficulties as to the manner of prosecuting the case, and getting it speedily under way again. In particular, because Galileo denied in his hearing that which is evident in the book he wrote, it would necessarily follow from his negative attitude that there would be greater rigor in the proceedings, and less regard for the delicacies in this business. Finally I proposed a means: that the Holy Congregation grant me power to deal extra-judicially with Galileo to the end of convincing him of his error, and bringing him to the point, when he understood, of confessing it. It appeared at first sight too daring a proposal; there seemed little hope of succeeding by means of reasonable persuasion; but when I mentioned my basis for advancing the idea, they gave me the power. And not to lose time, I went to reason with Galileo yesterday after luncheon, and after many exchanges between us, I gained my point by the grace of God, for I made him see plainly his error, so that he clearly knew he was in the wrong, and that in his book he had gone too far. This he expressed in heartfelt words, as if he found consolation in the recognition of his error. He agreed to confess it judicially, but he asked me for a little time to make honest (*honestare*) his confession, which I hope will in substance follow the line mentioned. I felt obliged to let you know at once, having told no one else, so that His Holiness and you will be satisfied that in this way the case can be brought to a point where it can proceed without difficulty. The Tribunal will maintain its reputation (*sarà nella sua reputatione*), and may use benignity with the accused. However it turns out, Galileo will recognize the grace accorded him, and all the other satisfactory consequences that are desired will   215 follow. Today I plan to examine him to obtain the confession; and, with it in hand, as I hope, nothing will remain but to interrogate him on intention and permit him his defenses; this done, it will be possible to return him to his house for imprisonment as you mentioned to me.

Your Reverence's servant,
Vincenzio [Maculano] da Firenzuola

It is apparent from this letter that the trial was resumed only after Galileo had been induced to "cop a plea"; that is, had been promised a light sentence if he would cooperate by confessing to some lesser crime than that with which he was originally charged. It was a fair deal for both sides. Galileo could not hope to get off scot-free, and the inquisitors, with any kind of confession from him, could ignore the preponderance of the weight of Galileo's evidence over theirs on the crucial charge. Galileo's confession was duly handed in on April thirtieth. He said in effect that vanity had induced him to produce arguments of his own in favor of Copernicus without providing equally strong answers, but he insisted that there had been no wrong intention on his part. His defense, presented ten days later, explained the circumstances under which he had secured the affidavit from Bellarmine and stated that ". . . the two phrases in addition to 'hold' and 'defend,' which are 'teach' and 'in any way,' which I hear are contained in the command given to me and recorded, came to be as entirely new and [previously] unheard, and I do not think I should be doubted if in the course of fourteen or sixteen years they were lost to my memory. . . ."

Thus was the deal concluded, but it was not kept. It was this fact that led Galileo to hint in later years that deep intrigues and personal malice lay behind his troubles. Life imprisonment is not a light sentence, even when one is allowed to dwell in one's own house instead of a dungeon. Why did the inquisitors inflict such a drastic penalty, after they had obtained the confession for which they had bargained through Maculano?

At the end of April, the intention had been to make Galileo's punishment very light: probably a short term of imprisonment and some conventional religious penances. Maculano, a young

216

man, had acted in good faith when he approached Galileo with that solution in mind. But by the time the Cardinals of the Inquisition met again to pass sentence, at least one among them must have doubted the wisdom of letting him off lightly. It is noteworthy that three of the ten cardinals abstained from signing the final condemnation, one of the three being Francesco Barberini. W emay suppose that one of the other cardinals argued somewhat as follows: "Once Galileo is out of our power, once he is returned to his home in Tuscany, there will be nothing to prevent his telling the whole story as he sees it—how he was summoned to Rome to answer charges based on a false account of the earlier events; how he successfully countered these with his bona fide certificate from Bellarmine, and how the Inquisition was then obliged to admit his essential rectitude. We all know Gallileo's pugnacious character. Influential men all over Europe will accept his story, and the Holy Office will suffer a heavy blow to its reputation." As the other cardinals listened to this warning, it became clear to most of them that a light sentence was impossible, whatever had been previously intended. The only solution was to keep Galileo under physical arrest, while making the conditions of his detention easy for him. So long as he remained in the custody of the Inquisition, he would not dare breathe a word against that institution or in favor of Copernicanism, for the penalty against "relapsed heretics" was death.

Maculano himself may have been upset at this decision; he had been the instrument of the negotiation and had conducted it in good faith. But if he said anything, he was told that these were matters of state, and that it was not his responsibility that a previous error in judgment had to be rectified at Galileo's expense for the good of the Church.

When Galileo heard the sentence of life imprisonment pronounced on him, he was hardly able to believe his ears. As his incredulity wore off, he came to believe that he had been the victim of deliberate bad faith and intrigue of the most reprehensible kind. Hints of this are to be found in some of his letters, smuggled out by friends, in which it is intimated that if he could speak out, he could unfold a tale of despicable behavior on the part of his enemies. His bitterness toward the Jesuits is particularly evident, and it is likely that as time went on, his feeling of persecution (which was largely justified) led him to believe that as early as 1616 he had been calculatingly trapped by Bellarmine.

III.

Galileo has been much criticized (even by his partisans) for his signing of the confession prepared for him to read when sentence was passed on him, because that confession explicitly included an admission that he had received a precept not to hold, defend, or teach in any manner the Copernican doctrine. In all the hearings and in all the documents he had signed before, this admission was never made. The general view among Galileo's supporters has been that this final concession was made simply from prudence; the alternative was torture and death, and in view of his age and physical condition, to say nothing of his having already achieved his principal goal by publishing to the world the arguments for his position, most people have argued that Galileo should be forgiven for having yielded to the instinct of self-preservation.

But if the foregoing account of the events of 1616 is correct, Galileo may now be absolved from even this one charge of weakness. For in the last analysis there was nothing literally false in the admission that the strong precept had been given to him— just as there had been nothing dishonest in his having evaded or denied this throughout the trial. There were, so to speak, two "truths" about the events of that memorable morning in February 1616: one physical, and the other juridical. In terms of the sound-waves that had passed through the audience chamber of Cardinal Bellarmine, the truth was that the precept had been given; but in terms of Church law and procedure, the truth was that it had not been given. One need think only of our present legal procedure, under which the members of a jury are told to disregard statements uttered in court but "stricken from the record," to understand this duality of truth. And if one puts one-self in Galileo's position at the time of the trial in 1633, assuming the events postulated above, one may see the extraordinary difficulty of his situation and applaud the manner in which he handled it.

Appendix A

Likewise, it appears to me that much of the criticism which has been leveled against the Church for its actions in this matter may be undeserved. The behavior of one or two individuals may easily have brought about the injustice that was wrought; and in the essential incident, if the postulated events are correct, the behavior of at least one individual was actually contrary to the policy and procedures of the Church as an institution. Moreover, the preservation of the documents as we have them today is itself testimony of the good faith of the Church as an institution. Let us recall, for example, Bellarmine's certificate. This exists in the form of a copy in Galileo's handwriting which he submitted at the first hearing, a document which alone would have even less authority than the unsigned minute in the records of the Inquisition. But it exists also in the original, in Bellarmine's handwriting, submitted by Galileo later to support his written defense. Now, had Galileo been the victim of a heartless and deliberate conspiracy, it would have been a simple matter to destroy the original when it was handed in. Had that been done, no one today could escape the suspicion that Galileo's entire account of the matter (and his whole defense) might have been a colossal bluff; and this could easily have been foreseen by the conspirators. Or the original could have been abstracted and conveniently 'lost' at any time during the period from 1633 to 1867, when the records were first opened to the inspection of scholars. If the Church officially, or its custodians of documents personally, had wished to strengthen its position by fraud, especially during the two decades immediately preceding publication of the records (during which time violent debate raged among scholars on this subject), it could have been done in this way. That it was not, speaks eloquently for the authenticity of the records as they stand.

Moreover, such frauds are very hazardous; perhaps that is why they are seldom employed by institutions of great age. Experience shows that it is hard to suppress all trace of any event. In this instance, when Galileo visited Bellarmine (in May 1616) to request some means of answering the false rumors against him, the Cardinal first drafted his certificate and then copied it out in final form for Galileo; and the original draft in Bellarmine's hand has since been found among his papers. 219

Galileo Galilei

Thus any attempt to suppress the original evidence would eventually have backfired on its perpetrators in a way which they could scarcely have anticipated.

There is also the letter of Maculano to Francesco Cardinal Barberini. This letter, with its remarkable reference to the necessity for the Inquisition to save face by extra-judicial negotiation with Galileo, was found among the Barberini papers by a devout Vatican librarian who was under no obligation to reveal its existence to the general public. Yet he published it nearly a decade after the documents of the trial had been put in the public domain, at a time when the Church was under the most severe criticism for its handling of the case, and he did so under the official imprimatur of the Church.

In conclusion, I wish to repeat that what has been said here is neither pure history nor pure fiction. It may be that I have overlooked some contradiction between an actual document and the events I have postulated; and whether or not such a contradiction is discovered, it is most unlikely that the actual events were precisely those here postulated. What has been attempted is no more than the opening of a line of historical research concerning these problems which may do away with the subjective biases that appear to me to have entered into previous investigations.

May others come and do it better.
—Ludwig Wittgenstein

Appendix B
Reply to Stillman Drake
by Giorgio de Santillana

Mr. Drake's hypothesis deserves our attention. He would like to have peace descend upon a centuries-old controversy, and I too believe that a way should be found to a reconciliation. His theory is ingenious and carefully documented, as one would expect of him, and it has the great merit of providing a natural explanation for several features of this old and bewildering puzzle. It explains for instance why the record of the injunction was left unsigned. It explains the inner conflict in the records. It reminds us that Galileo must have known certain things from Bellarmine himself a few days after the encounter, and finally, it makes the character of the Cardinal shine ethically throughout, as it was right to expect.

Still, there is a crucial problem that Mr. Drake has not solved. He suggests that when the Cardinal made his notification, the Father Commissary of the Holy Office broke in upon the proceedings to serve his injunction, whereupon the Cardinal reprimanded him and told Galileo (we must assume he told him either then or later, but explicitly) to disregard this unauthorized intervention and erase it from his memory. Galileo dutifully forgot—and this would explain his subsequent behavior. But the record of that injunction existed, and came back to life sixteen years later. At that point everyone was trapped by the past. This would solve the conflict between the text of the *Decreta* and the acts of the trial. Does it really explain anything else? Does it present a plausible picture of Galileo's behavior?

My impression is that Mr. Drake, whom a kind fate never exposed to special tribunals, had in mind our own judicial procedures, where jurors can be instructed to disregard this or or that piece of evidence. But this was the Inquisition, and Galileo was no juror but the accused, and he would certainly have been in no frame of mind to forget this ominous move by his persecutors. He knew that Popes and Cardinals come and go, but that the Holy Office remains, with its own policy and its own records.

Yet the text of the interrogation proves undeniably that when he came to trial in 1632, he never suspected there might be trouble over the Father Commissary's minute of 1616. We cannot forget his genuine puzzlement when the Commissary of the trial asks him searchingly whether anyone else was present on the famous occasion. "There were some brothers of St. Dominic present," he says, "but I do not remember any of them speaking to me." On being asked again more urgently, he quotes again the Cardinal's words, and becomes more specific. "As to those Dominican fathers, I do not remember whether they were there first or came afterward, nor do I recall whether they were present when the Cardinal told me that the same opinion could not be held." This is directly said and without hedging. The slightest suspicion of danger from that quarter would have caused Galileo to reconsider, and to admit at least that Fr. Seghizzi had been present and had spoken. In his carefully considered defense memorandum of a month later, when his memory should have been amply refreshed by his private conversation with the Commissary, he insists on the fact that those words "not to teach in any way" were new to him entirely, and that he can bring up no recollection of them. We have that memorandum; its tone is firm and a shade contemptuous. It suggests: "enough of this nonsense." He must have checked that line of defense with Fr. Maculano and found it acceptable.

But there is more. Even on his first interrogation, Galileo was not caught entirely by surprise. There is a letter of his to Geri Bocchineri, dated February 27, during his long wait before he was called before the Holy Office, which shows that he was forewarned. "We (i.e., he and the ambassador) hear at last that the many and so grave imputations are reduced to one and the rest have been dropped. Of this one I shall have no difficulty in disposing. . . . " And the ambassador on his side two days later: "As far as I can learn, the main grievance consists in this, that these authorities here maintain that in 1616 he was ordered not to discuss the question, nor to converse about it. He says, on the contrary, that these were not the terms of the injunction, which were that that doctrine was not to be held or defended." So Galileo knew exactly the line of action of the authorities, he knew at what point they intended to strike. He faced the questions of the Inquisitor fully forewarned. Any "instruction" of Bellarmine to forget had proved misleading. And how then can we be asked to believe that, on being questioned, he tried to dodge at the crucial point, to pretend that no one else had spoken, lying openly to the Inquisitor in the hope that if he did not mention the fact, it would just go away?

To go back to the central point of my thesis, if Galileo had ever known of or even suspected an injunction, he would never have written the *Dialogue* until he had received sufficient assurance that he was in the clear. To assume the contrary would make him an utter fool. What moderns used to constitutional freedoms seem not to realize, is that any kind of warning from the Holy Office changed a man's status from that of a free citizen to that of a dangerous suspect under perpetual surveillance. Mr. Drake will insist: he *was* practically in the clear. His suggestion is all the more cogent, in that it explains why the Pope in audience felt he had to reassure him further, and give him a certificate of good behavior. I am willing to grant Mr. Drake all the background he has built up so discerningly. I could even agree with him that Galileo's mind had been lulled to rest through all these years. Even so, I doubt that Galileo could have ever felt really in the clear beyond doubt, if ever he had met the Inquisition face to face even for a moment. As I already said, Popes and Cardinals come and go, but the Holy Office stayed on and kept the records. As the Inquisitor says in Schiller's *Don Carlos*

> . . . . Der Seil
> an dem er flatterte, war lang, doch unzerreissbar

This is what filled people with dread at the mere mention of the Inquisition. If Mr. Drake had lived under the Gestapo, or the G.P.U., his perception of his point would be notably enhanced.

Still, for the sake of argument, let us grant that Galileo had dismissed the episode from his mind. But here, even before the start of the trial, comes news that the authorities are chiefly concerned with an injunction which seems to have taken place on the occasion of Bellarmine's audience. This should have struck Galileo like a thunderbolt, bringing to nought all his flimsy self-reassurances. The words he had heard that day from the Commissary stood on the record, with their ominous conclusion *sub poenis;* there was no Bellarmine to support him, he was trapped.

His line of defense henceforward should have been to seek for extenuating details, to tell of Bellarmine's reassurances, not to ignore the injunction. Niccolini, who had been told beforehand by Riccardi under the seal of secrecy, would have advised him before the trial to throw himself on the mercy of the Court. We know Niccolini wrote to Florence: "this particular would be enough to undo Mr. Galileo utterly." We see Galileo instead suggesting airily: "If they think I was exposed to any kind of threats on that day, I have a little paper with me to surprise them." We also notice from Niccolini's letters that he felt secure to the point of still planning a reasoned defense of his book and wanting to challenge their Lordships to stand reason. And then let us go back to the record of the interrogation, and ask ourselves whether it is compatible with any guilty memory of the accused. He desperately and explicitly denies that anyone else had spoken to him—and then we notice that the Inquisitor does carefully refrain from telling him that someone else *did* actually speak to him, so as to leave him floundering and doubting whether the words of Bellarmine himself may not have contained some small fatal clause; and it is this floundering, this confusion, not any direct challenge, which leads him at last shakily to admit that something may have been said to him that he cannot remember.

So we can confirm beyond doubt and peradventure that nothing at all had been said at Bellarmine's audience by the Inquisitor or by anyone except Bellarmine himself, and that the record does not correspond to facts.

There remains the last point raised by Mr. Drake: why did Galileo later admit the existence of that injunction in the text of his recantation? The answer is, as above, that he had to do not with an American police court but with a special tribunal, and was told to sign or else. The Court needed that statement to validate the whole trial, and it needed it badly.

I can agree with Mr. Drake that the authorities have been scrupulous in preserving the file intact, with all the doubts and contradictions it entailed. Let me hope, with him, that they will bring the issue to a close and a reconciliation, by declaring the trial invalid, or at least subject to reasonably doubt, and rehabilitating the victim.

Notes

Introduction

[1] The twenty volumes were reprinted, with some additions, in 1929–39. Among the other principal works of Favaro we shall mention here only the following: *Galileo Galilei e lo Studio di Padova* (2 vols, Florence, 1883); *Galileo Galilei e Suor Maria Celeste* (Florence, 1891; 2d. ed. 1935); and the superb *Bibliografia Galileiana* (1568–1895) compiled and annotated by Favaro in collaboration with A. Carli (Rome, 1896). Some of his minor works will be mentioned in the ensuing text.

[2] For his work, *Galilei und sein Kampf für die copernicanische Lehre* (Hamburg, 1909 and 1926. The second volume was posthumous, Wohlwill having died in 1912.)

[3] For his work, *Galilei und seine Zeit* (Halle, 1927). [Although Professor Olschki taught at that time in Germany, and later in the United States, he was born at Verona and educated in Florence.—Tr.]

[4] For his work, *Etudes Galiléenes* (3 vols., Paris, 1939).

[5] *Galileo Galilei und das kopernikanische Weltsystem* and *Der Galilei Prozess* (Freiburg, 1909).

[6] V. Ronchi, *Galileo e il cannochiale* (Udine, 1942) [revised edition, *Il cannochiale di Galileo e la scienza del Seicento* (Turin, 1958)]; A. Banfi, *Galileo Galilei* (Milan, 1949); G. de Santillana, *The Crime of Galileo* (Chicago, 1955), written in English because the author is presently Professor History and Philosophy of Science [at Massachusetts Institute of Technology] in the United States. This book has subsequently been translated into French and Italian.—Tr.]

Chapter 1: Galileo's Youth

[1] [Tradition makes Galileo's father a wool merchant as well as a musician. The researches of Professor Favaro throw grave doubt on this tradition, which appears to be no older than the beginning of the nineteenth century. It may have originated from no better evidence than the fact that Vincenzio accepted a part of Julia's dowry in cloths. Contemporary documents which referred to his occupation consistently called him a lutenist.—Tr.]

[2] A. Banfi, *Galileo Galilei* (Milan, 1949), p. 72.

[3] [*La Bilancetta* will be found in English translation in an appendix to *Galileo and the Scientific Revolution* by Laura Fermi and Gilberto Bernardini (New York, 1961), pp. 134–40.—Tr.]

Galileo Galilei

⁴ Galileo journeyed to Rome for the first time in 1587 for the purpose of seeking support, but without success.

⁵ [Galileo's salary is said to be the equivalent of about £100 or $300 today. The salary here attributed to Mercuriale is equivalent to some £3350 or $10,000, but in the university rolls reprinted by Favaro the maximum stipend reported at Pisa during those years was 660 scudi, equivalent to £1100 or $3300. Most young professors were expected to augment their official salaries by private tutoring, and the official appointment was of great assistance to them in getting pupils.—Tr.]

⁶ In Timpanaro's preface to the second volume of the collection of works by Galileo published at Milan, 1936–38. [Wohlwill's expressed opinion in his principal work is more guarded; cf. *Galilei und sein Kampf für die copernicanische Lehre* (Hamburg, 1909), p. 110.—Tr.]

⁷ A. Koyré, *Etudes Galiléenees* (Paris, 1939), III, 45. [Emphasis added by Professor Geymonat.—Tr.]

⁸ [While it is true, as Koyré remarks, that Galileo's early investigations of motion take on their full significance only when related to the Copernican theory, I believe this to be a *new* significance, and not one which Galileo entertained at the time. Galileo's "marble sphere" is definitely placed at the center of the universe; and if, as Koyré himself declares (a few lines after the passage cited below), this sphere represented the earth, then Galileo was not a Copernican at the time. Elsewhere in these same writings, Galileo spoke of the center of heavy bodies (which to him meant the center of the earth) as being also the center of the universe. On the whole, the available evidence appears to go against the belief that Galileo personally adopted the Copernican system in his Pisan period. Cf. *Motion and Mechanics*, pp. 72–76.—Tr.]

⁹ [Concerning these papers, see *Motion and Mechanics*, where most of them are translated and all are described.—Tr.]

¹⁰ [Benedetti's work was published at Turin in 1585. Inasmuch as Professor Geymonat, in the ensuing discussion, assumes that Galileo had studied this book before setting down his own ideas on motion (about 1590), it may be remarked that the evidence for this is purely circumstantial, as neither Galileo nor any of his correspondents ever mentioned Benedetti. It is true that Jacopo Mazzoni, a colleague of Galileo's when he taught at Pisa, knew of Benedetti's work by 1597; but by that time Galileo had left Pisa and had become a convinced Copernican.—Tr.]

¹¹ [It should be added that Aristotle held the speed of a body to be inversely proportional to the density of the medium, from which he inferred that motion in a vacuum would have to be instantaneous. Since he considered instantaneous motion absurd, he employed this argument in proof of the impossibility of a vacuum or, more exactly, the impossibility of the existence of a "void" in the sense of Democritus and the atomists.—Tr.]

¹² I, 285. All citations of Galileo's works will be thus referred to, the
Roman numeral indicating the volume and the arabic numeral the page

Notes

in Favaro's National Edition of the works of Galileo. [*Motion and Mechanics*, p. 50]

13 [It put him at a disadvantage when he wished to visit with girls, Galileo complained; moreover, it was an intolerable expense to the more impecunious professors, who had to wear woolen togas in place of velveteen; and so on. Professor Geymonat has included in Italian an extract from this lampoon, but it is virtually impossible to preserve the humor in English translation.—Tr.]

14 *Op. cit.*, p. 59. [It is worth noting that in later life Galileo moderated his criticism of Tasso, and in fact referred to him in the *Dialogue* as "the divine poet."—Tr.]

15 [Equivalent to about £ 150 or $450 today.—Tr.]

Chapter 2: The Paduan Period

1 In the sixteenth century every kind of heterodox Aristotelianism was called "Averroist," whether inspired by the commentaries on Aristotle written by Averroes himself or by those of Alexander of Aphrodisias.

2 VIII, 49. [Cf. *Two New Sciences*, p. 1.—Tr.]

3 An example of the latter is the manner in which he exploited the telescope; see Chapter 3.

4 From a letter of Galileo to "Sig. Vesp." written in February 1609. X, 232–33.

5 From a letter of Galileo to Belisario Vinta [Tuscan Secretary of State] dated May 7, 1610. X, 350. [See *Discoveries*, pp. 60–64, for this entire letter. —Tr.]

6 [Professor Geymonat is correct in saying that this question had caused much debate, some writers having gone so far as to accuse Galileo of deliberate hypocrisy on this score. The curious thing is that the whole debate is pointless unless Galileo did suppress mention of a rival theory. In the very tract under discussion, Galileo advised his students that a contrary theory had been proposed and that "there have not been lacking very great philosophers and mathematicians who, deeming the earth to be a star, have endowed it with motion." Inasmuch as it was Copernicus himself who first applied this particular expression of "star" to the description of the earth, and it was precisely the eradication of this "error" which constituted the principal "correction" eventually ordered by the Church to be made in later editions of Copernicus' book, it is absurd to charge Galileo with having suppressed mention of the theory. He goes on immediately to say, "Nevertheless, following the opinions of Aristotle and Ptolemy, we shall adduce those reasons for which it may be believed quite motionless." (II, 223) It is difficult to see how this was any more hypocritical than it is for a modern teacher of elementary physics to mention relativity and go on to teach Newtonian mechanics, or for a high school teacher to mention non-Euclidean geometry and go on to explain Euclid. The curriculum required Galileo to expound a particular book, which he did.—Tr.]

Galileo Galilei

[7] II, 198–202.

[8] X, 67.

[9] ["Advance notice of cosmographical theses containing the world-structural mystery of the remarkable proportions of the celestial orbs, and the true and essential reasons for the number of the heavens, their sizes, and their periodic motions, demonstrated by the five regular geometric solids." The scientific value of the book is accurately portrayed by its title.—Tr.]

[10] ["I came round to the opinion of Copernicus many years ago, and from his theory I have found the causes of many natural phenomena which doubtless cannot be explained by the ordinary theory."—Tr.]

[11] [It is pretty certain that Galileo did not reply, and that the principal reason was his disappointment at the contents of Kepler's book after the hopes raised in him by its preface. It should be noted that, contrary to tradition, there is good evidence that Kepler had never heard of Galileo until he received the letter of thanks for his book. The book had been put in Galileo's hands by Kepler's friend Paul Hamberger, who had been given two copies to take to Italy, and who left them with Galileo, bearing back to Kepler Galileo's hasty note of thanks. Kepler's first book consisted principally of the sort of neo-Platonist mathematical mysticism which was utterly distateful to Galileo.—Tr.]

[12] [Much misunderstanding occurs in this matter because it is widely supposed that Galileo spoke of "proofs" as such. What he said was that he had found certain natural phenomena which could be explained by the motions of the earth and could not be explained without them—scientifically, that is. There is no doubt that he had in mind principally the tides, as Kepler himself immediately surmised and as he wrote to another friend at the time. Many authors had believed that a motion of the earth would cause tides. Kepler correctly rejected this notion. What he did not know, however, was that Galileo had formulated a new theory, on mechanical principles, invoking the double motion of the earth assumed by Copernicus. To this theory Galileo clung all his life, believing it his greatest discovery. He did not publish it until 1632, and it much offended the Pope, who had forbidden him to use "physical" proofs in favor of Copernicus.—Tr.]

[13] [It might be safer to say that he considered the nova to destroy certain arguments of Aristotle and certain notions associated with Ptolemy's system. But since Galileo was unwilling to consider any third alternative, perhaps this comes to the same thing as saying that he considered the nova to support Copernicus.—Tr.]

[14] [It is true that Galileo never published a book on the nova of 1604 as his own, but he took part in the writing of a dialogue in the rustic Paduan dialect which ridiculed the Aristotelian professors. This witty satire was quite popular and went through two editions. (II, 307ff.) Galileo probably also drafted a serious book on the subject, as suggested by a letter to Guidobaldo dal Monte (XX, 597–98), and the bulk of it may have been published in a pseudonymous attack on Galileo's inept foe, Lodovico delle Colombe, (X, 176).—Tr.]

Notes

[15] For this category of students Galileo also composed, about 1593–94, two works entitled *Brief introduction to military architecture* and *Treatise on fortification.*

[16] Galileo returned to the study of magnets in 1626.

[17] X, 115.

[18] VIII, 198 [Cf. *Two New Sciences,* p. 169.]

[19] [Guidobaldo did little or nothing to advance the principle of virtual velocities, though it is true that in certain of his statements about levers and pulleys he came close to the idea. Most historians of science credit it to Jordanus Nemorarius, a writer of the thirteenth century, whom Guidobaldo ridiculed. Galileo expressly credits Aristotle with the principle, which he adopted and generalized not only in his *Mechanics* but in his *Bodies in Water* and the *Two New Sciences.* Galileo's disciple Evangelista Torricelli brought the principle still closer to its modern form.—Tr.]

[20] [Granting readily the general correctness of Professor Geymonat's view in this matter, it is still not quite accurate to say that Galileo lacked any interest in pure mathematics. The notion of the one-to-one correspondence of the positive integers and their squares (*The New Sciences,* pp. 31ff.) is strikingly original, and far in advance of his time. Other examples could be given. See Ch. 9.—Tr.]

[21] In addition to Olschki and Koyré, discussed below, we may mention as among the more authoritative supporters of a Galilean Platonism (though with very different shadings among themselves) Banfi, in the work previously cited; Ernst Cassirer, in *Das Erkenntnisproblem in der Philosophie und Wissenschaft der neueren Zeit* (1906) [also in his *Galileo's Platonism,* in *Studies and Essays in the History of Science and Learning* (ed. M. F. Ashley Montagu, N.Y., 1944)—Tr.] and elsewhere; Augusto Guzzo in the volume *La Scienza* (Turin, 1955.) [Professor A. C. Crombie of Oxford has remarked that the versatility and accuracy of Galileo's writings have made it possible for enthusiasts to find in them traces of every great philosophy, including some which had not yet been propounded in his day. —Tr.]

[22] *Op. cit.,* III, 53, n. 4.

[23] [In translating this paragraph, I have used the word *justification* (or *justify*) throughout, whereas the author employs various words or phrases which appear to me to be intended synonymously. Also, I have used the term *operationalist* in place of the Italian word *strumentalistica,* because I believe it is widely understood in English as a general philosophical term, whereas *instrumentalist* is a more restricted term employed principally in the philosophy of mathematics.—Tr.]

Chapter 3: The First Fortunate Astronomical Observations

[1] [Galileo has been so long, so bitterly, and so widely attacked for supposedly having claimed to be the inventor of the telescope that even modern Italian authors hesitate to defend him. But it is only by a strained inter-

pretation that such a claim can be attributed to Galileo. In his first published book on the subject (1610), he openly announced that he had first heard, and then read, an account of the existence of such an instrument in Holland. A week or two before he presented his instrument to the Senate, a foreign rival had shown one there. As to suggestions Galileo might have received from the writings of others, a comment is made in note 3, below.—Tr.]

2 [Mention might also be made of the Englishmen Thomas Digges and William Bourne, who had performed and described numerous experiments with magnifying instruments, principally concave mirrors alone or in combination with convex lenses.—Tr.]

3 [Kepler's book was first heard of by Galileo in 1610, and he promptly sent for a copy. Porta's book, which Galileo had doubtless seen, was translated into English in 1658 and reprinted in facsimile in 1957 by Basic Books, Inc., New York. Thus the reader may easily determine for himself whether Porta's suggestions would be useful in inventing a telescope. The celebrated passages occur in the English translation on p. 368. Modern scholars question whether they were meant to suggest a telescope or bifocal spectacles.—Tr.]

4 [The only evidence that lenses had been combined into a telescope before 1608 is contained in a diary entry made by Isaac Beeckman in 1634. According to this entry, the first telescope made in Holland dated from 1604, and was copied from an Italian model dated 1590. Beeckman had this information from a man who was not born until 1611, seven years after the purported event, and who wanted to establish priority for his father, who was only sixteen years of age in 1604. In later years he filed an affidavit falsifying his own age and swearing that his father had made a telescope in 1590, when in fact even the father was only two years old. Hence little credit can be given to the story, even though Beeckman himself was a man of great integrity.—Tr.]

5 [As previously remarked, Galileo freely admitted in print that he had heard of the instrument before he attempted to make one. He denied, however, that he had actually seen one before that time. Reasons for accepting his account, despite the existence of contrary rumors, were set forth in my paper, "Galileo's First Telescope at Padua and Venice," in *Isis*, September 1959, pp. 245ff.—Tr.]

6 [The arguments of Professor Geymonat are persuasive. It is nonetheless important to note that not only in 1610, but for many years afterward, very few telescopes made by others than Galileo were sufficiently powerful to reveal the principal astronomical phenomena he had described. The instruments reported in France and Holland magnified three to four times, as did Galileo's first model. Within a month, however, he was able to construct a thirty-power instrument. This may have been merely luck, as many scholars contend that it was; on the other hand, it may have involved theoretical knowledge which Galileo did not care to divulge.—Tr.]

232   7 [Jean Tarde was a French clergyman. After visiting Galileo, he re-

Notes

turned to France and wrote a book on sunspots in which he ridiculed Galileo's (correct) views and made absurd claims concerning discoveries of his own. In his diary he attempted to efface all record of the information he had received about sunspots during his visit to Galileo, but fortunately this can still be read under his cancellations. If Galileo did not care to pass on all his knowledge of telescope construction to this casual visitor (who did turn out to be somewhat lacking in honesty, or at least courtesy), this scarcely proves Galileo to have been ignorant. As a matter of fact, he was evasive even when his good friend Sagredo wrote to him for instruction on the theory of the telescope. Scientific secrecy concerning valuable discoveries was even more prevalent then than it is now, and the telescope was Galileo's greatest claim to fame at that time. While it may be true that he was incapable of understanding elementary optics, it may also be true that he was merely reluctant to give away his stock in trade. Both are doubtless reprehensible traits, but in Galileo's case it is usually safer to assume selfishness than ignorance in explanation of his behavior. —Tr.]

8 [At the very least, we may express surprise that Kepler seemed unable to construct a telescope after reading Galileo's *Starry Messenger* of 1610, where the process was described; for several months he complained that he could not find one that would enable him to verify Galileo's discoveries. In the eyes of Galileo's modern adversaries, this proves only Galileo's stinginess, and not Kepler's lack of knowledge or resourcefulness. If, as Professors Ronchi and Geymonat contend, Kepler's publication of 1604 had already put him in a position to proceed with the invention, and if, as Imperial Mathematician, he could call on the resources of court craftsmen to do the manual work, it is hard to account for his inaction.—Tr.]

9 [The relative merits of Galilean and Keplerian telescopes for observations made in those days are at least debatable. Galileo's telescopes presented an erect image, which was a considerable advantage for everything but astronomical purposes. As will be seen later in this chapter, it even had an advantage astronomically at that time, as it served to prove that the telescope did not distort familiar objects, and hence was trustworthy when applied to the heavens. The Galilean telescope had sufficient magnifying power for the startling first discoveries, but not enough to introduce insuperable difficulties of management at a time when suitable telescopic mountings had not yet been devised. The real advantages of the Keplerian instrument belong mostly to the period of greater refinement in astronomical observation.—Tr.]

10 [Here, as in the title to this chapter, the author emphasizes the element of luck in the first astronomical discoveries made with the telescope. No one can deny such an element; still, it is easy to overestimate its importance. Even today it is not simple to observe the satellites of Jupiter with a completely homemade Galilean telescope, though we have better materials and tools to work with than Galileo did. To recognize the moons

Galileo Galilei

of Jupiter required not only luck but also a good memory of what had been seen before, for not even he had yet charted the numerous new fixed stars he was observing nightly. It is interesting that no one anticipated Galileo's discovery of the phases of Venus, which lagged several months behind the publication of his first announcements, as Venus was then too close to the sun to be observed. It takes more than luck to make even "simple" discoveries.—Tr.]

[11] X, 357. [Letter to Matthew Carosio.]

[12] XI, 106.

[13] X, 327. [In Galileo's letter of acceptance (X, 373) he asked for the title of mathematician as well as philosopher to the Grand Duke, which was duly granted in the ducal patent (X, 400).—Tr.]

[14] [It is probable that a misunderstanding which arose at the time of Galileo's acceptance of the reappointment accounts both for the strong feelings of the Venetian rules and for Galileo's indifference to those feelings. A reconstruction of the events is set forth in the paper mentioned in note 5 above.—Tr.]

[15] [Galileo makes one of his interlocutors in the *Dialogue* of 1632 declare that he had observed the sunspots while still at Padua. In later years Fra Fulgenzio Micanzio wrote that he recalled the event, and the interest shown in it by Fra Paolo Sarpi. Nevertheless, the point is doubtful. The earliest reliable evidence of Galileo's sunspot observations would place them at Rome in April 1611, and his first written mention of sunspots in surviving correspondence occurs in October of that year.—Tr.]

[16] XI, 69–70.

[17] [Mayr's claim was not made until 1614, four years after Galileo's publication. For several reasons it is peculiarly implausible, but has never lacked defenders. Galileo's own comments are given in *Discoveries*, p. 233. —Tr.]

[18] XI, 165. [Every commentator on this letter has agreed with the interpretation here placed on it. To me, Cremonini appears in a very different light, as a sage old professor fond of his joke. I fancy that looking through the spectacles of those days did literally give one a headache, and that Cremonini sensed that looking through Galileo's two lenses would give him a double headache—one of them philosophical. At his age and in his position he could well do without this. He was well paid, enjoyed the respect of his colleagues, and was already in trouble with the Inquisition.—Tr.]

[19] [It is not easy to show others the use of the telescope, even now when good tripods are available and optical conveniences are provided for correct placement of the eye. With a hostile audience and a primitive instrument, it is little wonder that Galileo failed. The wonder is that he achieved what he did by his own observations.—Tr.]

[20] X, 343.

Notes

[21] X, 441–42. [Lodovico Cardi da Cigoli was an eminent painter and a close friend of Galileo.—Tr.]

[22] XI, 115.

[23] [The celebrated exclamation of Julian the Apostate, turned by pun into "Galileo, you have conquered." A more famous pun between "Galileo" and "Man of Galilee" is mentioned in the next chapter; Latin lent itself neatly to this device.—Tr.]

[24] III, 188.

[25] [The *Accademia dei Lincei* (Academy of the Lynx-eyed) was the first specifically scientific academy, and had vast influence on all future societies of this type. It collapsed with the death of Cesi in 1630, but was later reorganized and is again a powerful factor in the scientific world.—Tr.]

[26] XI, 79.

[27] ["Let it be seen whether in the trial of Doctor Cesare Cremonini mention is made of Galileo, Professor of Philosophy and Mathematics." XIX, 275.—Tr.]

[28] A. Müller, *Galileo Galilei: Studio Storico Scientifico* (Rome, 1911) p. 71. [This work is an Italian translation of the two works by Müller cited in the preface.—Tr.]

[29] *Ibid.*, p. 100.

[30] [Most scholars have rejected Mayr's claim; see for example] E. Wohlwill, *op. cit.*, App. III [and cf. note 17 above.—Tr.]

[31] Müller, *op. cit.*, p. 100.

[32] XI, 146–47.

[33] XI, 142. [As a modern philosopher, Professor Geymonat admires the aptness of this phrase. Most readers, however, will find greater relish in another remark of Galileo's in the same letter. He said he would gladly accept this crystalline substance, and would then declare it to be so distributed as to produce mountains ten times as high, and craters ten times as deep, as those he had actually seen.—Tr.]

Chapter 4: The Ambitious Program

[1] Concerning Scheiner, see the interesting study of A. Favaro in his series *Oppositori di Galileo* (*Atti del Reale Instituto Veneto*, v. 78, 1918–19).

[2] A few months before, a booklet had appeared on the subject by Johann Fabricius, *De maculis in sole observatis et apparente earum cum sole convectione narrati* (Wittemberg, 1611), based on observations made at the end of 1610. ["Recital of spots observed in the sun and of their apparent turning with the sun." This book had not been heard of by either Scheiner or Galileo.—Tr.]

[3] It should be noted that the "History" replied not only to the first three letters of Scheiner, but also to a new study he published on the subject in September 1612, with the title of *De maculis solaribus et stellis circa iovem errantibus accuratior disquisitio* ("A more accurate thesis on sunspots and the stars moving about Jupiter").

Galileo Galilei

⁴ [That is, *The Ursine Rose*, a ponderous dedication of the book to the house of Orsini, the word *rose* being here an allusion to the sun. This book opened with an attack of unprecedented violence against Galileo, inspired chiefly by a sarcastic reference to Scheiner that had been made by Galileo in a book on the comets of 1618–19 through the pen of his pupil Mario Guiducci.—Tr.]

⁵ [Bruno, a brilliant but erratic writer who had spent some years in England, was turned over to the Church authorities during a return to Italy and was eventually burned at the stake for heresy in 1600. One of his most characteristic works, *Of the Infinite Universe and Worlds*, has been translated into English by Dorothy Waley Singer, in *Giordano Bruno: His Life and Thought* (N.Y., 1950).—Tr.]

⁶ Among the advocates of an actual continuity of thought between Galileo and Bruno we may mention V. Spampanato, *Quattro filosofi napolitani nel carteggio di Galileo* (Portici, 1907); G. Gentile, *Studi sul Rinascimento* (Florence, 1936); S. Timpanaro, *Scritti di storia e critica della scienza* (Florence, 1952). [Concerning the failure of Galileo to mention Bruno by name, it would seem evident that his program of winning support from the Church, as set forth in the present chapter, would preclude his championing in any way the recently executed heretic, or acknowledging any debt to him.—Tr.]

⁷ One might repeat almost the same thing of comparisons between Galileo and Thomas Campanella, and it serves to explain the reasons behind Galileo's perenial coldness toward the unfortunate friar, who on his part supported Galileo with the warmest and most sincere enthusiasm. Campanella even offered to undertake personally the task of defending him before the ecclesiastical authorities, but Galileo prudently avoided acceptance of the offer. [Campanella was a brilliant and original writer on political topics who was imprisoned by the Spanish Inquisition for some twenty-seven years and was freed only when the Roman Inquisition demanded his custody under pretex of punishing him, and then set him free. His philosophical works include a *Defense of Galileo* published in 1622 and numerous attacks on the ancient metaphysics.—Tr.]

⁸ *Op. cit.*, p. 134.

⁹ IV, 140 [The "place occupied" is that of the chip plus that of the air lying between the top of the chip and the level of the water.—Tr.]

¹⁰ IV, 627.

¹¹ [Kepler certainly held such a view, but there is little evidence that Galileo subscribed to it any more than to other ideas of Kepler's. Galileo's interest in the rotation of the sun appears to me to have lain more in its mechanical implications, particularly in its support of his ideas of inertia and of the conservation of angular momentum, adumbrated in his early unpublished writings and first set forth in print in the *Letters on Sunspots*. —Tr.]

¹² IV, 229 [*Discoveries*, p. 139].

Notes

13 IV, 257 [Cf. *Discoveries*, p. 139, for a similar passage.—Tr.].

14 Even in the last century, Father Filippo Anfossi could write in a little anonymous book published at Rome in 1822 that Kepler's laws, Newtonian attractions, and the deviation of freely falling bodies toward the east "are things that do not deserve the least attention when confronted with so many and such clear expressions of Scripture that constantly assert the motion of the sun and the immobility of the earth, without once asserting the contrary." And he adds further: "Did the Holy Spirit know of these later discoveries, or not? If it knew of them, why did the saintly men inspired by it say more than eighty times that the sun moves, without saying once that it is immovable and fixed?" (The reference and citations are taken from S. Timpanaro, *Scritti di storia e critica della scienza*, pp. 95–96.)

15 In his letter to Monsignor Dini, he asked that his *Letter to Castelli* be brought to the attention of the mathematicians of the Collegio Romano, and if possible also to that of Cardinal Bellarmine.

16 [Brahe, who wrote after Copernicus, could not bring himself to accept the earth's motion in view of the apparent mechanical difficulties, as well as the biblical contradictions. Accordingly he proposed a system in which the earth remained fixed, while the sun and moon traveled round it, and the planets in turn revolved about the sun. This system was adopted by the more intelligent elements in the Church, particularly the Jesuits, as a means of avoiding difficulties in the ancient Ptolemaic system caused by the telescopic observations. Galileo never missed a chance to jeer at Tycho's system. Kepler, who personally rejected it for the Copernican theory, nevertheless recognized in all his works the mathematical equivalence of the two.—Tr.]

17 V, 282–83 [From Galileo's *Letter to Castelli*, discussed in Ch. 5, section 3. Cf. *Discoveries*, pp. 181–86, where similar ideas are expressed in the *Letter to Cristina*.—Tr.]

18 V, 284.

19 V, 322 [*Discoveries*, p. 189].

20 XV, 25 [Fromond was a Belgian Jesuit who had vigorously opposed Galileo and other Copernicans.—Tr.].

21 V, 365.

22 VII, 62 [*Dialogue*, p. 38]

23 V, 367 [*Discoveries*, p. 168].

24 As a faithful interpreter of the Galilean spirit, Prince Cesi was to write to Galileo on May 11, 1613, these significant words: "We need captains as well as soldiers in our philosophical militia, though not so many of the former, since we have the best, and a few suffice to lead a great army" (XI, 507).

25 It is interesting to note how Galileo explained, in a letter to Paolo Gualdo dated June 16, 1612, the reasons that led him to write his answer to Apelles in Italian: "I wrote it in the colloquial tongue because I must

have everyone able to read it, and for the same reason I wrote my last book
in this language. I am induced to do this by seeing how young men are
sent through the universities at random to be made physicians, philosophers,
and so on; thus many of them are committed to professions for which they
are unsuited, while other men who would be fitted for them are taken up
by family cares and other occupations remote from literature. . . . Now I
want them to see that just as nature has given to them, as well as to
philosophers, eyes with which to see her works, so she has also given
them brains capable of penetrating and understanding them" (XI, 327)
[*Discoveries*, p. 84].

Chapter 5: The First Discomfiture

[1] [It is customary to refer to the proceedings of 1615–16 as Galileo's
first trial, though in fact he was not actually subjected to formal trial until
1633.—Tr.] For a detailed study of the two trials of Galileo, refer to the
works mentioned in the Preface, and especially to that of Santillana. See
also the following special studies recently published: three articles by G.
Morpurgo Tagliabue under the general title *I processi di Galileo e l'epis-
temologia* (*The trials of Galileo and epistemology*) in the *Rivisista di
Storia di Filosofia*, 1946–47; an essay by Ferdinando Flora, *Il processo di
Galileo* (*The trial of Galileo*), published as appendix to the *Vita di Galileo*
(*Life of Galileo*) of Vincenzio Viviani (Milan, 1954); Flora's essay *Il
Dramma di Galileo* (*The drama of Galileo*) in the journal *Il Ponte*, 1953,
Vol. IX, and the interesting debate between Flora and Santillana which
ensued in the same journal in 1955 and 1956.

[2] This letter is set forth and commented on at length in the volume by
Müller previously cited, pp. 74, 326. [It is at least debatable whether in
Kepler's mind the "imprudent behavior" was that of Galileo or the Catho-
lic censors. Kepler was a Protestant.—Tr.]

[3] *Didaci a Stunica Salmaticensis Eremitae Augustiniani In Job Com-
mentaria* [first published at Toledo in 1585], Rome, 1591. It is interesting
to note, in support of the importance attributed to this work in the highest
Catholic circles, that Cardinal Conti made reference to it in a reply to
Galileo dated July 7, 1612. Galileo had asked him about the possibility
of reconciling the Copernican theory with the Bible. Here are Conti's words:
"As to the motion of the earth and of the sun, a question may be raised
about either of two motions of the earth. One is a straight motion, made by
a change of its center of gravity; and whoever would give it this motion
does not contradict Scripture, for this is an accidental motion of the
earth. . . . The other is a circular motion, such that the heavens would
stand still and would appear to us to move because of the motion of the
earth, as the shore appears to sailors to be moving, and this opinion was
held by the Pythagoreans and was followed later by Copernicus . . . and
others; and this seems less in conformity with the Bible. . . . Nevertheless,

Notes

Diego de Zuñiga, on the ninth chapter of Job, verse 6, says that it is more in agreement with Scripture for the earth to move, though his interpretation is not generally followed" (XI, 354–55).

⁴ XII, 171–72 [For translation of Bellarmine's entire letter, see *Discoveries*, pp. 162–64.—Tr.] Some critics, and in particular the French philosopher Pierre Duhem, claim that these words of Bellarmine's are to be interpreted as a declaration in favor of positivism; that is, as a statement that scientific theories cannot achieve absolute truth, but merely reason *ex suppositione.* Yet it is clear, as Santillana well shows (*op. cit.,* pp. 107–8), that such an interpretation will not stand up, since Bellarmine, while he made himself the defender of a relativistic attitude inside a limited field of knowledge, placed this attitude within an absolutist conception of truth based upon a physical and metaphysical realism of the scholastic type. [Duhem's contention that not Galileo but Bellarmine was the true positivist is utterly refuted by Galileo's manuscript reply, which includes the statement: "No greater truth may or should be sought in a theory than that it corresponds with all the particular appearances" (V, 369; *Discoveries,* p. 169)—Tr.].

⁵ [It should be noted that the tradition which places this clever pun in the mouth of Caccini has no source earlier than a century after his sermon. The text of the sermon was taken from the book of Joshua.—Tr.]

⁶ [The phrase *black and white dogs of the Lord* embodies an ancient and favorite pun on *Domini . . . canes,* embellished with references to the two garbs used in the order, those of the Blackfriars and the Whitefriars.—Tr.]

⁷ XIX, 297–98. [Lorini was a desperately heavy-handed writer, virtually impossible to do injustice to in translation; Galileo called him a *goffo dicitore* (clumsy speaker) at the time of his classic imbecility of calling Copernicus "Ipernicus."—Tr.]

⁸ XIX, 318–19 [Lest the reader wonder how Galileo could have got mixed into the theological disputations, it may be added that these views were attributed to a Dominican novice known to favor Galileo's scientific opinions. Galileo's guilt was by association.—Tr.].

⁹ XII, 231.

¹⁰ [Ciampoli was a brilliant literary man and devoted friend of Galileo who rose rapidly in the Church.] At the end of 1632, Ciampoli was sent away from his high post in Rome to Montalto, and thence to other places, as punishment. The principal cause of his demotion was the friendship that had linked him so closely to Galileo.—Tr.]

¹¹ XII, 145–47.

¹² XII, 184.

¹³ XII, 223; January 8, 1616.

¹⁴ XII, 228; January 23, 1616.

¹⁵ XII, 230; February 6, 1616.

¹⁶ *Ibid.*

¹⁷ On this theory he wrote a celebrated letter, dated January 1616 and   239

addressed to Cardinal Orsini, giving it the title "On the ebb and flow of the sea," but it remained unpublished at the time. [The nature of Galileo's theory is discussed in Ch. 7.—Tr.]

[18] XII, 226–27.

[19] XII, 207; December 5, 1615.

[20] *Op. cit.*, p. 155. [Galileo had announced that the sun revolves upon its axis with a period of about one month.—Tr.]

[21] XIX, 323. [It should be noted here that the phrase "taught the same doctrine" means not Copernicanism as such, but the doctrine that Copernicanism is consistent with the Bible; it was this that Foscarini had done, and it was for this reason that his book was utterly condemned. This point is not generally understood, but it is important to a full explanation of the difficulties mentioned by the author in the ensuing paragraph.—Tr.]

[22] [Galileo's book on sunspots, though it supported Copernicus, made no reference to the Bible; see note 21 above.—Tr.]

[23] XIX, 321.

[24] XIX, 322.

[25] XII, 244.

[26] XIX, 348.

Chapter 6: The Years of Silence

[1] [A newly created arm of the Church designed to combat the inroads of Protestantism by spreading the official doctrines. Ingoli was a jurist of Ravenna.—Tr.]

[2] XIII, 48–49.

[3] [Leopold was brother to Maria Madeleine, wife of Cosimo II; he had recently visited Galileo at Florence. For a possible reason (not mentioned in the text) which would account for Galileo's actions in sending him the treatise on the tides, see *The Controversy of the Comets of 1618*, xii. —Tr.]

[4] XII, 390–91.

[5] *Op. cit.*, 178–79.

[6] According to Aristotle's physics, the terrestrial globe (fixed at the center of the universe) was composed of four spheres—earth, water, air, and fire, as one moves outward—which constituted the "natural places" of the four basic "elements." Beyond the sphere of fire lay the various heavens, of spherical form, which rotated with uniform circular motion with their centers at the center of the earth. The "first heaven," which was lowest of all, was the heaven of the moon.

[7] [The Collegio Romano was the center of Jesuit learning then, as it is now. At present it is known as the Gregorian University, in honor of the pope who confirmed it in 1583. Several books mentioned below are available in English in *The Controversy on Comets* (Philadelphia, 1950.)—Tr.]

Notes

8 [Galileo attacked not the Tychonic view as such, but the main argument by which Grassi supported it. In order to undermine that argument he suggested the optical hypothesis of comets, but he did not espouse it positively.—Tr.]

9 [In Galileo's copy of this book he corrected the word *examinantur*, which means "examined" to *exanimantur*, which means "suffocated" or "deprived of soul."—Tr.]

10 [Dante, *Purgatorio*, ix, 5–6.]

11 VI, 221. [*Controversy*, 171–72.—Tr.]

12 VI, 277 [Ariosto, *Orlando Furioso* xxxv, 59.—Tr.]

13 *The Crime of Galileo*, p. 153.

14 *Op. cit.*, II, 18.

15 [A different viewpoint concerning the nature of Galileo's hypothesis will be found in the preface to *The Controversy on Comets*, cited above and referred to as *Controversy*. The attitude of Kepler in his work translated there does not appear unfriendly to Galileo.—Tr.]

16 *Galilei und seine Zeit*, p. 280.

17 See Timpanaro, Preface to *Opere di Galileo*, II, 53. [Cf. notes 8 and 15 above.—Tr.]

18 Flora, *op. cit.*, pp. 98–99.

19 VI, 264 [*Controversy*, 218].

20 VI, 337 [*Controversy*, 297–98].

21 VI, 339 [*Controversy*, 300].

22 VI, 341 [*Controversy*, 302].

23 VI, 281–82. [*Controversy*, 237. The understanding of Galileo's hypothesis concerning comets depends upon recognition of this skeptical approach.—Tr.]

24 *Op. cit.*, p. 284.

25 VI, 232 [*Controversy*, 183–84].

26 VI, 347 ff. [*Controversy*, 308 ff.].

27 VI, 347–48 [*Controversy*, 309–11].

28 VI, 232 [*Controversy*, 183–84].

29 *Op. cit.*, p. 176.

30 VI, 232 [*Controversy*, 183].

31 VI, 245 [*Controversy*, 198].

32 VI, 253 [*Controversy*, 206].

33 VI, 270 [*Controversy*, 224].

34 VI, 308 [*Controversy*, 226].

35 VI, 296 [*Controversy*, 252].

Chapter 7: The Copernican Manifesto

1 Francesco Barberini, who was very friendly toward Galileo.

2 XIII, 121.

3 XIII, 130–31.

Galileo Galilei

[4] VI, 201 [*Controversy*, 153].

[5] An ecclesiastical pension was in fact conferred on Vincenzio Galilei in 1627, connected with the Cathedral of Brescia. In 1630 another was conferred on Galileo himself, connected with the Metropolitan of Pisa.

[6] XIII, 182.

[7] It is worth noting that at this period Galileo still found time to devote himself to researches of a completely different kind. The most important of these were those which led him in 1624 to the construction of a compound microscope; in September of that year there was a letter from Galileo to Prince Cesi accompanying the gift to his Roman friend of an *occhialino per veder da vicino le cose minime* ("a small glass for closely examining the smallest things") and explaining its use and remarkable merits. In 1626 he made new investigations of magnetism, studies which he had begun many years before at Padua. In 1627, Galileo took part in the discussion of a curious problem of practical arithmetic: "A horse is truly valued at 100 scudi; its value is estimated by one man at 1000 scudi and by another at 10 scudi; the question is which one made the better estimate." Galileo's opinion was that the errors of estimate should be calculated according to geometric proportion [that is, that the two estimates in the above case were equal in error]. In support of Galileo's competence in practical problems, mention may be made of the opinion he gave to the Grand Duke in January 1631, concerning the project of several engineers to perform certain work in order to remedy the frequent floods along the Bisenzio River; this is contained in a letter of a few pages which despite its brevity is a true gem of scientific precision and technical expertness.

[8] VI, 511–12.

[9] VI, 561.

[10] VI, 535.

[11] VI, 536.

[12] VI, 540.

[13] VI, 543–44.

[14] VI, 547–48.

[15] VI, 545.

[16] VI, 549.

[17] VI, 545.

[18] VI, 549.

[19] A grandson to Galileo was born of this union in December 1629 and named after the great scientist. Two other grandsons (Carlo, 1632, and Cosimo, 1638) followed, but the direct line ended with them. [Vincenzio is often reported to have been a scapegrace and much trouble to Galileo, but this appears to be largely a confusion with another Vincenzio, son of Michelangelo and nephew to Galileo.—Tr.]

[20] [The nickname is supposed to have been friendly and to have arisen from Riccardi's prodigious memory, but it may have been given him because of his great physical size.—Tr.]

Notes

21 [Three fishes were an ancient cryptic religious symbol, and this device was mistaken in Rome as a devious attempt to suggest Church approval of the book. Galileo later had to send copies of other books published by Landini to refute this absurd charge.—Tr.]

22 It should be noted that the words *Two Chief Systems* emphasized Galileo's decision not to number among the "chief" world systems that of Tycho Brahe which had been appropriated by the Jesuits.

23 VII, 29 [*Dialogue*, 5].

24 VII, 30 [*Dialogue*, 6].

25 VII, 488 [*Dialogue*, 464].

26 VII, 128–29 [*Dialogue*, 103].

27 VII, 130 [*Dialogue*, 105].

28 VII, 367 [*Dialogue*, 339–40].

29 "Among all the great men who have philosophized about this remarkable effect, I am more astonished at Kepler than at any other. Despite his open and acute mind, and though he has at his fingertips the motions attributed to the earth, he has nevertheless lent his ear and his assent to to moon's dominion over the waters, to occult properties, and to such puerilities." VII, 486 [*Dialogue*, 462]. [It may be noted here that Galileo's mechanical explanation, though fallacious, is more in the spirit of modern science than rival theories, including Kepler's which recognized an attraction of the moon for water but not for other matter.—Tr.]

30 [*Dialogue*, 463.]

31 [Galileo's theory was quantitatively entirely wrong, but there is some question whether it may be condemned as utterly fallacious. Cf. "The Origin and Fate of Galileo's Theory of the Tides" in *Physis*, (1961) III, 185–94.—Tr.]

32 VII, 259–60 [*Dialogue*, 233].

33 *Op. cit.*, 202–3.

34 *Op. cit.*, 342ff.

35 *Op. cit.*, 227.

36 From the introduction to the *Dialogo* in the edition of Sandron, Rome 1945. [Emphasis added by Professor Geymonat.]

Chapter 8: The Collapse of the Galilean Program

1 XIV, 357; from Alessandro Caccia, May 26, 1632.

2 XIV, 363; from Fulgenzio Micanzio, July 3, 1632.

3 XIV, 364; from Fulgenzio Micanzio, July 17, 1632.

4 XIV, 366–67; from Thomas Campanella, August 5, 1632.

5 XIV, 360.

6 XIV, 373.

7 XIV, 383–84.

8 Banfi, *op. cit.*, p. 198.

9 *Ibid.*, p. 199.

Galileo Galilei

[10] XX, suppl. 571–72. [Cf, note 21 to Ch. 7.—Tr.]

[11] XX, suppl., 572.

[12] XIV, 375–76.

[13] XIX, 331–32.

[14] XX, 575–76.

[15] XV, 21.

[16] XIV, 406–8. Italics added by the author.

[17] [It was always politic to speak of the Copernican theory as a revival of views held in antiquity by the Pythagoreans, Aristarchus, and others. —Tr.]

[18] XIV, 408.

[19] XIV, 376.

[20] [Niccolini had in fact been given this information in great secrecy and confidence by Riccardi in September 1632, and had communicated it to the Grand Duke through the minister Cioli (XIV, 389). Whether the information had leaked to Galileo before February 1633 is not known.—Tr.]

[21] Santillana correctly observed that Galileo's confidence constitutes an indirect but irrefutable proof that he had not received any special precept on the twenty-sixth of February 1616: "And let us also recall the weeks preceding the trial; when he was finally told the well-guarded secret of 'Bellarmine's precept,' he wrote quite freely to Geri Bocchineri that of all the various charges, it appeared that nothing remained other than this; and thanks to the affidavit (of Bellarmine) it would be easy to handle this. Would it not have been the moment for him to feel chilled with fear when he was awakened to the inexorable record of the ill-starred intervention by the Commissary, from which it would be impossible to escape? Instead, it appeared to him that he had nothing more to fear at the hour when he should confront his judges. It is time, he says, that these gentlemen should take into account the entire persecution. And it was Niccolini who had to tell him that things would not fall out that way, and to advise him to 'satisfy them' as best he could." (*Il Ponte*, 1956, p. 424.)

[22] XV, 85.

[23] XIX, 341.

[24] XIX, 343.

[25] XIX, 346.

[26] [In the proceedings of the Inquisition it was not sufficient to show the facts, but it was also necessary to be satisfied as to the intention of the accused. This was the step at which various degrees of torture, when used at all, usually came into play. See further, below.—Tr.]

[27] On this point, the words written to Galileo by his friend and pupil Mario Guiducci on the succeeding twenty-third of July are very clear; Guiducci must have been quite conscious that he was interpreting a wish that had taken root months earlier in Galileo's mind: "It seems a thousand years before I shall see you once more in your accustomed repose, where, putting aside

Notes

the studies condemned by the Congregation, you may attend to others that are entirely beyond suspicion." (XV, 190)

[28] XVI, 116. [The interpretation Galileo and all subsequent commentators, have given to this remark may not be correct. There is evidence that Grienberger personally regretted all that had happened. His comment, taken objectively, implies only that Galileo made a mistake when he openly attacked the Collegio in the person of Grassi and thus alienated its support. This does not imply that the Collegio took part in his eventual prosecution, nor is there any evidence that they did. Scheiner, who intrigued at Rome against Galileo, was not connected with the Collegio.—Tr.]

[29] There is for example a letter of Filippo Magiotti to Mario Guiducci of August 1632 (XIV, 370); one from Gabriel Naudé to Pierre Gassendi of April 1633 (XV, 88); one from Descartes to Marin Mersenne of February 1634 (XVI, 56); one from Hugo Grotius to Gerard Voss of May 1635 (XVI, 266).

[30] [The question of the views and actions of Scheiner is central to the entire drama of Galileo's troubles, but it is very difficult and involved. On the particular scientific matter mentioned here, it is the opinion of the translator that Scheiner never embraced Copernicanism, even in his most secret thoughts, but that he wished to modify the Tychonic view, officially adopted by most of his fellow Jesuits, by allowing the earth a rotation on its axis without any revolution about the sun. Even this possible motion of the earth, however, appears only by implication in a posthumous book of Scheiner's, and was never openly espoused by him.—Tr.]

[31] [Cf. XV, 25; XVI, 458.—Tr.]

[32] [Although the question whether Galileo was actually tortured was once much debated, it is now generally agreed that no such action was taken. Afflicted as he was with arthritis and double hernia, it would be physically impossible for him to endure the rack and then almost immediately appear for public abjuration, let alone to undertake the journey to Siena a few days later. It is frequently argued that torture was not in any case applied to the aged and infirm under regulations of the Inquisition. Legally, however, there was no such bar; indeed, a doctor of Church law soberly argued, not long ago, that the authorities in charge of Galileo's trial committed a serious juridical error by *not* torturing him, since he had never admitted any wrong intention. See Orio Giacchi, *Considerazioni Giuridiche sui due Processi contro Galileo*, in *Nel Terzo Cenetenario della Morte di Galileo Galilei* (Milan, 1942), especially pp. 399 and 406.—Tr.]

[33] XIX, 362.

[34] For a complete account of the ceremony, the reading of sentence and abjuration, see XIX, 402–7. [Also see Santillana, *op. cit.*—Tr.]

[35] *Loc. cit.*

[36] [It is true that no contemporary document supports this story, which did not make its appearance in print until more than a century after the supposed event. It is, moreover, palpably absurd to suppose that these words

Galileo Galilei

were spoken by Galileo on the occasion in question. But the existence of a contemporary painting of Galileo in prison which bears the precise words makes it very probable that he did utter them on another occasion. See *Discoveries*, 291–92.—Tr.]

[37] XV, 165.

[38] XIX, 362.

Chapter 9: The Return to Pure Science

[1] XIX, 393.

[2] XIX, 389.

[3] XV, 98.

[4] XV, 167.

[5] XV, 181.

[6] XVI, 57.

[7] XVI, 85.

[8] Both outlived Galileo. Sister Arcangela died in 1659, Vincenzio in 1649.

[9] XVII, 393.

[10] XVI, 59.

[11] XVI, 112.

[12] XVI, 361.

[13] [The Elzevir press was at that time one of the most active in publishing works of an educational nature, and best able to circulate its publications widely. It is still active in this field, perhaps without break in continuity.—Tr.]

[14] [This was supposed to be published together with the Latin *Dialogue*, but Diodati's translation was delayed. The book was rigorously suppressed in Catholic countries.—Tr.]

[15] Viviani's *Historical Account of the Life of Galileo* [written in 1657] was first published posthumously at Florence in 1717. It is included in Volume XIX of the National Edition.

[16] XVI, 234.

[17] XVII, 247.

[18] From a letter to Fulgenzo Micanzio dated November 19, 1634. XVI, 163.

[19] The edition of 1638 ends with a Latin section bearing the title *Appendix in which are contained theorems and their demonstrations about the centers of gravity of solids written long ago by the same author*. This merely reproduces Galileo's youthful theorems mentioned in Ch. 1.

[20] [Viviani, *Scienza Universale delle Proporzioni* (Florence, 1674) pp. 1–77.—Tr.]

[21] It is worth noting that in the so-called Sixth Day, Simplicio is replaced as interlocutor by Paolo Aproino, a nobleman of Treviso who had been a pupil and a good friend of Galileo's in his Paduan days.

[22] [Cf. *Two New Sciences*, p. 3.—Tr.]

[23] [Cf. *Two New Sciences*, pp. 74–75.—Tr.]

Notes

24 [That is, all pendulums of the same length beat together, but one four times as long takes twice as much time to complete each swing—Tr.]

25 [By *moment* is meant the product of the force and the distance at which the force acts, which together determine the efficacy of the action.—Tr.]

26 VIII, 175 [*Two New Sciences*, p. 137].

27 VIII, 296 [*Two New Sciences*, p. 276. A century earlier, Tartaglia had published the result that an angle of 45° gives maximum distance.—Tr.].

28 VIII, 345. [Mersenne, the translator of Galileo's early treatise on mechanics, says in his preface that Galileo experimented by striking a heavy chest many thousands of times with a spinet hammer, and found that it had actually moved.—Tr.]

29 XVI, 163.

30 [Published in 1635, this book is generally considered to be the first important step toward invention of the calculus.—Tr.]

31 [Professor Geymonat here adds the words "as later actually happened." This refers to Cavalieri's publication in 1632 of the parabolic trajectory of projectiles. Galileo heard of this before he saw the book (*Lo Specchio Ustorio*), and was at first annoyed. When the book came, however, he found to his satisfaction that Cavalieri had given him very generous acknowledgment.—Tr.]

32 XIII, 390; February 29, 1626.

33 XIII, 312; March 21, 1626.

34 XIII, 381; December 17, 1627.

35 [Not published until 1632. Cavalieri was first to introduce logarithms into Italy.—Tr.]

36 XIV, 263; May 21, 1631.

37 XVI, 15.

38 VIII, 85–86. [*Two New Sciences*, p. 40]

39 VIII, 72. [Cf. *Two New Sciences*, p. 25]

40 [VIII, 77ff. *Two New Sciences*, pp. 31ff.—Tr.]

41 [Cf. *Two New Sciences*, p. 37; XIX, 83. Galileo's remarks on this paradoxical statement seem to me to show that far from displaying neo-Platonic confusion, he had anticipated by three centuries the methods used today in dealing with certain paradoxes of the infinite.—Tr.]

42 In the *Scritti* previously cited, p. 97.

43 VII, 173 [*Dialogue*, p. 147].

44 VII, 243 [*Two New Sciences*, p. 215].

45 "*Salviati:* Then in order for a surface to be neither downward nor upward, all its parts must be equally distant from the center. Are there any such surfaces in the world?

"*Simplicio:* Plenty of them; such would be the surface of our terrestrial globe if it were smooth." (VII, 174 [*Dialogue*, p. 148].)

46 [All critics today describe Galileo's restricted enunciation in the *Dialogue* as an "error." It certainly lacks generality, but whether that is a scientific "error" may be debated. What Galileo stated was true, and was

limited to his field of observational data. The full generalization of inertia by Descartes, praised by Koyré, might equally well be branded an "error" in the absence of the gravitational law, later discovered by Newton. Galileo's terrestrial observations justified no more than the restricted statements he made. Newton's celestial observations justified its generalization. Today, relativity has destroyed the absolute notion of a straight line required by the inertial laws of Descartes and of Newton himself. Galileo's enunciation remains unscathed, because he prudently refrained from discussing the behavior of bodies in empty space.—Tr.]

[47] [The ball is assumed to roll along a level table and then off the edge. Koyré contends that Galileo was incapable of thinking separately of the inertial effect which, in the absence of gravity, would carry the ball along in its straight motion whether the table continued to support it or not.—Tr.]

[48] *Op. cit.*, pp. 263ff. (III-113ff) [If inertia alone were considered, the motion would continue to be straight. This completes Koyré's argument.—Tr.]

[49] [The parallelogram of movements states that a body subjected to two movements will follow a resultant path having a speed and direction represented by the diagonal of the parellelogram. Thus if the lengths of A and C represent the speeds of the two motions, acting respectively in the directions of A and C, then B represents the direction, and its length the speed, of the resultant motion:

If one or both motions change speed or direction according to any rule, the same method may still be used to determine the resultant path at any given point.—Tr.]

[50] VIII, 273. [Cf. *Two New Sciences*, p. 250. But Sagredo goes on next to question the validity of the assumptions.—Tr.]

[51] VIII, 212 [*Two New Sciences*, p. 178].

[52] The device of studying the fall of bodies along an inclined plane rather than vertically has the obvious purpose of slowing acceleration. It assumes, however, that this retardation does not affect the laws which govern such fall. [Since some have questioned whether Galileo ever actually performed these experiments, and even whether they could have produced the results he claimed, it is worh noting that recently they have been repeated and found both practicable and adequate. See T. B. Settle, "An Experiment in the History of Science," in *Science*, January 6, 1961, pp. 19–23.—Tr.]

[53] *Op. cit.*, p. 145 (II, 71).

[54] For the ideas briefly mentioned here I refer principally to Cassirer's *History of Philosophy*, cited in Ch. 2, section 5, above, and to Banfi's work (pp. 278, 307, and elsewhere), which on this problem faithfully reproduces the essential lines of Cassirer's interpretation. For reasons of space, I cannot discuss Cassirer's thesis of the close relations between Galileo and

Notes

Kant. On this whole quesion, consult the brief and pointed note of Franz Brunetti concerning the two interpretations of Galileo's experimental method in *Belfagor*, 1956, I, 79–88.

55 *Individuo e Cosmo nella filosofia del Rinascimento* (Florence, 1935), p. 264.

56 XVIII, 12–13.

57 VIII, 327.

58 We shall see in the next chapter that this tendency reappeared with extraordinary clarity in his last letters, written in 1640.

59 VII, 80 [*Dialogue*, p. 55].

60 Previously cited in Ch. 7, section 4. [*Dialogue*, p. 339.]

61 VIII, 213. [*Two New Sciences*, p. 178–79.]

62 "Galileo makes use of *deduction* and specifically of reasoning; for if on the one hand, he makes a mathematical or *quantitative* 'resolution' and 'composition' of the qualitative or empirical, by which he formulates the *idea* of the 'proportionality of the spaces to the squares of the times' as true *hypothesis* of the cause of the fall of heavy bodies; on the other hand, he has the *proof* of the *truth* of his hypothesis, which thereby becomes a causal *law*, not *in its own right* (as reason) . . . but *specifically* because of the technical *experiment* which, insofar as it supplies the *disproof* or *elimination* of competing facts . . . permits reason really to overcome the fundamental difficulty . . . of diverse antecedents of the same fact." *Logica come scienza positiva* (2d ed., Messina, 1956), p. 226. On Della Volpe's polemic against Cassirer, see the article of Brunetti cited in note 54 above.

Chapter 10: The Serene Conclusion of an Embattled Life

1 The principle that the relations [of space and time] demonstrated for the vertical fall of heavy bodies hold unchanged for their descent along any inclined plane.

2 XVIII, 125–6.

3 For several years Galileo had returned to problems of the moon, and it was to this subject that he had devoted his final telescopic observations in 1637, before going blind. He gave an account of these in a letter dated February 20, 1638 (XVII, 291–97), of which the subject was the so-called problem of lunar perturbations. It constitutes a treatise, brief but complete, which is exemplary for its methodological rigor and clear style. Galileo's previous thesis of the affinity or cognate relation of earth and moon is strongly reinforced. The letter ends with some bitter remarks about Scheiner.

4 XVIII, 232–36. The second version of Galileo's letter to Leopold was inserted in Book II of Liceti's *De Lunae suboscura luce prope coniunctiones ineclipsibus observata* (*On the moon's pale light near conjunctions, observed in eclipses*), published in 1641.

5 XVIII, 314–16.

6 *Op. cit.*, p. 239.

[7] Alessandra Bocchineri was born in the opening years of the seventeenth century. She died in 1649.

[8] XIV, 100.

[9] XVIII, 313.

[10] XVIII, 319.

[11] XVIII, 374.

[12] VIII, 511.

[13] VIII, 499.

[14] VIII, 521.

[15] VIII, 542.

[16] [This and ensuing passages are from the letter mentioned above.] XVIII, 247-51.

[17] VI, 296 [*Controversy*, p. 252] cited in Ch. 6, section 4.

[18] VIII, 175 [*Two New Sciences*, p. 137] cited in Chapter IX, §5.

[19] VIII, 327; cited in Ch. 9, section 8.

[20] In fact this letter faithfully repeats the words of Salviati paraphrased in Ch. 9, section 9: "Does not Aristotle affirm that whatever is demonstrated to us by experience and our senses should be placed above any reasoning, even if it appears extremely well-founded?" (VII, 80; *Dialogue*, p. 55) Thus Galileo knows and openly declares that this methodological canon goes back to Aristotle himself.

[21] Here the considerations developed in the last two sections of Ch. 3 and in Ch. 4 should be remembered.

[22] XVIII, 295.

[23] [It might be better to say that he was convinced, rightly or wrongly, that any philosophical (or social) consequences of the scientific revolution were certain to be good. For Galileo, the search for truth could yield only changes for the better. This is rather different from a complete disregard for consequences. Galileo's dangerous, courageous, and disastrous battle in 1615-16, with its philosophical as well as its social overtones, appears to me to exclude the idea of his having been unconcerned about the implications of his scientific revolution.—Tr.]

[24] *Galileo Galilei: a philosophical symbol.*

[25] [XIX, 623]

[26] [XIX, 624. The body was laid to rest in Santa Croce, where the ancestral tomb is, but was not placed in that tomb. Until 1737 it remained in a narrow room at the end of the corridor leading to the sacristy. Viviani's body, at his request, was laid beside Galileo's in 1703.—Tr.]

[27] XVIII, 379-80.

[28] XIX, 399. The monument was in fact erected in the Cathedral of Santa Croce in 1737, and is the work of the sculptors G. B. Foggini and G. Ticciati. [Galileo's final resting place is at the left as one enters Santa Croce, directly opposite that of Michelangelo.—Tr.]

[29] [*Cimento* means a severe test, here a reference to experiment. Publication of the proceedings of this Academy in 1667 set the precedent for similar

Notes

reporting by scientific societies which has become the indispensable tool of every scientist.—Tr.]

[30] [Prince Leopold de' Medici was made a cardinal in 1667. It was he who had given the Academy its principal support. The collapse of the Academy in the same year has been variously interpreted.—Tr.]

[31] XIX, 419.

[32] XIX, 421.

Index

Index

Index

Index

Index

Index

Index

Index

242